ADVANCED LEVEL

A2

CHEMISTRY

JOHN ATKINSON • CAROL HIBBERT

For AQA

Contents

Module 5 Thermodynamics and further inorganic chemistry

Heinemann Educational Publishers
Halley Court, Jordan Hill, Oxford, OX2 8EJ
Part of Harcourt Education
Heinemann is the registered trademark of Harcourt Educational Limited

First published 2001

ISBN: 978 0 435581 31 2

10 09 08 07
12 11 10 9

Development editor Paddy Gannon

Edited by Mary Korndorffer

Designed and typeset by Ian Foulis and Associates, Plymouth Devon

Illustrated by Ian Foulis and Associates, Plymouth Devon

Printed and bound in China through Phoenix Offset

Acknowledgements
The authors and publishers would like to thank the following for permission to use photographs:

(L = left, R = right, B = bottom, M = middle)

Cover photo: Science Photo Library
p2 T SPL, **M** Gareth Boden, **B** SPL; **p4**, **p16**, **p52**, **p60**, **p66**, **p67**, **p72** & **p87** – all Andrew Lambert; **p102 L&M** Andrew Lambert, **R** Peter Morris, **ML** Ace Photo Library, **MM** SPL, **MR** Ace Photo Library, **BL** Ace Photo Library, **BR** SPL; **p106**, Corbis; **p109** SPL; **p110**, **p154**, **p177**, **p179**, **p182**, **p184**, **p193**, **p195**, **p204**, **p219** – all Andrew Lambert; **p223** Corbis; **p225**, **p242**, **p245**, **p250**, **p252** & **p255** – all Andrew Lambert.

Other photographs by Carol Hibbert and Kevin Greenhead College, Huddersfield.

Thanks to Geoff Hallas (University of Leeds) for the use of his spectra.

The publishers have made every effort to trace the copyright holders, but if they have inadvertently overlooked any, they will be pleased to make the necessary arrangements at the first opportunity.

Introduction

To the student

This book has been written specifically for Advanced Level Chemistry and matches AQA Specification 6421. It covers all of the material you will need written in a clear and concise way with no added extras.

How to use this book

The book is divided into three **Modules**.

Module 4 – Further physical and Organic Chemistry
Module 5 – Thermodynamics and Further Inorganic Chemistry
Module 6 – Synoptic Assessment

- At the beginning of each Module you will find an **introduction**, which give you an overview of the Module, and a **concept map** showing you the various links between the topics in that Module.
- Each Module is divided in units, each one of which covers a main topic area. Module and unit titles are shown at the top of each page for easy reference
- At the the start of each unit, where appropriate, there is a **summary** of the content covered. This is followed by a Memory Jogger box, which summarizes what is covered at AS level.Where appropriate, worked examples of calculations are included for quantitative aspects of the units. Within the pages there are **questions** for you to answer about the information on the pages. Some are **synoptic questions**; these are indicated by the symbol Ⓢ. You should do these questions as you work through the units, as they will check your understanding. The answers are at the back of the book.
- At the end of each unit there are **key ideas** which you can use as a check list for revision.
- At different points in the text you will find key words in bold type. It is important that you understand these terms. Their meaning is given in the text and in the **glossary** at the end of the book.
- There are short-answer examination questions at the end of each unit to test your knowledge and understanding of that topic and longer questions at the end of each module which link the topics within the module and across modules to test your application of knowledge. The answers to the end of unit questions are at the end of the book with mark allocations shown in brackets.

AS book and further resources

An AS book is also available for the first year of A-level study.
Both books have an accompanying resource pack with further questions and the answers to all of the end of module questions in the book.

John Atkinson BA (Oxon)
Carol Hibbert BSc (Liverpool) CChem FRSC
Lecturers, Greenhead College, Huddersfield

Introduction to Module 4

This module builds upon the concepts of physical chemistry and extends the organic chemistry studied at AS level to include some more functional groups and benzene chemistry.

The first three units are physical chemistry units. In Unit 1 the ideas about rates of reaction are revisited to show the effect that changing the concentrations of the reactants involved has on the rate. In Unit 2 the concept of chemical equilibrium is developed to include a quantitative treatment and the principles of acid–base equilibria are introduced in Unit 3. This unit includes pH as a measure of acidity, the theory of acid-base indicators and the action of buffer solutions. Quantitative aspects of all of these topics are vital to their study, including titrations and associated calculations.

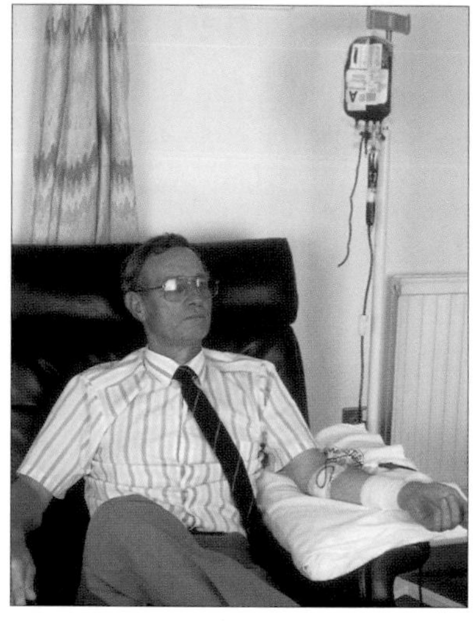

Figure 1 *Blood transfusion – blood is buffered to pH 7.4*

The Units 4–10 revisit Organic Chemistry. Aspects of isomerism studied at AS are expanded in Unit 4 to include optical isomerism, which plays a very important role in the chemistry of natural organic compounds. In Unit 5 the chemistry of the carbonyl group, which was studied at AS for aldehydes and ketones, is extended to other homologous series including carboxylic acids, esters and acyl chlorides. Two new mechanisms are introduced involving nucleophilic addition. Aromatic chemistry is introduced in Unit 6. The aromatic chemistry studied at A2 is based on the chemistry of benzene. This includes an understanding of the structure of benzene and its reactions with electrophiles.

Figure 2 *Articles made from natural or synthetic polymers*

The chemistry of amines, which you first met at AS level, is studied in Unit 7. This overlaps with Unit 8, which has a biochemical flavour. The unit includes natural and synthetic polymers. Proteins are natural polymers made up of a sequence of amino acids. Amino acids have special chemical properties because they have both an amine and a carboxylic acid functional group in their structures.

In Unit 9 methods used to determine the structure of organic compounds are introduced. These include mass spectrometry, infra-red spectroscopy and proton magnetic resonance spectroscopy. These are instrumental techniques and the unit concentrates on how the spectra are interpreted to give information about the structure of compounds.

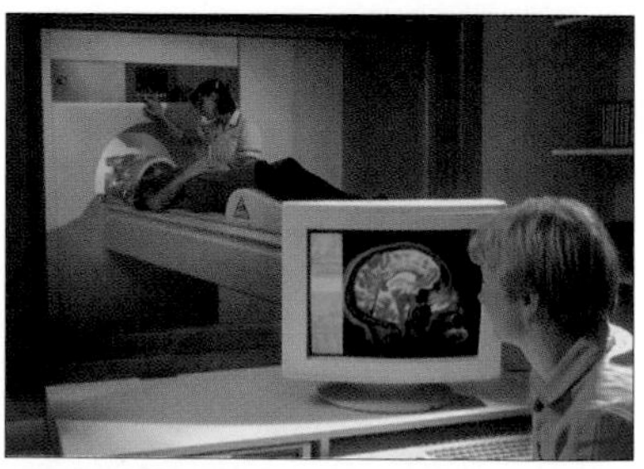

Figure 3 *N.m.r. spectroscopy is the basis of medical imaging*

In the final Unit of this Module the chemistry of the different functional groups are drawn together. The unit concentrates on the reactions of the different functional groups and using this knowledge in synthesis and analysis.

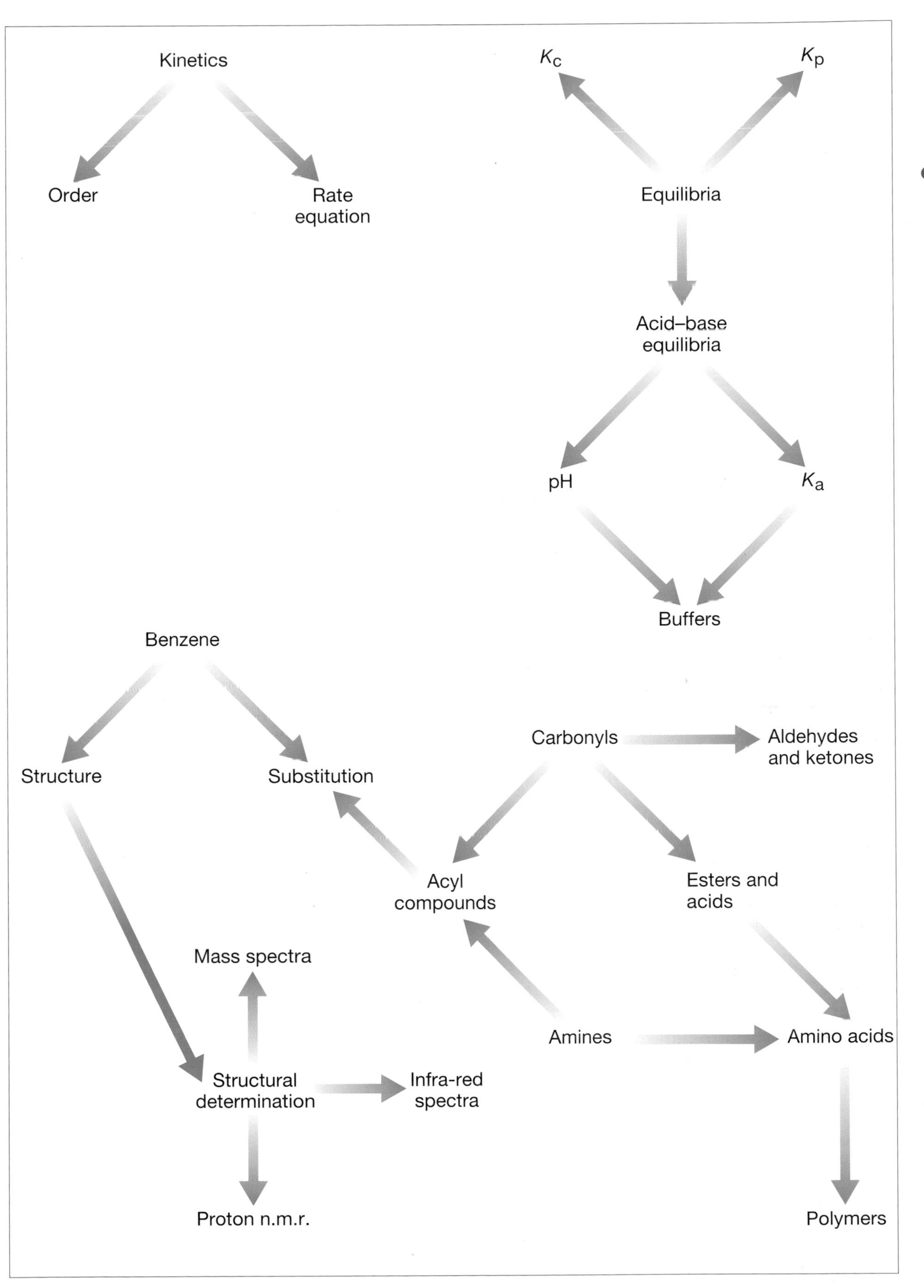
Kinetics
Order
Rate equation
K_c
K_p
Equilibria
Acid–base equilibria
pH
K_a
Buffers
Benzene
Structure
Substitution
Carbonyls
Aldehydes and ketones
Acyl compounds
Esters and acids
Mass spectra
Amines
Amino acids
Structural determination
Infra-red spectra
Proton n.m.r.
Polymers

1 Kinetics

At AS level you will have studied the factors that affect the rate of a chemical reaction, including the effect of temperature, addition of a **catalyst** and the concentration of reactants in solution. In A2 Chemistry we will focus on how changing the concentration of each reactant affects the rate of reaction. The approach is **quantitative**. This means you will study by how much altering the concentration of a reactant will affect the rate.

Collision theory

At AS level you will have learnt that there are two ways of increasing the rate of chemical reaction:

1 increasing the frequency of collisions
2 increasing the percentage of particles with energies equal to or greater than the **activation energy**, E_a

In practice increasing the frequency of collisions is accomplished by increasing the concentration of the reactants in solution, increasing the pressure of gaseous reactants or increasing the surface area of solid reactants.

In order to increase the percentage of particles with energy equal to or greater than the activation energy, the temperature of the reactions is increased and/or a catalyst is added.

The order of reaction

The best way to study the effect of altering the concentration of the reactants on the reaction rate is to perform some experiments. One example of a reaction that is easy to follow experimentally is the reaction between iodate(V) and sulphite ions in the presence of an acid. The apparatus is shown in Figure 1. This experiment is often referred to as an iodine 'clock' experiment.

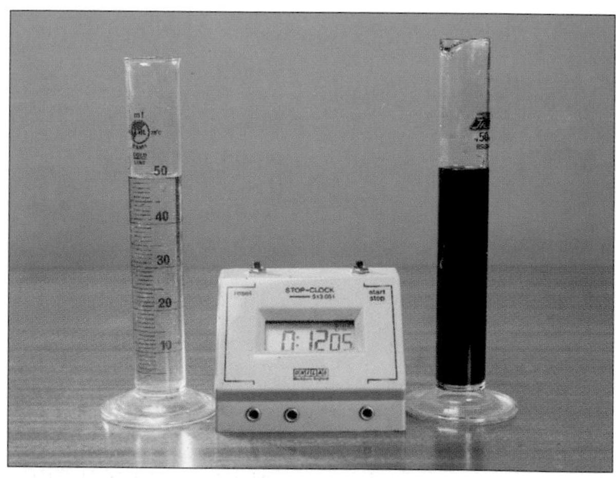

Figure 1 *The iodine clock experiment*

The stoichiometric (balanced) equation for the reaction is:

$$2IO_3^-(aq) + 5SO_3^{2-}(aq) + 2H^+(aq) \rightarrow I_2(s) + 5SO_4^{2-}(aq) + H_2O(l)$$

This reaction can be followed by using starch solution to detect the formation of iodine. Starch turns blue-black in the presence of iodine.

Several different combinations of the reactants are trialled. These are called 'runs'. The concentration of one of the reactants is varied while the concentrations of the other reactants are kept constant. The time taken for the reaction, indicated by the blue-black colour, is recorded.

By comparing the results we can see how changing the concentration of individual reactants affects the rate of the reaction. This allows us to determine the **order** with respect to each of the reactants.

Table 1 below shows some typical results of four different 'runs'.

Run	IO_3^-(aq)/cm^3	SO_3^{2-}(aq)/cm^3	H^+(aq)/cm^3	water/cm^3	time/s
1	10	10	10	20	24
2	10	20	10	10	24
3	10	10	20	10	12
4	20	10	10	10	6

Table 1 *Rate of reaction*

By comparing runs 1 and 3 we can see that the only concentration that varies is the acid. Doubling the concentration of the acid reduces the time taken for reaction by half so doubling the concentration of the acid increases the rate of reaction by a factor of two, i.e. the rate doubles. Since the change in rate is proportional to the change in concentration of the acid we can say that the reaction is **first order** with respect to the acid. Mathematically:

rate $\propto$ [reactant]

Comparing runs 1 and 4 the only concentration that varies is that of the iodate ions. When the iodate concentration is doubled the rate of reaction increases by a factor of four. Since the change in rate is proportional to the square of the change in concentration (i.e. 2^2) we can say that the reaction is **second order** with respect to the concentration of iodate. Mathematically:

rate $\propto$ [reactant]^2

1 What would be the effect on the rate of reaction of tripling the concentration of the acid in the above reaction?

In runs 1 and 2 the only concentration that varies is that of the sulphite ions. But the change in concentration of sulphite has no effect upon the rate of reaction. Therefore the rate of reaction is **zero order** with respect to the sulphite.

2 Give two ways in which the rate of the above reaction can be quadrupled.

The rate equation

Having found the rate of reaction with respect to each of the reactants we can now write a **rate equation** for the reaction which summarises mathematically the experimental findings.

From the results of the 'runs':

$$\text{rate} \propto [H^+]^1[SO_3^{2-}]^0[IO_3^-]^2$$

In this expression notice that the powers of the concentration terms (in mol dm^{-3}) are the orders with respect to each of the reactants.

Any term raised to the power of zero equals 1 so, since $[SO_3^{2-}]^0 = 1$, then this term is omitted from the equation. Also, standard notation is not to show a power of 1 as in $[H^+]^1$. This gives an equation:

$$\text{rate} \propto [H^+]\,[IO_3^-]^2$$

Introducing a constant of proportionality, k, gives the rate equation for the reaction. k is the known as the **rate constant**.

$$\text{rate} = k[H^+][IO_3^-]^2$$

Notice that the rate equation bears *no* relation to the stoichiometric equation for the reaction:

$$2IO_3^-(aq) + 5SO_3^{2-}(aq) + 2H^+(aq) \rightarrow I_2(s) + 5SO_4^{2-}(aq) + H_2O(l)$$

Rate equations can *only* be determined by experiment.

3 For the reaction X + Y → Z the rate equation is found to be:

rate = $k[Y]^2$

a) Why is [X] omitted from the rate equation?

b) What effect will doubling [Y] have on the rate of reaction?

The **overall order** of the reaction is equal to the sum of the indices of the concentration terms in the rate equation.

In this reaction the overall order is 1 + 2 = 3, i.e. **third order**. This means if both the concentrations of $H^+(aq)$ and $IO_3^-(aq)$ are doubled at the same time the rate will increase by a factor of 8, i.e. 2^3

The general form of a rate equation is:

$$\text{rate} = k[A]^m[B]^n$$

where

- k is the rate constant for the reaction.
- m and n are the orders of reaction with respect to the reactants A and B.
- the overall order = m + n

Measuring rates of reaction

The rate of a reaction is measured experimentally. The rate at the start of the reaction is the greatest. This is called the **initial rate** and is the easiest to measure. From these measurements we can find the order of reaction and hence determine the rate equation.

Consider the reaction:

$$A(aq) + B(aq) \rightarrow C(aq) + D(aq)$$

The rate of the reaction is defined as the change in concentration of a reactant or product with time. So the rate of the above reaction could be found by measuring the decrease in concentration of A or B or the increase in concentration of C or D.

$$\text{Rate} = \frac{-d[A]}{dt} = \frac{-d[B]}{dt} = \frac{d[C]}{dt} = \frac{d[D]}{dt}$$ where d[ ] = change in concentration and dt = change in time.

So the units for rate are mol $dm^{-3}s^{-1}$.

We looked at measuring rates in AS Chemistry and obtained graphs like those shown below:

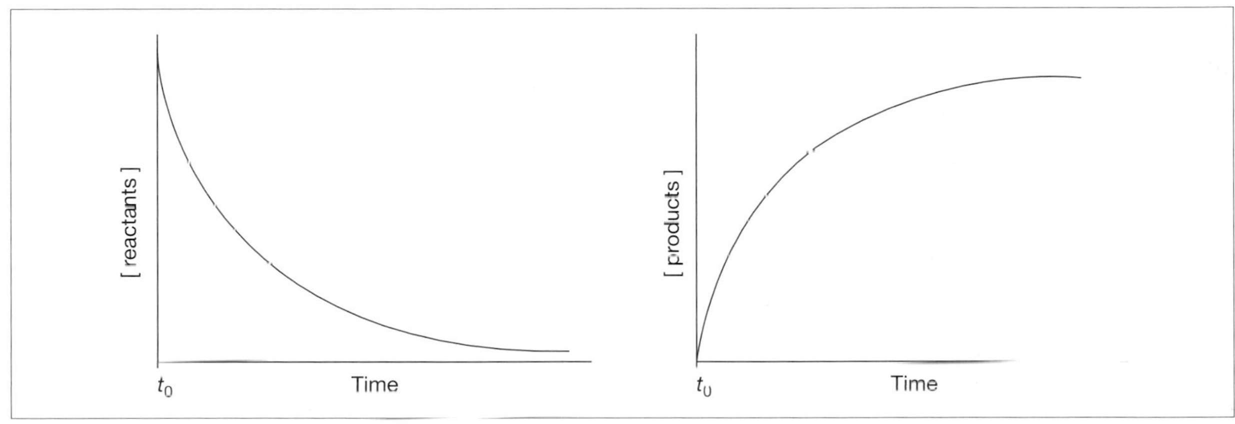

Figure 2 *Measuring the rate of a reaction*

The rate is continually changing throughout the reaction. The initial rate, at t_0, is the greatest, where the curve is steepest. Gradually it gets less as the reaction proceeds. The rate at any value of t can be determined by taking a tangent to the curve and measuring the gradient. The most accurately measured gradient is that at t_0. The measurement of the initial rate of a reaction is used to determine the order of reaction. The method is shown in Figure 3:

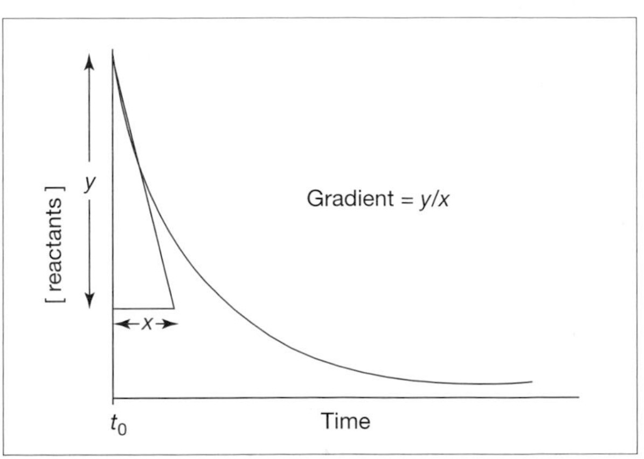

Figure 3 *Measuring the initial rate from a graph*

Determining order

This involves a series of experiments ('runs') in which the concentration of one reactant is varied whilst the concentrations of the other reactants are kept constant. The initial rate of the experiments allows the order with respect to the reactant to be determined. The experiments are then repeated to find the order with respect to each of the reactants.

The order can found by inspection or graphically.

Inspection method

The following examples illustrate how inspection can be used to determine the order with respect to the separate reactants.

Table 2 gives the initial rate of reaction at various concentrations of the reactants A and B.

Comparing runs 1 and 2, in which the concentration of A is constant and the concentration of B is doubled, we find that the rate doubles. This shows that the reaction is first order with respect to reactant B.

Run	Initial concentration of A/mol dm^{-3}	Initial concentration of of B/mol dm^{-3}	Initial rate/ mol dm^{-3} s^{-1}
1	0.1	0.2	1.6×10^{-2}
2	0.1	0.4	3.2×10^{-2}
3	0.2	0.2	6.4×10^{-2}

Table 2

Comparing runs 1 and 3, in which the concentration of B is constant and the concentration of A doubles, we find that the rate quadruples. This shows that the reaction is second order with respect to reactant A.

Having determined the order with respect to each of the reactants then the rate equation for the reaction can be written:

$$\text{rate} = k\,[A]^2[B]$$

Here is a more difficult example:

Table 3 gives the initial rate of reaction at various concentrations of the reactants X, Y and Z.

Q 4 What would be the initial rate of reaction in the above example if the concentrations of A and B where 0.2 and 0.4 mol dm^{-3} respectively?

Run	Initial concentration of X/mol dm^{-3}	Initial concentration of Y/mol dm^{-3}	Initial concentration of Z/mol dm^{-3}	Initial rate/ mol dm^{-3} s^{-1}
1	0.10	0.10	0.10	2.40×10^{-3}
2	0.10	0.10	0.30	7.20×10^{-3}
3	0.05	0.10	0.10	2.40×10^{-3}
4	0.10	0.40	0.10	3.84×10^{-2}

Table 3

Comparing runs 1 and 2:
Tripling the concentration of reactant Z while keeping the concentrations of X and Y constant triples the rate of reaction so the reaction is first order with respect to reactant Z.

Comparing runs 1 and 3:
Halving the concentration of reactant X while keeping the concentrations of Y and Z constant has no effect on the rate of reaction so the reaction is zero order with respect to reactant X.

Comparing runs 1 and 4:
Quadrupling the concentration of reactant Y while keeping the concentrations of X and Z constant increases the rate of reaction by a factor of 16, i.e. 4^2, so the reaction is second order with respect to reactant Y.

Using this information the rate equation for the reaction is:

rate = $k[Y]^2[Z]$

Graphical method

The initial rates at various concentrations are found and the results plotted as shown below:

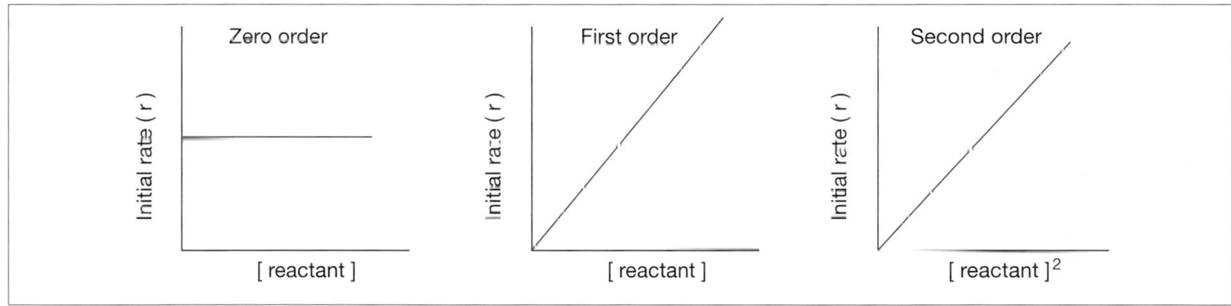

Figure 4 *Graphs to represent zero, first and second order reactions*

The graphs confirm what has been discussed previously:

- For an overall zero order reaction the increase in concentration of reactants has no effect on the rate.
- For an overall first order reaction the rate is proportional to the concentration of the reactants.
- For an overall second order reaction the rate is proportional to the square of the change in concentration of the reactants.

For a reaction where the rate equation is of the type:

rate = $k[A]$

then the gradient of the first order reaction graph shown above equals the value of k, the rate constant. Similarly for a reaction where the rate equation is of the type:

rate = $k[A]^2$

then the gradient of the graph for the second order reaction equals the value of k.

Worked examples

The rate of the reaction between compounds A and B was studied at a given temperature.
The results obtained are given in Table 4.

Run	[A]/mol dm^{-3}	[B]/mol dm^{-3}	Initial rate/ mol $dm^{-3}s^{-1}$
1	0.2	0.3	1.60×10^{-4}
2	0.2	0.6	3.20×10^{-4}
3	0.4	0.6	1.28×10^{-3}
4	0.5	0.3	To be calculated

a) Use the data in Table 4 to deduce the order of reaction with respect to A and B. Hence write the rate equation for the reaction.

b) Calculate the initial rate for run 4.

Answer
By comparing runs 1 and 2 it can be seen that the rate doubles when [B] doubles. The reaction is first order with respect to B.

By comparing runs 2 and 3 it can be seen that when [A] doubles the rate quadruples. The reaction is second order with respect to A.

The rate equation for this reaction is: rate $= k[A]^2[B]$.

This can be verified by comparing runs 1 and 3. When both [A] and [B] are doubled the rate increases by a factor of 8 (2^3).

To calculate the initial rate for run 4 we need to compare runs 1 and 4. The concentration of B is unchanged but the concentration of A has increased by a factor of 2.5. Since the reaction is second order with respect to A the initial rate of run 4 is increased by a factor of $2.5^2 = 6.25$.

So the initial rate of run 4 is $(1.60 \times 10^{-4}) \times 6.25 = 1 \times 10^{-3}$mol $dm^{-3} s^{-1}$.

Alternatively the value of k can be calculated using the rate equation and the concentrations from runs 1 ,2 or 3 and this value, substituted into the rate equation to find the initial rate for run 4 (see page 13)

2 The initial rate of reaction between X and Y was measured in a series of experiments and the following rate equation derived:

rate = k $[X]^2[Y]$

Complete the data for this reaction in Table 5.

Run	[Y]/mol dm^{-3}	[X]/mol dm^{-3}	Initial rate/ mol $dm^{-3}s^{-1}$
1	0.2	0.2	1.20×10^{-4}
2	0.4	0.4	9.60×10^{-4}
3	a)	0.4	2.40×10^{-4}
4	0.6	0.3	b)

 **Table 5**

Answer

a) Comparing runs 2 and 3:

The initial rate of reaction has been reduced by a factor of 4. Since the concentration of X remains constant this change is due solely to a reduction in the concentration of Y. The reaction is first order with respect to Y so its concentration has been reduced by a factor of 4.

The answer is 0.4/4 = 0.1 mol dm^{-3}

b) Comparing runs 1 and 4:

[Y] has been tripled and [X] has been increased by a factor of 1.5 so overall the rate has been increased by $3^1 \times 1.5^2 = 6.75$, taking in account the orders of reaction with respect to Y and X.

This means the initial rate for run 4 = $6.75 \times 1.20 \times 10^{-4} = 8.1 \times 10^{-4}$ mol dm^{-3} s^{-1}

Key Ideas 4 – 11

- **The order of reaction with respect to a reactant depends upon the effect that changing the concentration of that reactant has on the rate of reaction.**
- **The rate equation relates the rate of reaction to the concentrations of the reactants.**
- **The overall order of reaction is the sum of the powers of the concentration terms in the rate equation.**
- **The order of reaction and the rate equation can be derived from experimental data relating the initial rate of reaction to the concentrations of the reactants.**

2 The rate constant

The rate constant, k, in the rate equation has a particular value for a particular reaction providing the temperature is kept constant. Its value can be determined from experimental data.

The rate constant is temperature dependent

The rate constant is a temperature dependent constant. Its value for a specific reaction, at a particular temperature is constant but the value increases as temperature increases.

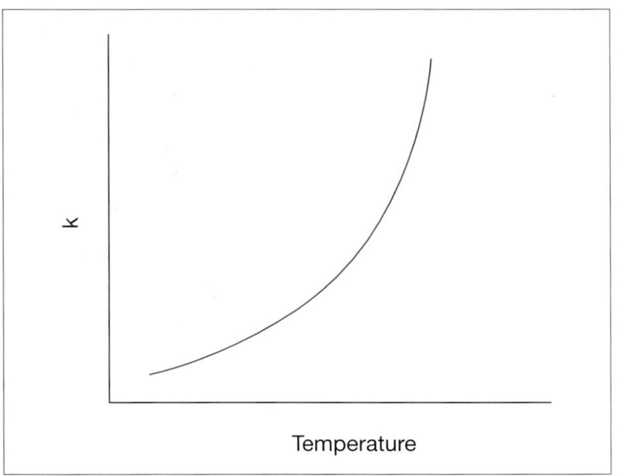

Figure 1 *The rate constant, k, increases with temperature*

You will remember from AS chemistry that increasing the temperature increases the proportion of molecules having the minimum activation energy needed to react. This means that the rate of reaction increases with temperature.

Consider the reaction between oxygen and gaseous nitrogen(II) oxide (NO):

$$2NO(g) + O_2(g) \rightarrow 2NO_2(g)$$

The rate equation for this reaction is:

$$\text{rate} = k[O_2][NO]^2$$

If the temperature increases then the rate increases and therefore the value of k must increase when the concentration of the gases are constant.

Calculating the units of k

The units of the rate constant vary depending on the overall order of the reaction. These are shown in Table 1.

The units of the rate constant are calculated as shown below.

Consider a reaction where the rate equation is found to be:

$$\text{rate} = k\,[A]^2[B]$$

Overall order	Units of k
First	s^{-1}
Second	$dm^3\ mol^{-1}\ s^{-1}$
Third	$dm^6\ mol^{-2}\ s^{-1}$

Table 1 *Units of the rate constant*

Rearranging this gives:

$$k = \frac{\text{rate}}{[A]^2[B]} \quad \text{where the units are} \quad \frac{\text{mol dm}^{-3}\ \text{s}^{-1}}{(\text{mol dm}^{-3})^3}$$

Cancelling this gives the units as $\text{dm}^6\ \text{mol}^{-2}\ \text{s}^{-1}$.

5 Calculate the units for the rate constant, k, for the rate equation:

r = k [A][B]

Calculating the value of k

From the rate equation the value of the rate constant can be calculated. Consider the following example:

$$\text{Rate} = k\,[X]^2[Y]$$

Run	[X]/mol dm^{-3}	[Y]/mol dm^{-3}	Initial rate/mol $\text{dm}^{-3}\text{s}^{-1}$
1	0.20	0.20	1.20×10^{-4}
2	0.40	0.40	9.60×10^{-4}
3	0.40	0.10	2.40×10^{-3}
4	0.25	0.30	To be calculated

Table 2

6 The value of k is constant for a particular reaction at constant temperature. Verify this statement by calculating the value of k for the above reaction using the results from run 2.

All measurements were taken at the same temperature.

$$k = \frac{\text{rate}}{[X]^2[Y]}$$

Using the results from run 1:

$$k = \frac{1.20 \times 10^{-4}}{(0.2)^2\,(0.2)} = \frac{1.20 \times 10^{-4}}{0.008} = 1.5 \times 10^{-2}\,\text{dm}^6\ \text{mol}^{-2}\ \text{s}^{-1}$$

Once the value of k has been calculated it can be used, in conjunction with the rate equation, to find the initial rate of reaction for run 4:

$$\text{rate} = k\,[X]^2[Y]$$

where $k = 1.5 \times 10^{-2}\,\text{dm}^6\ \text{mol}^{-2}\ \text{s}^{-1}$, $[X] = 0.25\,\text{mol dm}^{-3}$ and $[Y] = 0.30\,\text{mol dm}^{-3}$.

Substituting these values:

$$\text{rate} = 1.5 \times 10^{-2} \times (0.25)^2 \times 0.30 = 2.8 \times 10^{-4}\text{mol dm}^{-3}\text{s}^{-1}$$

Key Ideas 12 – 13

- **The rate constant for a particular reaction can be calculated from the rate equation.**
- **The value of the rate constant increases with temperature.**

Unit 1 Questions

3

1. Chloroethane is hydrolysed by hot aqueous sodium hydroxide solution according to the equation below:

$CH_3CH_2Cl + OH^- \rightarrow CH_3CH_2OH + Cl^-$

This reaction was studied using different concentrations of reactants and the initial rates measured. The data obtained are shown in below:

$[CH_3CH_3Cl]$/mol dm^{-3}	$[OH^-]$/mol dm^{-3}	Initial rate/mol $dm^{-3}s^{-1}$
0.01	0.02	8.60×10^{-8}
0.02	0.02	1.72×10^{-7}
0.02	0.06	5.16×10^{-7}

a) (i) What is the order of reaction with respect to chloroethane?
(ii) What is the order of reaction with respect to hydroxide ions? (2)

b) (i) What is the overall order of reaction?
(ii) Explain how you arrived at this answer. (2)

c) Name the mechanism of the reaction between a haloalkane and aqueous sodium hydroxide solution. (1)

2. The rate equation for the reaction between X and Y is given below:

rate = k [X] $[Y]^2$

a) Complete the table of data below for this reaction carried out at 60°C:

Run	[X]/mol dm^{-3}	[Y]/mol dm^{-3}	Initial rate/mol $dm^{-3}s^{-1}$
1	0.01	0.02	1.6×10^{-5}
2	0.03	0.02	
3	0.01		4.0×10^{-6}
4	0.02	0.04	

(3)

b) (i) Calculate the value of the rate constant, k, for this reaction at 60°C.
(ii) How will the value of k alter if the temperature is increased to 80°C?
(iii) How will the value of k alter if the concentration of Y is increased to 0.06 mol dm^{-3} at 60°C? (5)

(3) Hydrogen peroxide decomposes in the presence of a catalyst according to the equation below:

$2H_2O_2 \rightarrow 2H_2O + O_2$

The change in concentration of peroxide during an experiment was measured and the results are shown in below:

$[H_2O_2]$/mol dm^{-3}	0.156	0.115	0.092	0.081	0.073	0.062
Time/s $\times 10^3$	0.00	3.90	6.90	8.55	10.2	12.9

a) Plot a graph of these data and determine the initial rate of the reaction. (6)

b) Name a suitable catalyst for the reaction. (1)

(4) Benzenediazonium chloride (**A**) undergoes decomposition in water according to the equation below:

$$\underset{\textbf{A}}{C_6H_5N_2^+Cl^-(aq)} + H_2O(l) \rightarrow C_6H_5OH(l) + N_2(g) + HCl(aq)$$

At 50°C the rates of reaction at two different initial concentrations are shown on the graph below:

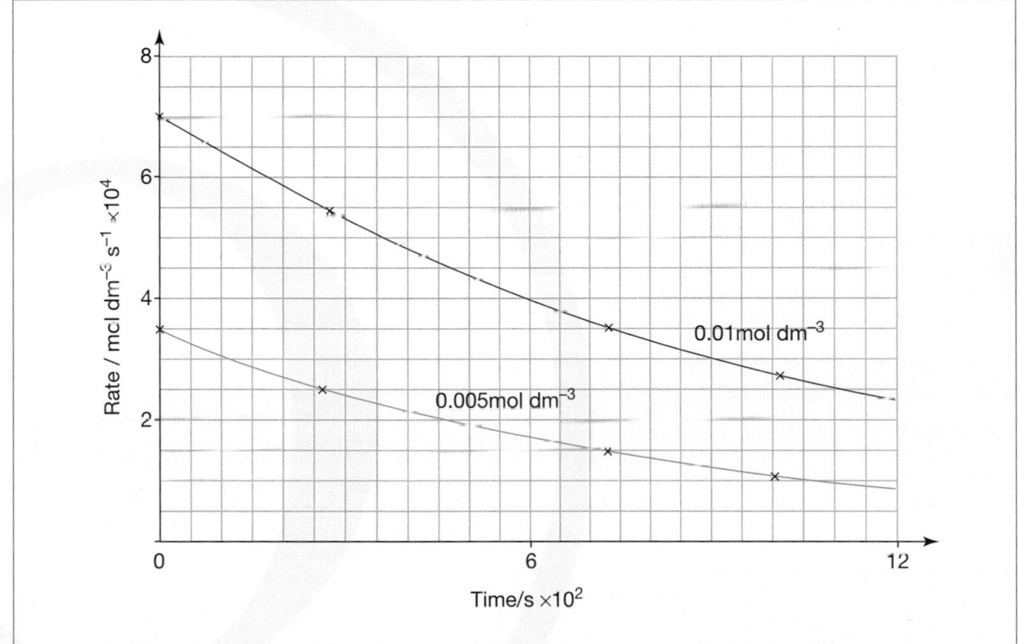

Figure 1

a) Suggest a suitable experimental method which could be used to monitor the rate of this reaction. (3)

b) Use the information on the graph to determine the order of reaction with respect to **A**. Explain how you arrived at your answer. (2)

c) If the concentration of **A** remains constant, what would be the effect of increasing the temperature on the rate of reaction? Explain your answer. (3)

1 Qualitative equilibria

At AS level you have studied the qualitative effects of changes in temperature, pressure and concentration on the position of a chemical equilibrium. The effect of these changes can be understood using **Le Chatelier's Principle.** In this unit we revisit these ideas and develop them to study quantitative aspects of equilibria, introducing the equilibrium constants, K_c and K_p for homogeneous systems.

Qualitative aspects of chemical equilibria

In a reversible reaction a **dynamic equilibrium** is established when the rate of the forward reaction equals the rate of the backward reaction. The equilibrium is established in a **closed system**. If external changes are made then the equilibrium position will shift to oppose these changes.

The effect of changes on the equilibrium position is summarised in Le Chatelier's Principle which states that:

> If one or more of the factors that affect the position of a chemical equilibrium are altered then the equilibrium will shift so as to oppose that change.

A summary of these effects, based upon AS Chemistry, is given below. All the examples used are homogeneous equilibria.

1 What do you understand by the term 'homogeneous equilibria'?

Changing the concentration

Increasing the concentration of one of the reactants will cause the equilibrium to shift to the opposite side of the reaction.

e.g. $2CrO_4^{2-}(aq) + 2H^+(aq) \rightleftharpoons Cr_2O_7^{2-}(aq) + H_2O(l)$

yellow (chromate), orange (dichromate)

If an acid is added to a solution containing chromate(VI) ions, then the solution will change colour from yellow to orange as the equilibrium shifts to the right, producing more dichromate(VI) ions.

2 What would you observe if a solution of potassium dichromate(VI) was treated with excess aqueous sodium hydroxide? Explain your answer in terms of Le Chatelier's Principle.

Changing the temperature

Increasing the temperature of an equilibrium favours the *endothermic* reaction.

e.g. $N_2O_4(g) \rightleftharpoons 2NO_2(g)$ ΔH +ve

In this reaction the forward reaction is endothermic so increasing the temperature will cause the equilibrium shift to the right. More dinitrogen tetroxide dissociates, producing nitrogen dioxide.

Decreasing the temperature of an equilibrium favours the *exothermic* reaction.

e.g. $N_2(g) + 3H_2(g) \rightleftharpoons 2NH_3(g)$ ΔH –ve

In this reaction decreasing the temperature will cause the equilibrium to shift to the right so more ammonia is formed.

3 Why is the manufacture of ammonia carried out at about 400°C when a lower temperature would favour the formation of ammonia?

Changing the pressure

Increasing the pressure moves the equilibrium to the side of the reaction with the fewer gaseous moles i.e. the lower volume.

e.g. $2SO_2(g) + O_2(g) \rightleftharpoons 2SO_3(g)$

In this reaction *increasing* the pressure pushes the equilibrium to the right so more sulphur(VI) oxide is formed.

If a reaction involves no change in the number of gaseous moles then pressure has *no effect* on the equilibrium position.

e.g. $H_2(g) + I_2(g) \rightleftharpoons 2HI(g)$

Adding a catalyst

A catalyst has *no effect* on the position of an equilibrium since it speeds up *both* the forward and backward reactions to the *same extent*. Addition of a catalyst does, therefore, increase the rate at which equilibrium is attained.

Key Ideas 16 – 17

- **An increase or decrease in the concentration of one or more of the reactants affects the position of the equilibrium. By Le Chatelier's Principle the equilibrium will shift in the direction which opposes the change.**
- **Endothermic reactions are favoured by an increase in temperature, exothermic reactions are favoured by a decrease in temperature.**
- **Pressure only affects gaseous equilibria where the reaction involves a change in volume. Increasing the pressure shifts the equilibrium in favour of the reaction with fewer gaseous moles.**
- **Catalysts have no effect on the equilibrium position.**

2 The equilibrium constant, K_c

For a homogeneous equilibrium reaction we can write an expression for an equilibrium constant, K_c, in terms of the concentrations of the reactants and products involved. K_c is basically a ratio of the concentration of the products to reactants.

Writing an expression for K_c

The general expression for an **equilibrium constant** for any reaction is shown below. In the reaction, *a* mol of A reacts with *b* mol of B to form *c* mol of C and *d* mol of D:

$$aA + bB \rightleftharpoons cC + dD$$

$$K_c = \frac{[C]^c[D]^d}{[A]^a[B]^b}$$ where [ ] represents the equilibrium concentration in mol dm^{-3}

Notice that in each case the concentration of the reactant or product is raised to the power of the number of moles shown in the equation for the reaction.

The following examples will help you to understand how to write expressions for equilibrium constants.

(1) $2SO_2(g) + O_2(g) \rightleftharpoons 2SO_3(g)$

$$K_c = \frac{[SO_3]^2}{[SO_2]^2[O_2]}$$

The units for this K_c value are:

$$\frac{(\text{mol dm}^{-3})^2}{(\text{mol dm}^{-3})^2(\text{mol dm}^{-3})} = \frac{1}{\text{mol dm}^{-3}} = \text{dm}^3\ \text{mol}^{-1}$$

(2) $CH_3COOH(aq) + CH_3CH_2OH(aq) \rightleftharpoons CH_3COOCH_2CH_3(aq) + H_2O(l)$

$$K_c = \frac{[CH_3COOCH_2CH_3][H_2O]}{[CH_3COOH][CH_3CH_2OH]}$$

The units for this K_c value are:

$$\frac{(\text{mol dm}^{-3})\ (\text{mol dm}^{-3})}{(\text{mol dm}^{-3})\ (\text{mol dm}^{-3})} = 1$$ Hence no units

Q

4 Write an expression for the equilibrium constants for the following reactions. In each case give the units of K_c

a) $PCl_5(g) \rightleftharpoons PCl_3(g) + Cl_2(g)$

b) $N_2(g) + 3H_2(g) \rightleftharpoons 2NH_3(g)$

Determining a value for K_c

Every reversible reaction has its own K_c. The value of K_c is constant for a particular reaction at constant temperature.

Initial moles of acid	Initial moles of alcohol	Moles of acid at equilibrium	Moles of alcohol at equilibrium	Moles of ester at equilibrium	Moles of water at equilibrium	K_c
1.00	0.18	0.829	0.009	0.171	0.171	3.92
1.00	0.50	0.575	0.075	0.425	0.425	4.12
1.00	1.00	0.333	0.333	0.667	0.667	4.01
1.00	2.00	0.150	1.150	0.850	0.850	4.12
1.00	8.00	0.033	7.033	0.967	0.967	4.02

Table 1 *Experimental data for esterification to calculate K_c*

The K_c value for the esterification reaction:

$$CH_3COOH(aq) + CH_3CH_2OH(aq) \rightleftharpoons CH_3COOCH_2CH_3(aq) + H_2O(l)$$

is found experimentally by adding known amounts of the acid and the alcohol into tubes containing some dilute hydrochloric acid catalyst. The tubes are sealed and heated to 373K until equilibrium is reached. The tubes are then rapidly cooled to 'freeze' the equilibrium, broken open and the amount of acid left determined by titration using a standardised solution of NaOH(aq) and phenolphthalein indicator.

The results obtained are shown in Table 1. From the data we can see that the average experimental value of K_c for this reaction is 4.01 at 373K. (see page 22 to calculate K_c).

As the amount of alcohol added is increased the equilibrium position shifts further to the right increasing the amount of products and decreasing the amount of acid at equilibrium. These changes *do not* affect the value of K_c.

It is important to remember that K_c is a constant at constant temperature. Altering the concentration of the reactants will shift the equilibrium position but the value of K_c remains constant.

The equation for the reverse of esterification, the **hydrolysis** of the ester, is:

$$CH_3COOCH_2CH_3(aq) + H_2O(l) \rightleftharpoons CH_3COOH(aq) + CH_3CH_2OH(aq)$$

$$K_c = \frac{[CH_3COOH][CH_3CH_2OH]}{[CH_3COOCH_2CH_3][H_2O]}$$

The value of K_c will be the reciprocal of the value of the original reaction, i.e. 1/4.01 = 0.248.

The value of the equilibrium constant depends upon the position of the equilibrium.

- If the value of the equilibrium constant is large then the equilibrium position lies to the right.
- If the value of the equilibrium constant is small then the position of the equilibrium lies to the left.

For the esterification reaction

$$CH_3COOH(aq) + CH_3CH_2OH(aq) \underset{K_c = 0.248}{\overset{K_c = 4.01}{\rightleftharpoons}} CH_3COOCH_2CH_3(aq) + H_2O(l)$$

The equilibrium lies to right since the K_c value for the forward reaction is greater than the K_c value for the reverse reaction.

Some more examples are shown in the table below:

Example	K_c at 298K
$H_2(g) + I_2(g) \rightleftharpoons 2HI(g)$	794
$H_2(g) + CO_2(g) \rightleftharpoons H_2O(g) + CO(g)$	1.00×10^{-5}
$N_2(g) + O_2(g) \rightleftharpoons 2NO(g)$	4×10^{-31}
$N_2O_4(g) \rightleftharpoons 2NO_2(g)$	0.05 mol dm^{-3}

Table 2

5 For which of these reactions does the equilibrium lie furthest to the left?

6 What is the K_c value for the reaction: $2NO_2(g) \rightleftharpoons N_2O_4(g)$?

Altering the value of K_c

At A2 we need to consider the effect that changes in reaction conditions have on the value of the equilibrium constant. It has already been stated that equilibrium constants are not affected by changes in concentration. Equally they are not affected by changes in pressure or addition of a catalyst but they are affected by changes in temperature.

If the forward reaction is exothermic an *increase* in temperature will favour the reverse reaction and the value of the equilibrium constant will *decrease*.

e.g. $H_2(g) + I_2(g) \rightleftharpoons 2HI(g) \quad \Delta H = -10.4\,kJ\,mol^{-1}$

The K_c values for this reaction at four different temperatures are shown below:

Temperature/K	K_c
298	794
500	160
700	54
1100	25

Table 3

Conversely a decrease in temperature for this reaction will favour the forward reaction and the value of the equilibrium constant will *increase*.

If the forward reaction is endothermic an *increase* in temperature will favour the forward reaction and the value of the equilibrium constant will *increase*. Whereas a *decrease* in temperature will favour the reverse reaction and the value of the equilibrium constant will *decrease*.

e.g. $H_2(g) + CO_2(g) \rightleftharpoons H_2O(g) + CO(g) \quad \Delta H = +39.3\,kJ\,mol^{-1}$

Table 4 shows the K_c values for this reaction at four different temperatures.

Temperature/K	K_c
200	1.00×10[illegible]
500	7.76×10^{-3}
800	2.88×10^{-1}
900	6.03×10^{-1}

Table 4

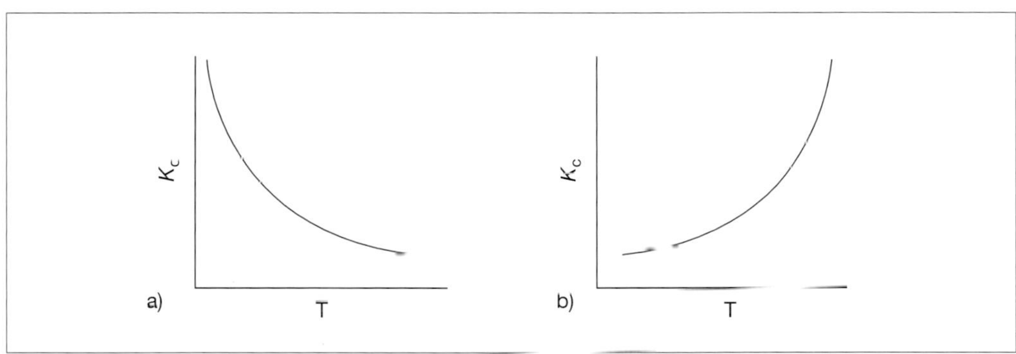

Figure 1 *Graphs to show the change in K_c with temperature for a) exothermic and b) endothermic reactions*

Q

7 a) The data below give the K_c values for the formation of nitrogen monoxide from nitrogen and oxygen at various temperatures. Is this reaction exothermic or endothermic? Explain your answer.

Temperature/K	K_c
293	4×10^{-31}
700	5×10^{-13}
1100	4×10^{-8}
1500	1×10^{-5}

Table 5

Ⓢ **b) Explain the formation of nitrogen monoxide in a car engine. What problems does it cause?**

Calculations involving K_c

We can calculate the value of K_c from the concentrations of the reactants and products at equilibrium. If these values are not quoted they can be calculated from the initial concentrations of the reactants. Study the worked examples given below.

In many of these examples the same two equilibria are used. These are:

$$H_2(g) + I_2(g) \rightleftharpoons 2HI(g)$$

$$CH_3COOH(aq) + CH_3CH_2OH(aq) \rightleftharpoons CH_3COOCH_2CH_3(aq) + H_2O(l)$$

The reason for this is two-fold:

1 These equilibria have been extensively studied and plenty of data are available.

2 By using the same examples in different questions it is easier to see how the question changes.

Worked examples

1 Table 6 shows the equilibrium concentrations for the following reaction at 700K:

$$H_2(g) + I_2(g) \rightleftharpoons 2HI(g)$$

$[H_2]$/mol dm^{-3}	$[I_2]$/mol dm^{-3}	[HI]/mol dm^{-3}
1.71×10^{-3}	2.91×10^{-3}	1.65×10^{-2}

Table 6

a) Write an expression for the equilibrium constant, K_c.

b) Calculate the value for K_c at 700K.

Answer

a) $$K_c = \frac{[HI]^2}{[H_2]\,[I_2]} \quad \text{(no units)}$$

b) Substitute the values quoted into this expression:

$$K_c = \frac{(1.65 \times 10^{-2})^2}{(1.71 \times 10^{-3})(2.91 \times 10^{-3})} = \frac{2.7225 \times 10^{-4}}{4.9761 \times 10^{-6}} = 54.7$$

2 $CH_3COOH(aq) + CH_3CH_2OH(aq) \rightleftharpoons CH_3COOCH_2CH_3(aq) + H_2O(l)$

0.829 mol 0.009 mol 0.171 mol 0.171 mol

The data given above show the number of moles of each component of this esterification reaction at equilibrium. Calculate the value for the equilibrium constant.

Answer

First you need to write an expression for K_c:

$$K_c = \frac{[CH_3COOCH_2CH_3][H_2O]}{[CH_3COOH][CH_3CH_2OH]} \quad \text{(no units)}$$

In this case we can use moles to find the value of K_c rather than molarity, because there are the same number of moles on both sides of the equation and so the volume terms cancel out. Substituting the values quoted into the expression gives:

$$K_c = \frac{(0.171 \times 0.171)}{(0.829 \times 0.009)} = 3.92$$

If the moles or molarity of the components of the reaction are not quoted at equilibrium then these need to be calculated first. Consider the esterification reaction:

8 For the equilibrium: $H_2(g) + I_2(g) \rightleftharpoons 2HI(g)$ calculate the value of K_c if the mixture at equilibrium contains 2.265 mol of hydrogen, 2.840 mol of iodine and 17.15 mol of hydrogen iodide at 764K

$$CH_3COOH(aq) + CH_3CH_2OH(aq) \rightleftharpoons CH_3COOCH_2CH_3(aq) + H_2O(l)$$

Suppose a mol of acid are reacted with b mol of alcohol and allowed to reach equilibrium at constant temperature so that x mol of ester are formed then:

	$CH_3COOH(aq)$ +	$CH_3CH_2OH(aq)$ $\rightleftharpoons$	$CH_3COOCH_2CH_3(aq)$ +	$H_2O(l)$
mol at start:	a	b	0	0
mol at equilibrium:	$a - x$	$b - x$	x	x

From the balanced equation 1 mol of acid reacts with 1 mol of alcohol to form 1 mol of ester and 1 mol of water. This means that

- The amount of the two products formed is the same (x)
- The amount by which the two reactants are reduced equals the amount of each product formed (x)

$$K_c = \frac{[CH_3COOCH_2CH_3][H_2O]}{[CH_3COOH][CH_3CH_2OH]}$$

$$K_c = \frac{(x/V) \times (x/V)}{(a-x)/V \times (b-x)/V} \quad \text{where V = volume in dm}^3.$$

Cancelling V gives:

$$K_c = \frac{x^2}{(a-x)(b-x)}$$

3 For the equilibrium:

$CH_3COOH(aq) + CH_3CH_2OH(aq) \rightleftharpoons CH_3COOCH_2CH_3(aq + H_2O(l)$

1.00 mol of acid is reacted with 0.330 mol of alcohol. At equilibrium 0.293 mol of ester is present. Calculate K_c.

Answer

	$CH_3COOH(aq)$ +	$CH_3CH_2OH(aq)$ $\rightleftharpoons$	$CH_3COOCH_2CH_3(aq)$ +	$H_2O(l)$
mol at start:	1	0.33	0	0
mol at equilibrium:	(1 − 0.293) = 0.707	(0.33 − 0.293) = 0.037	0.293	0.293

$$K_c = \frac{(0.293 \times 0.293)}{(0.707 \times 0.037)} = \frac{0.086}{0.026} = 3.31$$

Alternatively the values can be substituted into the expression:

$$K_c = \frac{x^2}{(a-x)\,(b-x)} \quad \text{where } x = 0.293,\ a = 1,\ b = 0.33$$

$$K_c = \frac{0.293 \times 0.293}{(1 - 0.293)(0.33 - 0.293)} = \frac{0.086}{(0.707 \times 0.037)} = 3.31$$

If you look back to page 19 you should now be able see where these data came from and how K_c was calculated.

9 One mole of ethanoic acid is reacted with 0.50 mol of ethanol. At equilibrium there are 0.414 mol of the ester present. Calculate K_c

4 For the equilibrium:

$CH_3COOH(aq) + CH_3CH_2OH(aq) \rightleftharpoons CH_3COOCH_2CH_3(aq) + H_2O(l)$

a) When 1 mol each of ethanoic acid and ethanol are mixed together at a fixed temperature 0.333 mol of acid remain at equilibrium. Calculate the value of K_c at this temperature.

b) At the same temperature the equilibrium mixture contains 0.142 mol of ethanoic acid and 1.142 mol of ethanol. Calculate the amount of ester present in this equilibrium mixture, assuming that none was present initially.

Answer

a) Here it is necessary to calculate the number of moles of ester at equilibrium:
If, from 1 mol of acid present initially, 0.333 mol remain at equilibrium then (1 – 0.333) mol must have been converted into ester and water:

	$CH_3COOH(aq)$ +	$CH_3CH_2OH(aq)$ ⇌	$CH_3COOCH_2CH_3(aq)$ +	$H_2O(l)$
mol at start:	1	1	0	0
mol at equilibrium:	0.333	0.333	1 – 0.333 0.667	1 – 0.333 = 0.667

$$K_c = \frac{(0.667)^2}{(0.333)^2} = 4.01$$

b) Once K_c has been calculated it is constant for a particular reaction at constant temperature so we can now use the value of K_c calculated in a) to find the amount of ester present in a different equilibrium mixture:

	$CH_3COOH(aq)$ +	$CH_3CH_2OH(aq)$ ⇌	$CH_3COOCH_2CH_3(aq)$ +	$H_2O(l)$
mol at equilibrium:	0.142	1.142	x	x

$$K_c = 4.01 = \frac{x^2}{(0.142 \times 1.142)}$$

$x^2 = (4.01 \times 0.142 \times 1.142) = 0.651$
$x = \sqrt{0.651} = 0.807\,\text{mol}$

Notice that in equilibrium calculations in which there are no changes in moles in the reaction we can use moles rather than concentration to calculate K_c.

10 For the reaction:
$N_2(g) + 3H_2(g) \rightleftharpoons 2NH_3(g)$
The value of K_c = 2.0 $mol^{-2}\,dm^6$ at 620 K.
What is the concentration of ammonia at equilibrium when the equilibrium concentrations of hydrogen and nitrogen are both 2.0 $mol\,dm^{-3}$?

11 When 8.28 g of ethanol were heated with 60.00 g of ethanoic acid 49.74 g of the acid remained at equilibrium. Calculate the value of the equilibrium constant.

Now consider the formation of hydrogen iodide:

$$H_2(g) + I_2(g) \rightleftharpoons 2HI(g)$$

Suppose a mol of hydrogen is mixed with b mol of iodine and allowed to reach equilibrium so that x mol of HI are formed then:

	$H_2(g)$	+	$I_2(g)$	$\rightleftharpoons$	$2HI(g)$
mol at start:	a		b		0
mol at equilibrium:	$(a - x/2)$		$(b - x/2)$		x

Table 7

From the balanced equation 1 mol of hydrogen reacts with 1 mol of iodine to form *two* mol of hydrogen iodide.

$$\text{So } K_c = \frac{x^2}{(a - x/2)(b - x/2)}$$

5 0.206 mol of hydrogen and 0.144 mol of iodine were heated at 683K. At equilibrium 0.258 mol of HI were present.

a) Calculate the value of K_c at this temperature.

b) If the value for K_c is 54 at 700 K deduce whether this reaction is exothermic or endothermic.

Answer

a)

	$H_2(g)$	+	$I_2(g)$	$\rightleftharpoons$	$2HI(g)$
mol at start:	0.206		0.144		0
mol at equilibrium:	(0.206 – 0.258/2) = 0.077		(0.144 – 0.258/2) = 0.015		0.258

$$K_c = \frac{(0.258)^2}{(0.077 \times 0.015)} = 57.63$$

b) As the temperature increases the value of K_c decreases so the forward reaction is exothermic.

For reactions that involve a change in the number of moles, the volume must be known in order to calculate concentrations before K_c can be determined. This is illustrated in the next worked example.

6 Consider the gaseous equilibrium:

$$N_2O_4(g) \rightleftharpoons 2NO_2(g)$$

At 300 K 1.0 mol of $N_2O_4(g)$ is 20% dissociated in a 2.0 dm^3 flask. Calculate the value of K_c for this reaction.

Answer

If N_2O_4 is 20% dissociated then 80% remains at equilibrium
i.e. 1.0 x 80/100 = 0.8 mol.
20% has been converted into nitrogen dioxide.

	$N_2O_4(g) \rightleftharpoons$	$2NO_2(g)$
mol at start:	1.0	0
mol at equilibrium:	0.8	2 x 0.2 = 0.4

$$K_c = \frac{[NO_2]^2}{[N_2O_4]} \text{ mol dm}^{-3}$$

It is not possible to use moles in the K_c expression since the units for K_c are mol dm^{-3}.

$$K_c = \frac{(0.4/V)^2}{0.8/V} = \frac{0.16}{0.8 \times V} \quad \text{where } V = 2\,dm^3$$

$$K_c = \frac{0.16}{0.8 \times 2} = 0.1 \text{ mol dm}^{-3}$$

12 a) Write an equation for the dissociation of PCl_5.

b) Write an expression for K_c for this reaction, stating the units.

c) 0.01 mol of PCl_5 was heated to 210°C in a 1 dm^3 vessel. At equilibrium 0.0042 mol remained. Calculate K_c.

13 Consider the following reaction:

$$CO(g) + Cl_2(g) \rightleftharpoons COCl_2(g)$$

A mixture of 2 mol of carbon monoxide and 5 mol of chlorine were allowed to reach equilibrium in a 10 dm^3 vessel. At equilibrium 1 mol of carbon monoxide remained. Calculate the value of K_c for this reaction.

Key Ideas 18 – 26

- K_c is an equilibrium constant expressed in terms of the concentrations of reactants and products.
- K_c is a constant for a particular reaction at a particular temperature.
- K_c is unaffected by changes in concentration or pressure and by the addition of a catalyst but varies with temperature.
- K_c can be calculated from the equilibrium concentrations of the reactants and products.

3 The equilibrium constant K_p

For homogeneous equilibrium reactions involving gases it is more convenient to use **partial pressures** of the reactants and products rather than concentrations in mol dm^{-3}. This leads to expressions for the equilibrium constant, K_p, in terms of the partial pressures of the reactants and products.

Writing an expression for K_p

The **partial pressure** of a gas in a mixture of gases is the pressure that the gas would exert if it alone occupied the available volume. Consider the equation for the Haber process:

$$N_2(g) + 3H_2(g) \rightleftharpoons 2NH_3(g)$$

$$K_p = \frac{(PNH_3)^2}{(PN_2)(PH_2)^3}$$ where PNH_3, PN_2 and PH_2 are the partial pressures of the three gases at equilibrium

Partial pressures are measured in pascals, Pa or kilopascals, kPa (an older unit is the atmosphere, where one atmosphere is 101,325 Pa)

The units of K_p for this reaction:

$$\frac{Pa^2}{Pa \times Pa^3} = \frac{1}{Pa^2} = Pa^{-2}$$

Knowing the values of the partial pressures of the gases at equilibrium, we can calculate the value of the equilibrium constant, K_p.

Worked example

1 **The partial pressures of the gases at equilibrium in the Haber process at 640K are hydrogen 40 kPa; nitrogen 10 kPa; ammonia 15 kPa.**

Use these data to calculate a value for K_p at 640K.

Answer

First write the equation and then an expression for K_p, with units:

$$K_p = \frac{(PNH_3)^2}{(PN_2)(PH_2)^3} \text{ kPa}^{-2}$$

Now substitute the values quoted into the expression:

$$K_p = \frac{(15)^2}{(10)(40)^3} = 3.5 \times 10^{-4} \text{ kPa}^{-2}$$

K_p is a constant

It is important to note that K_p like K_c is a constant at constant temperature. Altering the partial pressures of the reactants will shift the equilibrium position *but* the value of K_p remains constant.

If the partial pressure of nitrogen is doubled in the reaction:

$$N_2(g) + 3H_2(g) \rightleftharpoons 2NH_3(g)$$

then, by Le Chatelier's Principle, the equilibrium will shift to the right to produce more ammonia with an increased partial pressure, but K_p will still equal $3.5 \times 10^{-4}\,kPa^{-2}$.

14 Calculate the partial pressure of ammonia in the above reaction at 640 K if the partial pressure of nitrogen is doubled from 10 kPa to 20 kPa, while the partial pressure of hydrogen is maintained at 40 kPa.

If the temperature is altered then K_p will also alter.

- If the forward reaction is exothermic an *increase* in temperature will favour the reverse reaction and the value of the equilibrium constant will *decrease*.
- If the forward reaction is endothermic an *increase* in temperature will favour the forward reaction and the value of the equilibrium constant will *increase*.

This can be illustrated for the Haber process:

$$N_2(g) + 3H_2(g) \rightleftharpoons 2NH_3(g) \qquad \Delta H = -92.4\,kJ\,mol^{-1}$$

In this reaction the K_p values for the forward reaction, which is exothermic, decrease with temperature (see Table 1). Conversely the K_p values for the backward reaction would increase with temperature.

Temperature/K	K_p /kPa^{-2}
298	6.8×10^{4}
500	3.55×10^{-3}
700	7.8×10^{-6}
900	1.0×10^{-7}

Table 1

15 Calculate the K_p value for the dissociation of ammonia at 700 K.

16 Consider the following reaction:

$$H_2(g) + I_2(g) \rightleftharpoons 2HI(g) \qquad \Delta H = -10.4\,kJ\,mol^{-1}$$

a) Write an expression for the equilibrium constant in terms of partial pressures.

b) At a fixed temperature, X, analysis of the equilibrium mixture of the gases gave the following partial pressures: hydrogen 250 Pa; iodine 160 Pa; hydrogen iodide 1400 Pa.

Calculate the equilibrium constant for this reaction.

c) If the K_p value for this reaction is 54 at 700K deduce whether the temperature X above is higher or lower than 700K. Explain your answer.

Calculations using total pressure

The sum of the partial pressures of the individual gases in a mixture will equal the total pressure exerted by the mixture of gases.

In the Haber process:

Total pressure = $PNH_3 + PN_2 + PH_2$

This is a useful expression that will be needed in calculations.

Worked examples

2 **In the Contact Process, at equilibrium and with a total pressure of 120 kPa, the partial pressures of sulphur dioxide and sulphur trioxide are 33 kPa and 39 kPa respectively. Calculate a value of K_p stating the units.**

Answer

First write the equation for the process and then an expression for K_p, with units:

$$2SO_2(g) + O_2(g) \rightleftharpoons 2SO_3(g)$$

$$K_p = \frac{(PSO_3)^2}{(PO_2)(PSO_2)^2} \text{ kPa}^{-1}$$

Before the partial pressures can be substituted into the expression we need to find the partial pressure of oxygen, which is not quoted in the question.

Using: Total pressure = the sum of the partial pressures

$$120 = 33 + 39 + PO_2$$

$$PO_2 = 120 - (33 + 39) = 48$$

$$K_p = \frac{(39)^2}{48 \times (33)^2} = 0.029 \text{ kPa}^{-1}$$

Mole fractions

In AS Chemistry you will have studied the ideal gas equation, $pV = nRT$.

In a mixture of gases the volume and temperature are the same for each of the gases in the mixture, so the pressure of each gas is proportional to the number of moles present i.e. $p \propto n$. This means that the partial pressure of each gas is proportional to its **mole fraction**.

For example, if an equilibrium mixture contains 1 mol of ammonia, 3.6 mol of hydrogen and 13.5 mol of nitrogen then the total number of moles of gas present at equilibrium is 1 + 3.6 + 13.5 = 18.1 mol.

The mole fraction of ammonia = 1/18.1 = 0.055.
The mole fraction of hydrogen = 3.6/18.1 = 0.199.
The mole fraction of nitrogen = 13.5/18.1 = 0.746.
The sum of the mole fractions equals 1.

The partial pressures of the gases, and hence the K_p can be calculated from mole fractions using the expression:

The partial pressure of each gas = mole fraction × total pressure

3 A gaseous mixture contains 7 moles of X, 2 moles of Y and 1 mole of Z at equilibrium at a total pressure of 100 kPa. Calculate the value of K_p for the reaction:

$$X(g) + Y(g) \rightleftharpoons 2Z(g)$$

Answer

First calculate the mole fractions of each gas:

The total number of moles = 10

The mole fractions of the gases are: X 7/10 = 0.7; Y 2/10 = 0.2; Z 1/10 = 0.1.

Using: The partial pressure of each gas = mole fraction x total pressure

The partial pressures are: X 0.7 × 100 = 70 kPa; Y 0.2 × 100 = 20 kPa; Z 0.1 × 100 = 10 kPa

Knowing the values of the partial pressures of the gases at equilibrium, we can now calculate the value of the equilibrium constant, K_p

$$K_p = \frac{(PZ)^2}{(PY)(PX)} \quad \text{(no units)} \qquad K_p = \frac{(10)^2}{20 \times 70} = 0.071$$

17 The reaction: $PCl_5(g) \rightleftharpoons PCl_3(g) + Cl_2(g)$ is carried out at 120 kPa pressure. A sample of phosphorus(V) chloride is introduced into the reaction vessel. At equilibrium the partial pressure of phosphorus(V) chloride is 80kPa. Calculate the value of K_p.

18 $2SO_2(g) + O_2(g) \rightleftharpoons 2SO_3(g)$

Initially a vessel contained 12 moles of SO_2 and 6 moles of O_2. At equilibrium, at a total pressure of 200 kPa it was found that 90% of the SO_2 had reacted to form SO_3. Calculate the value of K_p for this reaction.

Key Ideas 27 – 31

- **The equilibrium constant for gaseous equilibria is calculated from the partial pressures of the gases present.**
- **The partial pressure of a gas in a mixture of gases is the pressure that the gas would exert if it alone occupied the available volume.**
- **The total pressure of a system equals the sum of the partial pressures of the individual gases.**
- **The partial pressure of a gas = the mole fraction of the gas × the total pressure.**

Unit 2 Questions

4

(1) Ethanol can be manufactured by the hydration of ethene in the presence of concentrated phosphoric(V) acid, which acts as the catalyst.
The equation for this reaction is:

$$C_2H_4(g) + H_2O(g) \rightleftharpoons C_2H_5OH(g) \qquad \Delta H = -46\,kJ\,mol^{-1}$$

The *position* of equilibrium and the *rate* at which equilibrium is attained are affected by the temperature and pressure at which the process is carried out. The conditions used industrially are 573K and 6000 kPa.
Complete the table below: (6)

	Effect on position of equilibrium	Effect on rate at which equilibrium is attained
A high pressure		
A high temperature		
The presence of the catalyst		

(2) Nitrogen dioxide dimerises into dinitrogen tetroxide and an equilibrium is established in the gaseous phase according to the equation below:

$$2NO_2(g) \rightleftharpoons N_2O_4(g)$$

dark brown — colourless

a) As the mixture is heated it becomes more brown in colour. What does this observation tell you about the ΔH value for the forward reaction? Explain your answer. (3)

b) What would be the effect on the yield of N_2O_4 of increasing the total pressure? Explain your answer. (3)

c) (i) Write an expression for the equilibrium constant K_p for the equilibrium.

(ii) At 298K and a total pressure of 200 kPa the mole fraction of NO_2 is 0.23. Use your answer to c)(i) and these data to calculate the value of K_p at this temperature.

(iii) How would this value change if the temperature were raised to 398K? (7)

(3) When 1.00 mol each of ethanol and ethanoic acid are mixed together at a fixed temperature the reaction mixture at equilibrium contains 0.66 mol of ethyl ethanoate.

a) Write an equation for this equilibrium. (1)

b) (i) The total volume of the reaction mixture is 0.10 dm^3. Calculate the equilibrium concentrations of ethyl ethanoate and ethanol.

(ii) Hence calculate the value of K_c at this temperature. (6)

c) This reaction is affected by the addition of a few drops of concentrated sulphuric acid.

(i) What is the role of concentrated sulphuric acid in this reaction?

(ii) What effect will this acid have on the rate of the reaction? Explain your answer.

(iii) What effect will this acid have on the K_c value calculated in b)(ii) above? (5)

(4) At high temperatures phosphorus(V) chloride dissociates according to the equation:

$$PCl_5(g) \rightleftharpoons PCl_3(g) + Cl_2(g)$$

An equilibrium mixture was found to contain 20.85 g of PCl_5, 20.625 g of PCl_3 and 14.20g of Cl_2 at 100 kPa pressure.

a) Calculate the number of moles of each component present at equilibrium and hence calculate their mole fractions. (4)

b) Use your answers in a) to calculate the partial pressure for each gas and hence calculate the value of the equilibrium constant, K_p, for this reaction: (4)

(5) **a)** The graph below shows how the K_c value for the reaction between A and B varies with temperature:

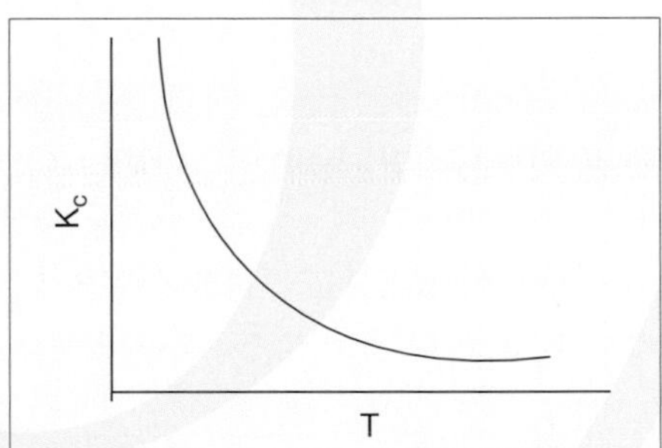

Use this graph to deduce whether the reaction:

$$A(g) + 2B(g) \rightleftharpoons C(g)$$

is exothermic or endothermic. Explain your answer. (2)

b) (i) At 400 K the value of K_c for this reaction is $2 \times 10^{-4} mol^{-2} dm^6$. Explain the significance of this value in terms of the equilibrium position of the reaction.

(ii) Give three ways in which the yield of C could be increased. (3)

1 Acids and bases

At GCSE you will have studied acids and bases. An **acid** is a substance containing a replaceable hydrogen atom. When an acid is added to water the acid ionises or **dissociates** releasing $H^+(aq)$ ions. A **base** is a substance that neutralises acids to form salts and water. A soluble base is called an **alkali**. In this unit we will take a more quantitative look at acids and bases.

The Brønsted–Lowry theory of acidity

When an acid is added to water the acid ionises releasing $H^+(aq)$ ions.

The **neutralisation** reaction between an acid and an alkali can be shown ionically as:

$$H^+(aq) + OH^-(aq) \rightarrow H_2O(l)$$

This theory of acidity, proposed by the Swedish chemist Arrhenius in 1884, is somewhat restrictive since it only applies to aqueous solutions. At A2 the ideas of acidity are further developed by studying the acid–base theory proposed independently by a British chemist, Lowry, and a Swedish chemist, Brønsted, in 1923.

Acids

According to the Brønsted–Lowry theory an acid is a **proton donor**.

In aqueous solution, acids ionise and donate protons, $H^+(aq)$, to the water molecules.

This is shown in the following equation using HA to represent any acid:

$$HA(aq) + H_2O(l) \rightarrow H_3O^+(aq) + A^-(aq)$$

Acids are classified as **strong** or **weak** depending upon the extent to which the acid ionises in solution.

Strong acids are *fully* (100%) ionised in solution. Examples include HCl, H_2SO_4 and HNO_3.

$$HCl + \text{water} \rightarrow H^+(aq) + Cl^-(aq)$$

$$H_2SO_4 + \text{water} \rightarrow 2H^+(aq) + SO_4^{2-}(aq)$$

$$HNO_3 + \text{water} \rightarrow H^+(aq) + NO_3^-(aq)$$

Weak acids are only *partially* ionised in solution. Examples of weak acids include organic acids such as ethanoic acid, CH_3COOH.

For any weak acid, HA:

$$HA(aq) + H_2O(l) \rightleftharpoons H_3O^+(aq) + A^-(aq)$$

In the forward reaction HA has donated an $H^+(aq)$ ion to water, leaving A^-. In the reverse reaction A^- accepts $H^+(aq)$ from $H_3O^+(aq)$ and reforms HA. HA is acting as an acid and A^- is acting as a base. The two species are described as a **conjugate pair** where A^- is the called the **conjugate base** of the acid HA.

This equilibrium lies very much to the left so the concentration of H_3O^+ ions in a solution of a weak acid is much less than that of a strong acid of the comparable concentration.

- Note that the terms strong and weak should not be confused with the terms concentrated and dilute. Strong and weak refer to the extent of dissociation of an acid or base. Concentrated and dilute refer to the amount of acid or base in a given volume of water.

1 a) What are the roles of H_2O and $H_3O^+(aq)$ in the equation below?

$$HA(aq) + H_2O(l) \rightleftharpoons H_3O^+(aq) + A^-(aq)$$

b) Write an equation to show the dissociation of ethanoic acid in water. Identify its conjugate base.

The acid dissociation constant, K_a

$$HA(aq) + H_2O(l) \rightleftharpoons H_3O^+(aq) + A^-(aq)$$

Since this is an equilibrium reaction we can write an expression for the equilibrium constant K_c for the reaction:

$$K_c = \frac{[H^+(aq)][A^-(aq)]}{[HA(aq)][H_2O(l)]}$$

where [ ] = the equilibrium concentrations ($mol\ dm^{-3}$) and $[H_3O^+(aq)] = [H^+(aq)]$

For a dilute weak acid the concentration of the water is effectively constant because it is in large excess, and it can be left out of the equilibrium expression.

$$K_a = \frac{[H^+(aq)][A^-(aq)]}{[HA(aq)]}\ mol\ dm^{-3}$$

where $K_a = K_c[H_2O(l)]$

The equilibrium established between ethanoic acid and water is:

$$CH_3COOH(aq) + H_2O(l) \rightleftharpoons CH_3COO^-(aq) + H_3O^+(aq)$$

The dissociation constant K_a for ethanoic acid is:

$$K_a = \frac{[H^+(aq)][CH_3COO^-(aq)]}{[CH_3COOH(aq)]}\ mol\ dm^{-3}$$

The value of K_a depends upon the extent of dissociation of the acid. The *weaker* the acid, the *smaller* the value of K_a. Some values of the **acid dissociation constant** are given in Table 1 overleaf.

Formula	Name	K_a /mol dm^{-3}
CH_3COOH	Ethanoic acid	1.7×10^{-5}
$HCOOH$	Methanoic acid	1.6×10^{-4}
$(COOH)_2$	Ethanedioic acid	5.9×10^{-2}
C_6H_5COOH	Benzene carboxylic acid*	6.3×10^{-5}
$CH_2ClCOOH$	Chloroethanoic acid	1.3×10^{-3}

Table 1

*also called benzoic acid

These values of K_a are quoted for 298 K. The dissociation of an acid is an *endothermic* process and therefore as the temperature increases the dissociation will increase. This will increase the value of the acid dissociation constant.

2 Which of the acids listed in Table 1 is the strongest?

3 Write an expression for the acid dissociation constant for benzene carboxylic acid.

4 Will the K_a value for ethanoic acid be greater or less than 1.7×10^{-5} mol dm^{-3} at 10°C? Explain your answer.

Bases

According to the Brønsted–Lowry theory a base is defined as a **proton acceptor**.

In solution bases accept protons from water molecules:

$B(aq) + H_2O(l) \rightarrow BH^+(aq) + OH^-(aq)$ where B is used to represent a base.

In this equation BH^+ is the **conjugate acid** of the base, B.

Bases can be strong or weak depending upon the extent to which they ionise in solution.

Strong bases are fully (100%) ionised in solution. Examples include potassium and sodium hydroxide, which are ionic compounds:

$$Na^+OH^- + \text{water} \rightarrow Na^+(aq) + OH^-(aq)$$

$$K^+OH^- + \text{water} \rightarrow K^+(aq) + OH^-(aq)$$

Weak bases are only partially ionised in solution. Examples include ammonia and the homologous series of amines:

$$NH_3(aq) + H_2O(l) \rightleftharpoons NH_4^+(aq) + OH^-(aq)$$

$$RNH_2(aq) + H_2O(l) \rightleftharpoons RNH_3^+(aq) + OH^-(aq)$$

5 Give the formula of the conjugate acid of methylamine.

Acid–base equilibria

Acid–base equilibria involve proton transfer. In such equilibria the acid donates a proton to the base. Since these reactions are reversible there is an acid and a base on both sides of the equation. The acid and its conjugate base and the base and its conjugate acid are called **conjugate pairs**.

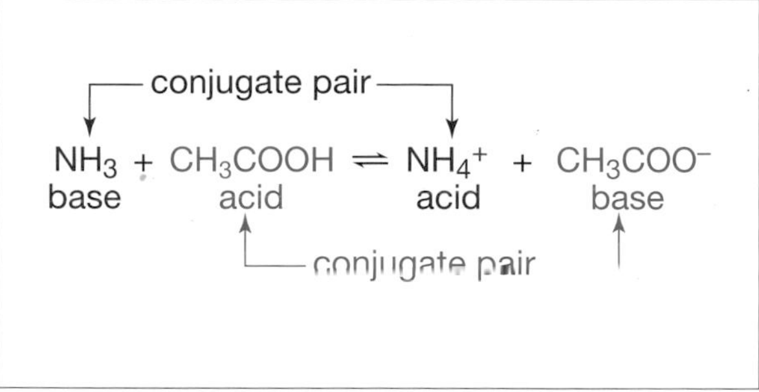

Figure 1 *Conjugate pairs*

Some more examples are shown in Table 2 below:

H_2SO_4 acid	HNO_3 base	⇌	HSO_4^- conjugate base	$H_2NO_3^+$ conjugate acid
NH_3 base	H_2O acid	⇌	NH_4^+ conjugate acid	OH^- conjugate base
HF base	HNO_3 acid	⇌	HF_2^+ conjugate acid	NO_3^- conjugate base
HCOOH acid	H_2O base	⇌	$HCOO^-$ conjugate base	H_3O^+ conjugate acid

Table 2 *Conjugate pairs*

Notice from the table that HNO_3, which is conventionally thought of as an acid, can also act as a base in its reaction with sulphuric acid. This is because sulphuric acid is stronger than nitric acid and assumes the role of a proton donor. Notice also that water, which is conventionally considered to be neutral, can act as an acid or a base depending on the other reactant. Since water can act as both an acid and a base, it can be described as **amphoteric**.

Q

6 Identify the acids and bases in the following reactions

a) $H_2SO_4 + CH_3COOH \rightleftharpoons HSO_4^- + CH_3COOH_2^+$

b) $CH_3CONH_2 + NH_3 \rightleftharpoons CH_3CONH^- + NH_4^+$

Key Ideas 34 – 37

- A Brønsted–Lowry acid is a proton donor
- A Brønsted–Lowry base is a proton acceptor
- The strength of an acid or base is determined by the degree of dissociation; Strong acids/bases are fully dissociated in solution whilst weak acids/bases are only partially dissociated in solution.

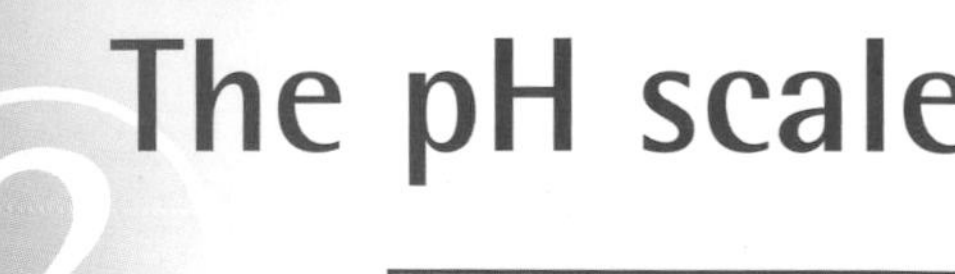

2 The pH scale

At GCSE the **pH** scale is a range of numbers from 0 to 14. It is used to show how acidic or alkaline a solution is; pH numbers of less than 7 represent acids and those above 7 represent alkalis. A solution of pH 7 is neutral. At A2 level the approach is quantitative and you will need to perform calculations to determine pH values.

Measuring pH

Universal indicator can be used to give an approximation of pH and hence the strength of an acidic or alkaline solution.

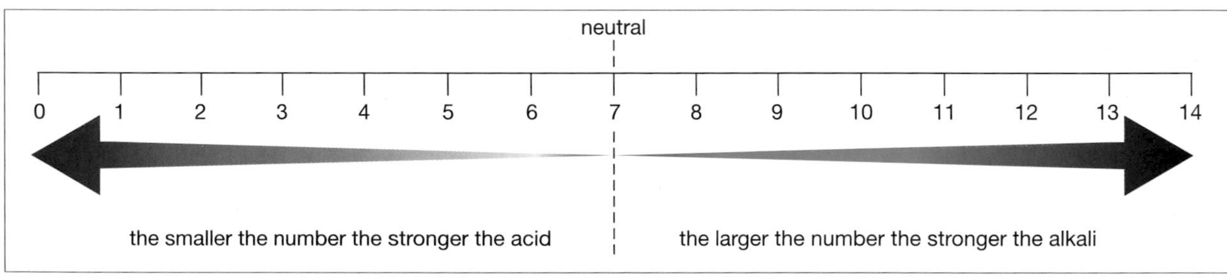

Figure 1 *Universal indicator chart*

At A level we need to be much more specific. It is no longer acceptable to say that hydrochloric acid is a strong acid with a pH of 1. The pH of an acid varies with concentration and temperature so the pH of hydrochloric acid is not always 1. A correct statement would be '0.1 M HCl has a pH of 1 at 298 K'.

An accurate pH value of a solution can be found using a **pH meter**.

Before use, a pH meter should be calibrated using buffer solutions of known pH. The pH meter should be used in several buffer solutions and a calibration curve of observed pH readings against known buffer pH values can then be plotted.

The calibration curve can then be used to adjust the observed pH of a solution as shown in Figure 2.

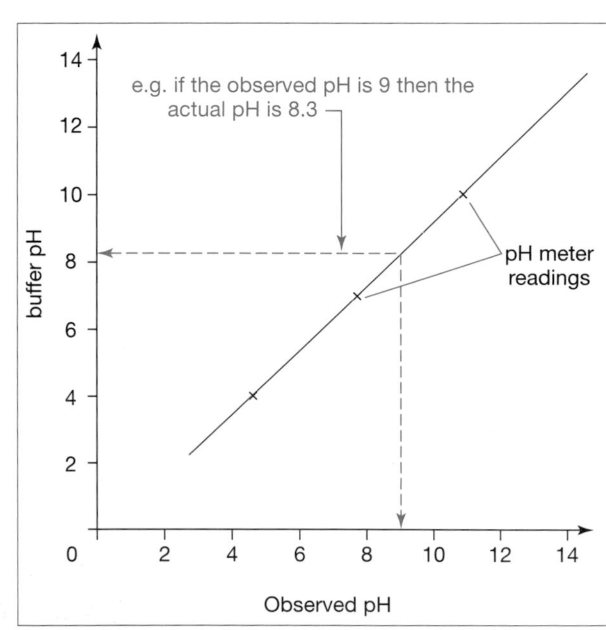

Figure 2 *pH calibration curve*

Calculating pH

The concentration of hydrogen ions in solution, $[H^+(aq)]$, can be expressed as a pH value where:

$$pH = -\log_{10}[H^+(aq)]$$

The pH scale is a logarithmic scale based on a factor of 10 and therefore when a pH value changes by one unit the $[H^+(aq)]$ has changed by a factor of 10. When the pH changes by 3 units the $[H^+(aq)]$ changes by a factor of 1000 (10^3). For example:

When $[H^+(aq)]$ is 1×10^{-4} mol dm^{-3} then pH $= -\log_{10}(1 \times 10^{-4}) = 4$

If $[H^+(aq)]$ mol dm^{-3} = 1.00 (1×10^0) then pH = 0

If $[H^+(aq)]$ mol dm^{-3} = 0.10 (1×10^{-1}) then pH = 1

For more complicated answers you will need to use a calculator:

If $[H^+(aq)]$ mol dm^{-3} = 0.05 then pH $= -\log_{10}0.05 = 1.3$

If $[H^+(aq)]$ mol dm^{-3} = 2.00 then pH $= -\log_{10}2.00 = -0.30$

As the concentration of $H^+(aq)$ *increases* the pH value *decreases*.

Notice that pH values can be negative. This only occurs with solutions of strong acids with a concentration greater than 1 M.

7 Calculate the pH of the following solutions.

a) $[H^+(aq)]$ = 0.025 mol dm^{-3} **b) $[H^+(aq)]$ = 0.005 mol dm^{-3}**

c) $[H^+(aq)]$ = 0.125 mol dm^{-3}

If we know the pH of a solution then we can calculate the $[H^+(aq)]$ of that solution. This is the reverse of the process used to find pH. You will need to change the sign of the pH value then find the inverse $\log_{10}$ of the value. Some examples are given below:

If pH = 1 then $[H^+(aq)]$ = 0.1 mol dm^{-3} i.e. 1×10^{-1}

If pH = 2 then $[H^+(aq)]$ = 0.01 mol dm^{-3} i.e. 1×10^{-2}

If pH = 3 then $[H^+(aq)]$ = 0.001 mol dm^{-3} i.e. 1×10^{-3}

For more complicated examples you will need to use a calculator:

If pH = 2.5 then $[H^+(aq)] = 3.16 \times 10^{-3}$ mol dm^{-3}

If pH = −0.15 then $[H^+(aq)]$ = 1.4 mol dm^{-3}

8 Calculate the $[H^+(aq)]$ from the following pH values.

a) 5.0 b) 3.5 c) −0.20 d) 4.25 e) 6.95 f) −0.09

Calculating the pH for strong acids

For a strong **monoprotic** acid the $[H^+(aq)]$ is equal to the concentration of the acid. This allows us to calculate the pH directly from the concentration of the acid.

$$HA(aq) + water \rightarrow H^+(aq) + A^-(aq) \quad \text{where } [HA(aq)] = [H^+(aq)]$$

For 0.1 M HCl the $[H^+(aq)] = 0.1$ so pH = 1.

For 0.2 M HNO_3 the $[H^+(aq)] = 0.2$ so pH = 0.7.

Sulphuric acid is a **diprotic** acid so each acid molecule produces two hydrogen ions in solution:

$$H_2SO_4 + water \rightarrow 2H^+(aq) + SO_4^{2-}(aq)$$

So, for 0.1 M H_2SO_4 the $[H^+(aq)] = 0.2$ and hence the pH = 0.7.

We can also calculate the concentration of a strong acid from its pH. For example:

If the pH of HCl is 1.7 then $1.7 = -\log_{10}[H^+(aq)]$

so $[H^+(aq)] = 0.02$

Therefore the concentration of the acid is 0.02 M.

9 Calculate the pH of the following acid solutions.

a) 1 M HCl
b) 0.25 M HNO_3
c) 0.15 M H_2SO_4

10 Calculate the concentration of the following strong acids from the given pH values:

a) HCl pH = 1.6 b) HNO_3 pH = 0.52

Calculating the pH of weak acids

We cannot use the same method to work out the pH of a weak acid that we used for strong acids. This is because a weak acid is only partially ionised in solution and therefore the hydrogen ion concentration is *not* the same as the concentration of the acid. In fact [HA] is much greater than $[H^+]$. Instead we calculate the pH using the acid dissociation constant, K_a

$$HA(aq) \rightleftharpoons H^+(aq) + A^-(aq) \quad \text{where HA is any weak acid}$$

$$K_a = \frac{[H^+(aq)][A^-(aq)]}{[HA(aq)]}$$

For the weak acid, HA, in solution $[H^+(aq)] = [A^-(aq)]$.

Hence

$$K_a = \frac{[H^+(aq)]^2}{[HA(aq)]} \text{ mol dm}^{-3}$$

If the concentration of the weak acid, HA, is c mol dm^{-3} then

$$[H^+(aq)]^2 = K_a c$$

therefore $\mathbf{[H^+(aq)] = \sqrt{(K_a c)}}$.

If the value of K_a and c are known then we can calculate the value of $[H^+(aq)]$ and hence the pH of the weak acid.

(This assumes that the quoted concentration of the acid, c, is the equilibrium concentration. In fact c = [HA(aq)] – $[H^+(aq)]$ but since $[H^+(aq)]$ is so small the approximation given above is valid.)

Worked examples

1 The weak acid CH_3COOH has a K_a value of 1.8×10^{-5} mol dm^{-3} at 300 K. Calculate the pH of a 0.1 M solution of this acid at this temperature.

Answer

Using $[H^+(aq)] = \sqrt{(K_a c)}$ and substituting the values for K_a and c

we get $[H^+(aq)] = \sqrt{(1.8 \times 10^{-5} \times 0.1)} = 1.34 \times 10^{-3}$ mol dm^{-3}

Since pH $= -\log_{10}[H^+(aq)]$

then pH $= -\log_{10}(1.34 \times 10^{-3}) = 2.87$

If the pH value and the molarity of a weak acid are known then the value of K_a can be calculated:

2 A 0.1 M solution of a weak acid, HA, has a pH value of 2.50. Calculate the value for the acid dissociation constant K_a

Answer

Using $\text{pH} = -\log_{10}[H^+(aq)]$

then $2.50 = -\log_{10}[H^+(aq)]$

so $[H^+(aq)] = 3.16 \times 10^{-3}$ mol dm^{-3}

But $K_a = \dfrac{[H^+(aq)]^2}{[HA]}$ mol dm^{-3}

Hence $K_a = \dfrac{(3.16 \times 10^{-3})^2}{0.1} = 1 \times 10^{-4}$ mol dm^{-3}

11 a) Define pH.

b) If the pH of a 0.1 M solution of ethanoic acid is 2.88 at 20°C calculate the hydrogen ion concentration of this solution at 20°C and hence a value for K_a

The pK_a scale

Since K_a values are very small it is convenient to use the pK_a scale where

$$pK_a = -\log_{10}K_a$$

For example.

If $K_a = 1.70 \times 10^{-5}$ mol dm^{-3}

Then p$K_a = -\log_{10}(1.70 \times 10^{-5}) = 4.77$

If $K_a = 2.30 \times 10^{-7}$ mol dm^{-3} then pK_a = 6.63.

For weak acids the pK_a is often a more useful tool than pH since it is independent of concentration. Some examples of pK_a values are given in Table 1.

Name	Formula	pK_a value
Trichloroethanoic acid	CCl_3COOH	0.7
Methanoic acid	HCOOH	3.8
Benzoic acid	C_6H_5COOH	4.2
Ethanoic acid	CH_3COOH	4.8
Propanoic acid	CH_3CH_2COOH	4.9
Carbonic acid	H_2CO_3	6.4

Notice that the stronger the acid, the *lower* its pK_a value.

Worked examples

3 Calculate the pH of a 0.1 M solution of a weak acid given that it has a pK_a value of 4.76 at 298 K.

Answer

Using pK_a = $-\log_{10}K_a$ i.e. 4.76 = $-\log_{10}K_a$

so K_a = 1.737×10^{-5} mol dm^{-3}

$[H^+]^2 = K_a c = 1.737 \times 10^{-5} \times 0.1 = 1.737 \times 10^{-6}$

$[H^+] = \sqrt{(1.737 \times 10^{-6})} = 1.318 \times 10^{-3}$ mol dm^{-3}

since pH = $-\log_{10}[H^+(aq)] = -\log_{10}(1.318 \times 10^{-3}) = 2.88$.

4 A 0.01 M solution of a weak acid, X, has a pH of 3.37 at 200 K. Calculate the pK_a value for X at this temperature.

Answer

Using 3.37 = $-\log_{10}[H^+(aq)]$ then the $[H^+(aq)]$ of X = 4.27×10^{-4} mol dm^{-3}

But $[H^+(aq)] = \sqrt{(K_a c)}$ so $[H^+(aq)]^2 = K_a c$

Rearranging this expression we get:

$$\frac{[H^+(aq)]^2}{c} = K_a$$

So $$K_a = \frac{(4.27 \times 10^{-4})^2}{0.01} = 1.82 \times 10^{-5}$$

pK_a = $-\log_{10}K_a$ = 4.74.

12 a) Define pK_a.

b) The K_a value for ethanoic acid is 1.99×10^{-5} at 35 °C. Calculate the pK_a value at this temperature.

Ionic product of water

Just because a solution contains H^+ ions it doesn't necessarily mean that the solution is acidic. All aqueous solutions will contain H^+ ions and OH^- ions, which are derived from the partial dissociation of the water.

For an acid solution $[H^+] > [OH^-]$, for an alkaline solution $[OH^-] > [H^+]$, for a neutral solution $[H^+] = [OH^-]$.

The partial dissociation of water is shown below:

$$H_2O(l) + H_2O(l) \rightleftharpoons H_3O^+(aq) + OH^-(aq)$$

The equation is usually simplified to:

$$H_2O(l) \rightleftharpoons H^+(aq) + OH^-(aq)$$

The expression for the equilibrium constant is

$$K_c = \frac{[H^+(aq)][OH^-(aq)]}{[H_2O(l)]}$$

Since the concentration of the water is effectively constant and in large excess we can simplify the expression to:

$\boldsymbol{K_w = [H^+(aq)][OH^-(aq)]}$ **mol² dm⁻⁶** where $K_w = K_c[H_2O]$

K_w is called the ionic product of water

At 298 K the value of K_w is 1×10^{-14} mol² dm⁻⁶

In pure water $[H^+(aq)] = [OH^-(aq)]$ so $K_w = [H^+(aq)]^2$

Hence $[H^+(aq)] = \sqrt{K_w}$

At 298 K $[H^+(aq)] = \sqrt{(1 \times 10^{-14})} = 1 \times 10^{-7}$ mol dm⁻³

So in pure water, at 298 K, the pH value is 7.

The dissociation of water is an *endothermic* process. The endothermic reaction is favoured by higher temperatures and therefore as the temperature *increases*, the value of K_w *increases*.

This means that at higher temperatures the concentration of $H^+(aq)$ in pure water will increase. This results in the pH of pure water *decreasing*. The water is still neutral since the concentration of hydrogen ions is the same as the concentration of the hydroxide ions. Consider the following example:

At 321 K the value of K_w is 4×10^{-14} mol² dm⁻⁶.

Since $[H^+(aq)] = \sqrt{K_w}$

Then $[H^+(aq)] = \sqrt{(4 \times 10^{-14})} = 2 \times 10^{-7}$ mol dm⁻³

Using $pH = -\log_{10}[H^+(aq)] = -\log_{10}(2 \times 10^{-7})$

So at 321 K the pH of pure water is 6.70.

13 a) Define the ionic product of water and state its units.

b) If the pH of pure water at 5 °C is 7.6 calculate the value for K_w at this temperature.

The pH of strong bases

The ionic product of water provides a method of calculating the pH for a solution of a strong base using:

$$K_w = [H^+(aq)][OH^-(aq)]$$

$$\text{Hence } [H^+(aq)] = K_w / [OH^-(aq)]$$

Worked example

5 Calculate the pH of 0.1 M KOH.

Since KOH is a strong base then for a 0.1 M solution of KOH the $[OH^-(aq)] = 0.1$.

If the temperature is 298 K then K_w is 1×10^{-14} mol² dm⁻⁶

Hence $[H^+(aq)] = \dfrac{1 \times 10^{-14}}{0.1} = 1 \times 10^{-13}$

Using $pH = -\log_{10}[H^+(aq)] = -\log_{10}(1 \times 10^{-13})$

Hence pH = 13

An alternative method for calculating the pH of an alkali at 298 K is to use the expression:

$$pH + pOH = 14$$

where $pOH = -\log_{10}[OH^-(aq)]$

This expression is only valid at 298 K, since the ionic product of water at this temperature results in a value of 14 for the expression.

If $[OH^-(aq)] = 0.1$ then pOH = 1

Hence pH + 1 = 14

Hence pH = 13

14 a) At 338 K the pH of pure water is 6.5. Calculate K_w at this temperature.

b) Hence calculate the pH of 0.01 M NaOH at 338 K.

Calculating pH after dilution

When a solution of an acid or base is diluted then the pH of the solution will change since the same number of H^+ ions is present in a greater volume.

Worked examples

6 Calculate the change in pH when 10 cm³ of 0.1 M HCl is added to 240 cm³ of water.

The initial concentration of $[H^+(aq)]$ is 0.1 mol dm^{-3} since the acid is a strong monoprotic acid, so $[H^+(aq)] = [HCl]$.

initial pH = $-\log_{10}[H^+(aq)] = -\log_{10}(0.1) = 1$

To calculate the new pH after the addition of water we need to calculate the new $[H^+(aq)]$:

initial moles of $H^+(aq)$ is found using *MV*/1000
initial moles of $H^+(aq)$ = 0.1 × 10/1000 = 0.001 mol

But the $H^+(aq)$ ions are in a new volume of 250 cm³ (240 + 10)

The final concentration is found using *M* = 1000 × moles/*V*.
Hence *M* = 1000 × 0.001/250 = 0.004 mol dm^{-3}
The final pH = $-\log_{10}[H^+(aq)] = -\log_{10}(0.004) = 2.40$
Therefore the change in pH is from 1 to 2.40

When a solution of an acid and an alkali are mixed then there is a reduction in the number of H^+ ions as well as a dilution effect.

The method used to tackle this type of calculation is to calculate the moles of acid and alkali present initially. From these answers the moles of acid/base remaining can be found. The final number of moles is then converted into a new concentration from which the pH can be calculated. The following example will illustrate this.

7 Calculate the pH of the final solution formed by mixing 25cm^3 of 0.1M HCl with 10cm^3 of 0.05M NaOH.

Using moles = *MV*/1000:

initial moles of HCl = $(0.1 \times 25)/1000$ = 0.0025 mol
initial moles of NaOH = $(0.05 \times 10)1000$ = 0.0005 mol

Therefore moles of acid unreacted is (0.0025–0.0005) = 0.002 mol. This amount of acid is present in a new volume = 35 cm^3

Hence the new concentration of the acid is $(0.002 \times 1000)/35$ = 0.057 M
Since the acid is a strong acid $[H^+]$ = 0.057 mol dm^{-3}
pH = $-\log_{10}[H^+(aq)]$ = $-\log_{10} 0.057$ = 1.25

15 An experiment was conducted in which 0.1 M NaOH was added slowly to 25 cm^3 of 0.1 M HCl.

a) Calculate the pH of the acid before reaction.

b) Calculate the pH of the solution after adding 5 cm^3 of 0.1 M NaOH.

Key Ideas 38 – 45

- **The $H^+(aq)$ concentration of a solution can be expressed as a pH value where pH = $-\log_{10}[H^+(aq)]$.**
- **The pH of a strong acid can be found directly from this formula providing its concentration is known.**
- **The acid dissociation constant for a weak acid, HA, is given by:**

$$K_a = \frac{[H^+(aq)][A^-(aq)]}{[HA]} \text{ mol dm}^{-3}$$

- **For a weak acid its $[H^+(aq)]$ and hence its pH is calculated using the expression: $[H^+(aq)] = \sqrt{(K_a[HA])}$**
- **The ionic product of water, $K_w = [H^+(aq)][OH^-(aq)]$ mol^2 dm^{-6}.**
- **For a strong base its $[H^+(aq)]$ and hence its pH is calculated using the expression:**

$$[H^+(aq)] = \frac{K_w}{[OH^-(aq)]}$$

- **At 298 K, pH + pOH = 14**

3 pH curves

In an acid–base titration we can follow the change in pH as the reaction proceeds by measuring the pH with a pH meter. The pH values can then be plotted on a graph to produce a pH curve. The shape of the curve depends upon the nature of the acid and base used.

The titration of a known volume of an acid against a base can be followed by recording the initial pH of the acid, adding small portions of the base from a burette, mixing the solution and recording the pH value until there is no further change in pH. Alternatively the acid may be added to a known volume of base.

The four typical pH curves for different combinations of strong and weak monoprotic acids with strong and weak bases are shown below:

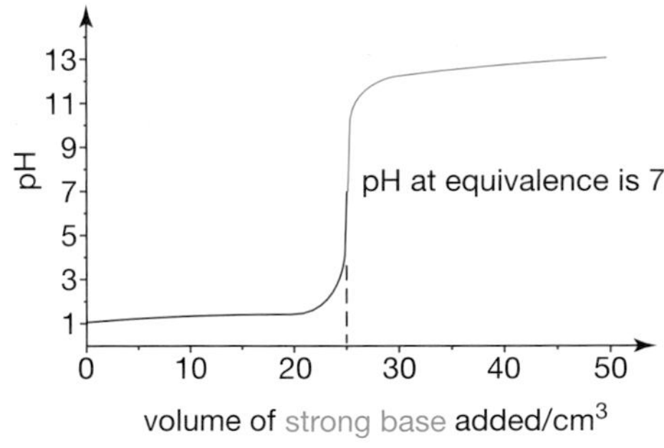

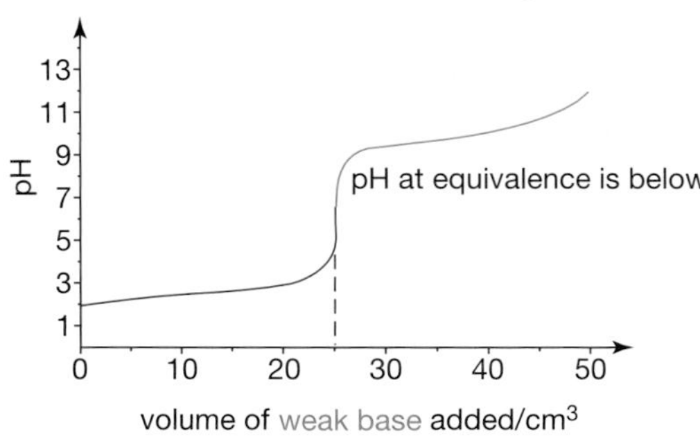

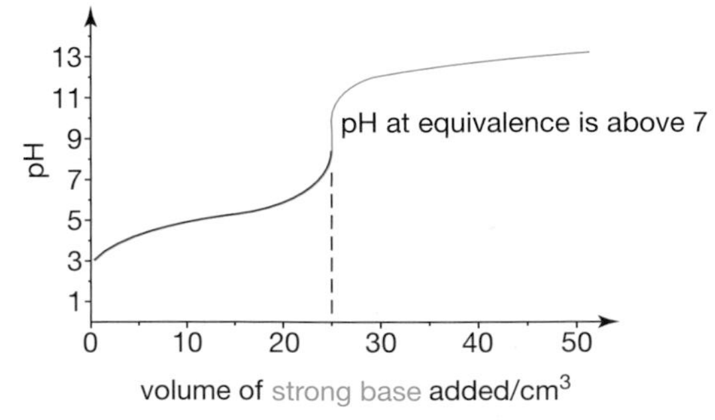

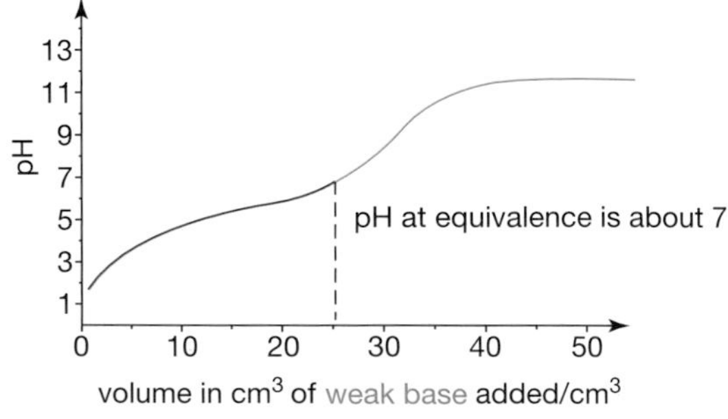

Figure 1 *pH curves*

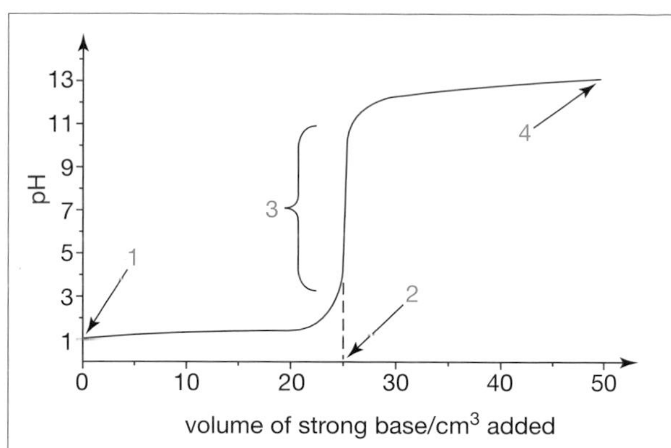

Figure 2 *The important features of pH curves*

The important features of these curves are:

1. The initial pH: this may be of the acid or base depending upon whether the acid is added to the base or vice versa.
2. The volume of acid or base required for **equivalence**: the point when equimolar amounts of both acid and base are present.
3. The pH range at equivalence.
4. The final pH.

Figure 3 *pH curves*

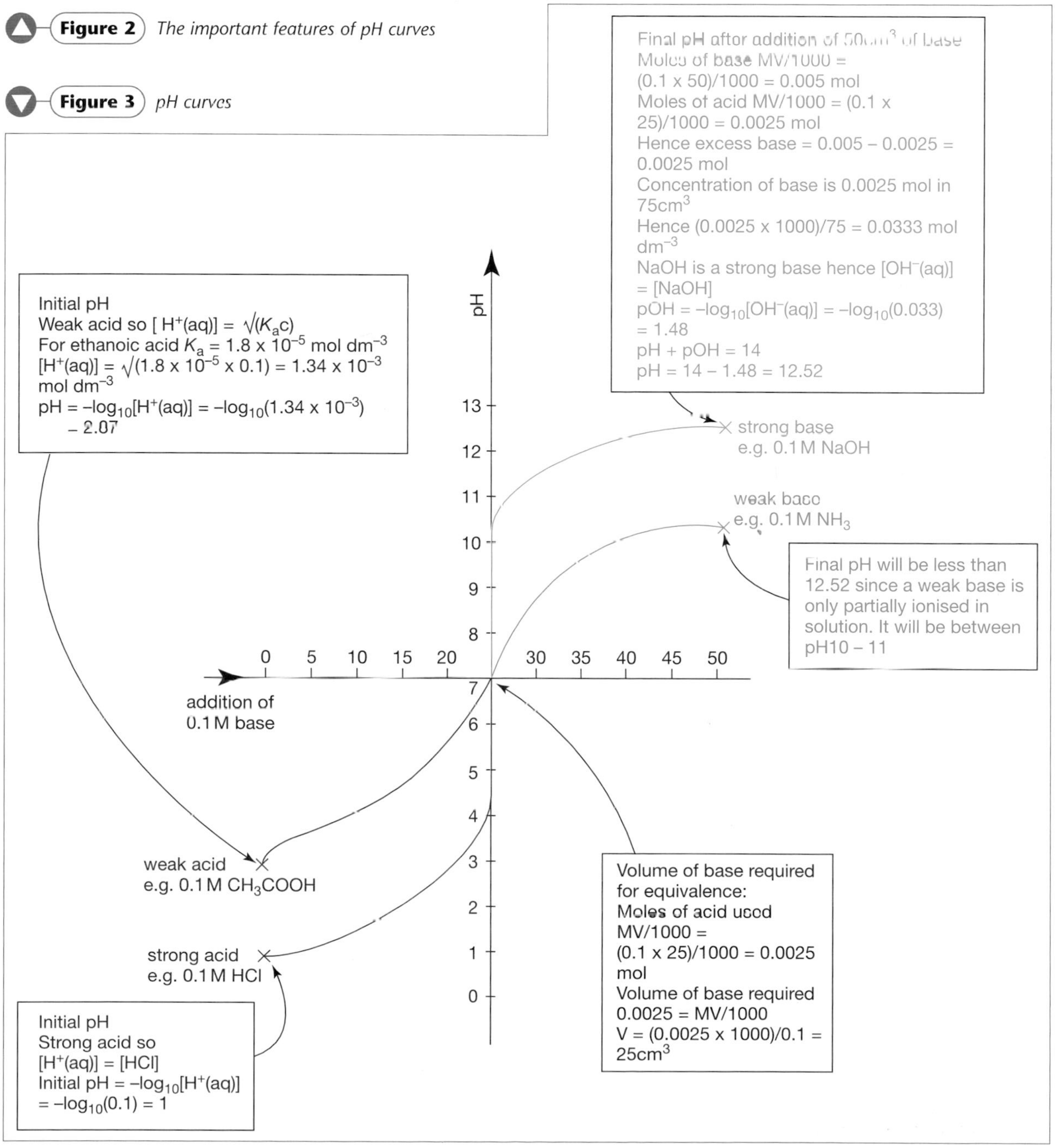

Final pH after addition of 50cm^3 of base
Moles of base MV/1000 = (0.1 x 50)/1000 = 0.005 mol
Moles of acid MV/1000 = (0.1 x 25)/1000 = 0.0025 mol
Hence excess base = 0.005 – 0.0025 = 0.0025 mol
Concentration of base is 0.0025 mol in 75cm^3
Hence (0.0025 x 1000)/75 = 0.0333 mol dm^{-3}
NaOH is a strong base hence $[OH^-(aq)]$ = [NaOH]
pOH = $-\log_{10}[OH^-(aq)] = -\log_{10}(0.033)$ = 1.48
pH + pOH = 14
pH = 14 – 1.48 = 12.52

Initial pH
Weak acid so $[H^+(aq)] = \sqrt{(K_a c)}$
For ethanoic acid $K_a = 1.8 \times 10^{-5}$ mol dm^{-3}
$[H^+(aq)] = \sqrt{(1.8 \times 10^{-5} \times 0.1)} = 1.34 \times 10^{-3}$ mol dm^{-3}
pH = $-\log_{10}[H^+(aq)] = -\log_{10}(1.34 \times 10^{-3})$ = 2.87

pH
13
12
11
10
9
8
7
6
5
4
3
2
1
0
0 5 10 15 20 30 35 40 45 50
addition of 0.1 M base

strong base
e.g. 0.1 M NaOH

weak base
e.g. 0.1 M NH_3

Final pH will be less than 12.52 since a weak base is only partially ionised in solution. It will be between pH10 – 11

weak acid
e.g. 0.1 M CH_3COOH

strong acid
e.g. 0.1 M HCl

Volume of base required for equivalence:
Moles of acid used MV/1000 = (0.1 x 25)/1000 = 0.0025 mol
Volume of base required 0.0025 = MV/1000
V = (0.0025 x 1000)/0.1 = 25cm^3

Initial pH
Strong acid so
$[H^+(aq)]$ = [HCl]
Initial pH = $-\log_{10}[H^+(aq)]$ = $-\log_{10}(0.1)$ = 1

> **Q** **16 The data in Table 1 show how the pH changes during a titration when aqueous 0.1 M NaOH is added to 10 cm^3 of aqueous ethanoic acid.**
> **a) Use these data to plot a pH curve.**
> **b) State the pH range at equivalence.**
> **c) Calculate the initial concentration of the ethanoic acid.**

Vol of NaOH/cm^3	0.0	1.0	2.0	4.0	6.0	7.0	8.0	8.5	10.0	14.0
pH	2.9	4.0	4.3	4.7	5.2	5.5	6.4	11.2	12.0	12.4

Table 1

pH curves for diprotic acids and bases

Ethanedioic acid is a weak, diprotic acid. When reacted with a strong base, e.g. sodium hydroxide, it successively loses two protons. Each loss has its own pK_a value and equivalence point.

The first equivalence point occurs when the following reaction is complete:

$$HOOCCOOH(aq) + OH^-(aq) \rightarrow HOOCCOO^-(aq) + H_2O(l) \text{ (at pH = 2.71)}$$

The second equivalence point occurs when the following reaction is complete:

$$HOOCCOO^-(aq) + OH^-(aq) \rightarrow {}^-OOCCOO^-(aq) + H_2O(l) \text{ (at pH = 8.36)}$$

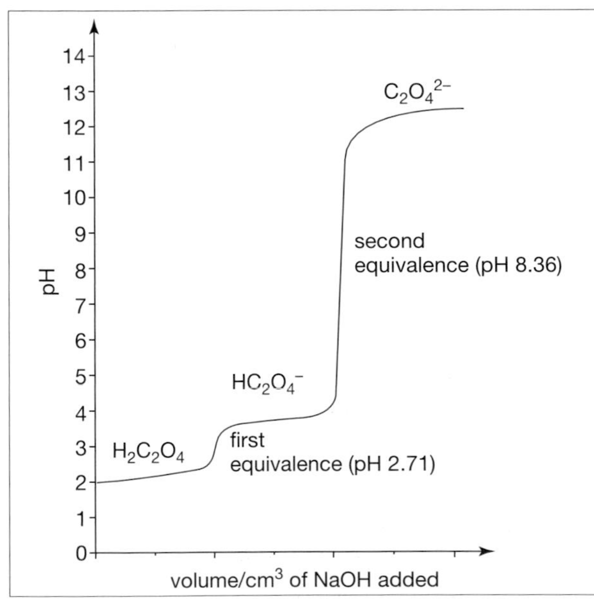

Figure 4 *The pH curve for ethanedioic acid against sodium hydroxide*

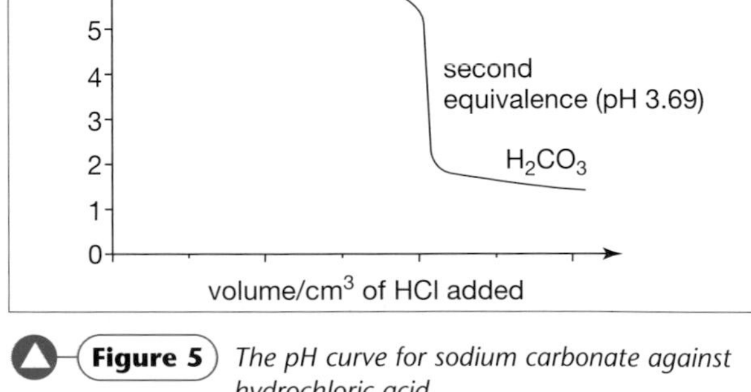

Figure 5 *The pH curve for sodium carbonate against hydrochloric acid*

If the pH is measured as NaOH (aq) is added to a solution of ethanedioic acid the pH curve will look like the one shown in Figure 4.

If sodium carbonate is titrated against a strong monoprotic acid e.g. HCl(aq) and the pH measured then the curve will resemble that in Figure 5.

The carbonate ion is the conjugate base of carbonic acid, a weak diprotic acid. It successively gains two protons from the hydrochloric acid. The two successive reactions lead to two equivalence points:

$CO_3^{2-}(aq) + H^+(aq) \rightarrow HCO_3^-(aq)$ (at pH = 8.31)

$HCO_3^-(aq) + H^+(aq) \rightarrow H_2CO_3(aq)$ (at pH = 3.69)

The carbonic acid produced releases carbon dioxide:

$H_2CO_3(aq) \rightarrow H_2O(l) + CO_2(g)$

Determination of the value of K_a for a weak acid

If a titration of a weak acid with a strong base is followed with a pH meter then the titration curve shown in Figure 7 is obtained.

For a weak acid

$$K_a = \frac{[H^+(aq)][A^-(aq)]}{[HA(aq)]} \text{ mol dm}^{-3}$$

When half of the acid has been neutralised then $[HA(aq)] = [A^-(aq)]$.

Therefore at this point (the half-equivalence point):

$K_a = [H^+(aq)]$

This allows us to find the value of K_a from the titration curve by finding the pH at the half-equivalence point. From the pH we can calculate $[H^+(aq)]$ and this will be equal to the value of K_a

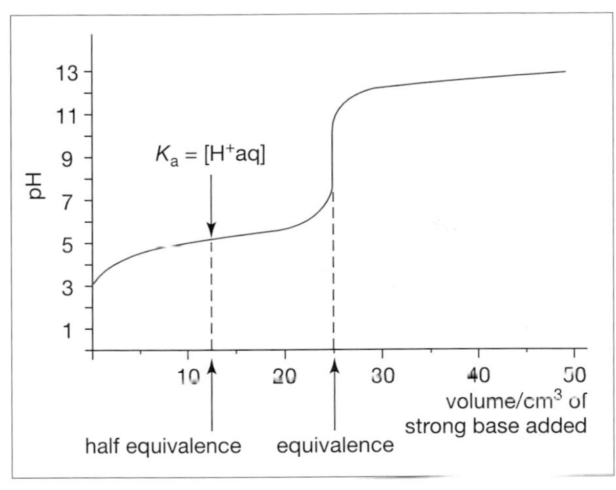

Figure 6 *Titration curve for weak acid against strong base*

or since pH = $-\log_{10} [H^+(aq)]$ and pKa = $-\log_{10} K_a$ then at half equivalence pH = pK_a.

For example:

When 20 cm^3 of 0.50 M hydrofluoric acid is reacted with 10 cm^3 of 0.50 M NaOH the pH of the resulting solution is found to be 3.45. Since the acid has been half neutralised then $pK_a = 3.45$ and $K_a = 3.55 \times 10^{-4}$ mol dm^{-3}.

An alternative method using the half-equivalence point is to carry out a titration using an indicator to find the volume of acid needed to neutralise a given volume of a base (e.g. 25 cm^3). Note the volume of acid required and then repeat the titration, without indicator, adding half of the volume of acid to a separate portion (e.g. 25 cm^3) of the alkali. The pH of the resulting solution is equal to pK_a

4 Acid–base indicators

You will have used a range of indicators at GCSE. An indicator is a substance that changes colour according to the $[H^+(aq)]$ of the solution to which it is added. To be an effective indicator it must have a distinct colour change over a small pH range.

How indicators work

Indicators are weak organic acids that have different colours in the undissociated form and the dissociated conjugate base. Methyl orange is a common indicator. Using HIn to represent the indicator:

$$\underset{\text{red}}{HIn(aq)} \rightleftharpoons H^+(aq) + \underset{\text{yellow}}{In^-(aq)}$$

Looking at the above equation: in the presence of an acid, excess $H^+(aq)$ ions will be present and, by Le Chatelier's principle, the equilibrium will shift to the left, turning methyl orange red. In the presence of alkali the $OH^-(aq)$ ions added will react with $H^+(aq)$ ions to form water, thus removing $H^+(aq)$ ions from the equilibrium. To restore the balance the equilibrium will shift to the right, causing the indicator to turn yellow.

To be effective an indicator must change colour quickly on the addition of a couple of drops of an acid or alkali. Most indicators operate in a narrow pH range. Different indicators change colour at different pH ranges.

Indicator	pK_a value (298 K)	pH range	Colour in acid	Colour in alkali
Methyl orange	3.7	3.0–4.4	red	yellow
Bromothymol blue	7.0	6.0–7.6	yellow	blue
Phenolphthalein	9.3	8.4–10.0	colourless	pink

Table 1 *Some common indicators with pH range*

For an indicator to work there must be a rapid change in pH at equivalence in the acid–base titration. Indicators are chosen which match the change in pH at equivalence (see Figure 1).

17 Bromocresol green is an acid–base indicator:

$$\underset{\text{yellow}}{HIn(aq)} + H_2O(l) \rightleftharpoons H_3O^+(aq) + \underset{\text{blue}}{In^-(aq)}$$

a) What colour would the indicator turn it was added to sodium hydroxide solution?

b) If the mid-point colour (green) exists at pH 4.7 what would you expect the pK_a value to be? Explain your answer.

Choosing the indicator for a titration

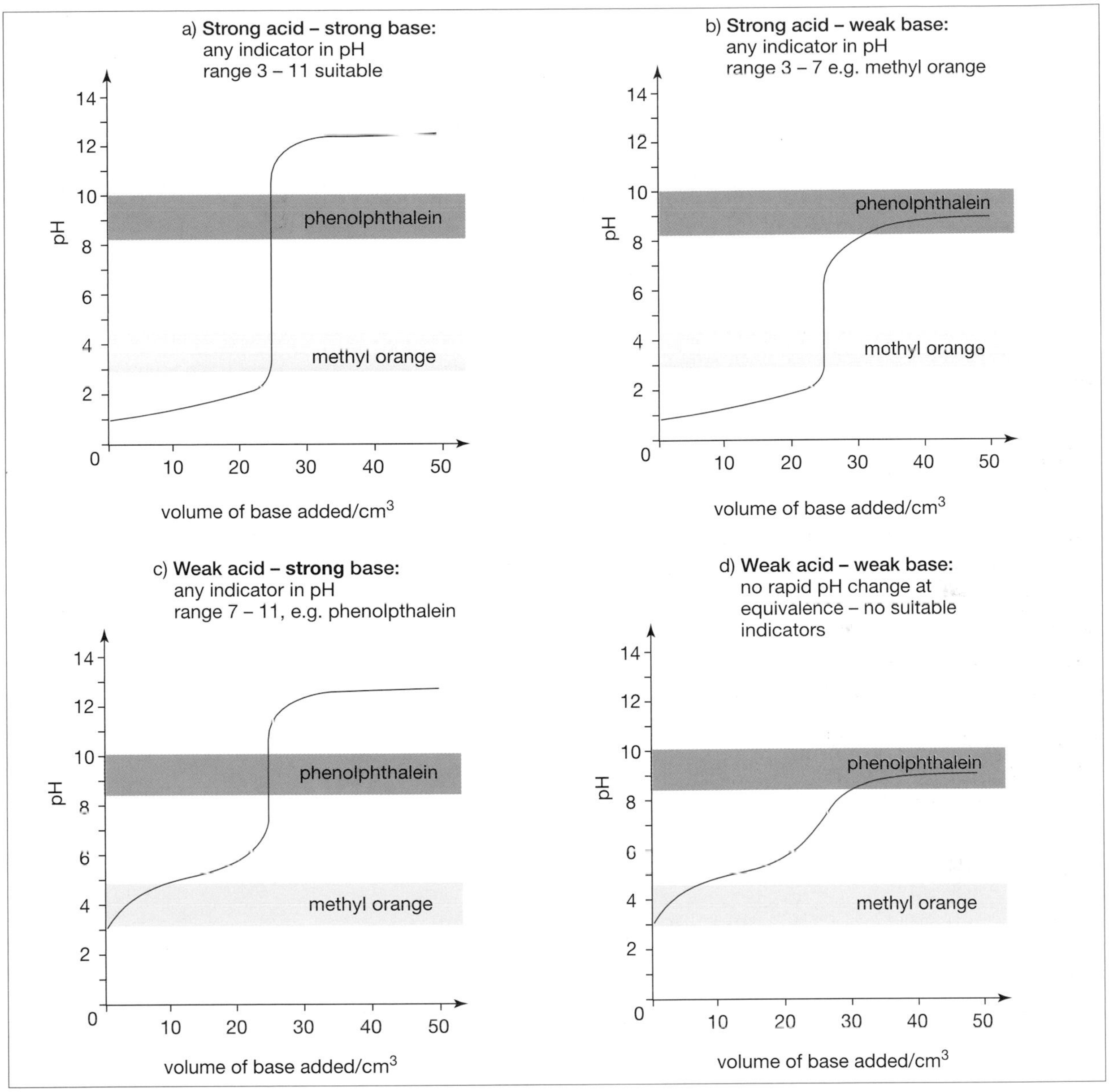
a) Strong acid – strong base:
any indicator in pH
range 3 – 11 suitable
b) Strong acid – weak base:
any indicator in pH
range 3 – 7 e.g. methyl orange
c) Weak acid – strong base:
any indicator in pH
range 7 – 11, e.g. phenolpthalein
d) Weak acid – weak base:
no rapid pH change at
equivalence – no suitable
indicators
pH
phenolphthalein
methyl orange
volume of base added/cm3
0
10
20
30
40
50
2
4
6
8
10
12
14

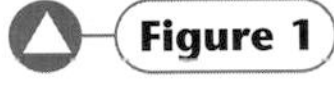

Figure 1 *pH curves to illustrate the principles of use of indicators*

Q

18 a) Sketch a graph of pH against 0.1 M HCl added to 10 cm^3 of 0.1 M Na_2CO_3.

b) Mark the equivalence points on the graph.

c) Which indicators would you use to follow the progress of this reaction?

5 Buffers

A buffer is a solution whose pH is resistant to change on the addition of relatively small quantities of an acid or a base.

Buffers have the ability to absorb added H^+ ions and OH^- ions. They can be acidic or basic.

How buffers work

An **acidic buffer** contains a weak acid and its salt formed with a strong base. An example of an acidic buffer is a solution containing ethanoic acid, CH_3COOH, and sodium ethanoate, $CH_3COO^-Na^+$.

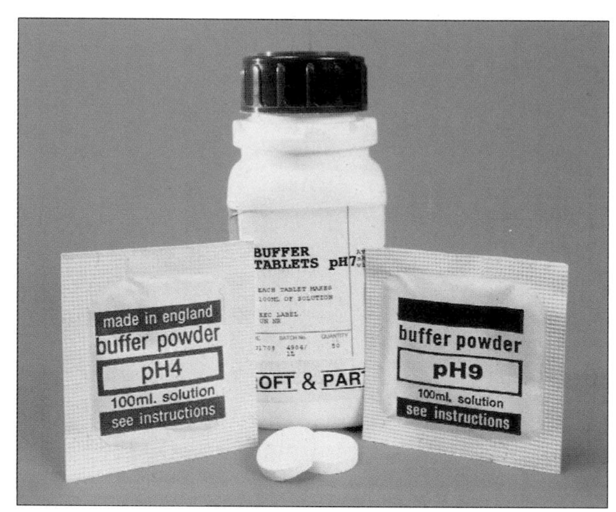

Figure 1 *Examples of buffers*

The important species present in the buffer solution are the undissociated weak acid and its conjugate base (CH_3COOH and CH_3COO^-).

The undissociated ethanoic acid can remove any added OH^- ions:

$$CH_3COOH(aq) + OH^-(aq) \rightarrow CH_3COO^-(aq) + H_2O(l)$$

The conjugate base CH_3COO^- can remove any added H^+ ions:

$$CH_3COO^-(aq) + H^+(aq) \rightarrow CH_3COOH(aq)$$

For a buffer to work effectively it must contain a *large* reservoir of the weak acid and its conjugate base.

$$CH_3COOH(aq) + H_2O(l) \rightleftharpoons CH_3COO^-(aq) + H_3O^+(aq)$$

$$K_a = \frac{[CH_3COO^-(aq)][H_3O^+(aq)]}{[CH_3COOH(aq)]} \text{ mol dm}^{-3}$$

Rearranging gives: $[H_3O^+(aq)] = K_a \times \dfrac{[CH_3COOH(aq)]}{[CH_3COO^-(aq)]}$

Hence, if there is large reservoir of *both* the free acid and its conjugate base, then the addition of small quantities of an acid or base will have little effect upon the $[H_3O^+(aq)]$. This means there will only be a small change in $[H^+(aq)]$ and hence a very small change in pH.

A **basic buffer** contains a weak base and its salt formed with a strong acid. An example of a basic buffer is a solution containing ammonia, NH_3 and ammonium chloride, NH_4Cl.

The important species present in the buffer solution are the undissociated weak base and its conjugate acid (NH_3 and NH_4^+).

The undissociated ammonia can remove any added H^+ ions:

$$NH_3(aq) + H^+(aq) \rightarrow NH_4^+(aq)$$

The conjugate acid, NH_4^+ can remove any added OH^- ions:

$$NH_4^+(aq) + OH^-(aq) \rightarrow NH_3(aq) + H_2O(l)$$

Making and calculating the pH of an acid buffer

An acid buffer can be made by adding the corresponding salt to the weak acid or by adding excess of the acid to the strong base. When performing pH calculations on buffers it is assumed that the acid is completely undissociated and the A^- ions are formed solely from the salt.

$$K_a = \frac{[H^+(aq)][A^-(aq)]}{[HA(aq)]} \text{ mol dm}^{-3}$$

Rearranging this gives:

$$K_a \times \frac{[HA(aq)]}{[A^-(aq)]} = [H^+(aq)]$$

It can be seen from the expression above that the $[H^+(aq)]$ and hence the pH of the buffer produced depends on the relative concentrations of the acid, HA and its conjugate base, A^-.

Worked example

1 a) Calculate the pH of a buffer solution produced by adding 3.28 g of sodium ethanoate to 1 dm^3 of 0.01 M ethanoic acid. The K_a of ethanoic acid is 1.84×10^{-5} mol dm^{-3} at 300 K.

b) Calculate the pH of this buffer if 10 cm^3 of 0.1 M HCl are now added.

Answer

a) **Step 1:** Find the number of moles of sodium ethanoate used.

The M_r = 82

Moles = mass/M_r = 3.28/82 = 0.04 = 4×10^{-2}

Step 2: Find the $[H^+(aq)]$ using:

$$[H^+(aq)] = K_a \times \frac{[CH_3COOH(aq)]}{[CH_3COO^-(aq)]}$$

$$= \frac{1.84 \times 10^{-5} \times 1 \times 10^{-2}}{4 \times 10^{-2}} = 4.6 \times 10^{-6} \text{ mol dm}^{-3}$$

Step 3: Find pH using

$$pH = -\log_{10}[H^+(aq)]$$

$$= -\log_{10} 4.6 \times 10^{-6} = 5.34$$

b) **Step 1:** Find the moles of acid added using

moles = MV/1000 = 0.1 × 10/1000 = 1×10^{-3}

since HCl is a strong acid then moles of $H^+(aq)$ added = 1×10^{-3}.

These ions will be 'mopped up' by the buffer but this will alter the concentrations of $[CH_3COO^-(aq)]$ and $[CH_3COOH(aq)]$.

Step 2: Find the new $[CH_3COO^-(aq)]$ and $[CH_3COOH(aq)]$

$$H^+(aq) + CH_3COO^-(aq) \rightarrow CH_3COOH(aq)$$
$$1 \times 10^{-3} \qquad 1 \times 10^{-3} \qquad 1 \times 10^{-3}$$

i.e. the no. of moles of $CH_3COO^-(aq)$ will have decreased by 1×10^{-3} and the no. of moles of $CH_3COOH(aq)$ will have increased by 1×10^{-3}

so the new $[CH_3COO^-(aq)] = \dfrac{(4 \times 10^{-2} - 1 \times 10^{-3}) \times 1000}{1010} = 3.86 \times 10^{-2}$

the new $[CH_3COOH(aq)] = \dfrac{(1 \times 10^{-2} + 1 \times 10^{-3}) \times 1000}{1010} = 1.09 \times 10^{-2}$

Step 3: Find the new pH.

$$[H^+(aq)] = K_a \times \frac{[CH_3COOH(aq)]}{[CH_3COO^-(aq)]}$$
$$= \frac{(1.84 \times 10^{-5}) \times (1.09 \times 10^{-2})}{(3.86 \times 10^{-2})}$$
$$= 5.19 \times 10^{-6} \text{mol dm}^{-3}$$
$$pH = -\log_{10} 5.19 \times 10^{-6}$$
$$= 5.28$$

Notice that the addition of $10 cm^3$ of 0.1 M HCl only alters the pH of the buffer by 0.06.

19 Calculate the pH of a buffer solution made by mixing 0.25 mol of a weak acid ($K_a = 2.4 \times 10^{-5}$ mol dm^{-3}) and 0.50 mol of a salt of the acid.

20 Calculate the mass of sodium ethanoate which must be dissolved in 500 cm^3 of 0.1 M ethanoic acid to produce a buffer solution with a pH of 4.0.

(The K_a value for ethanoic acid is 1.7×10^{-5} mol dm^{-3}.)

Key Ideas 50 – 54

- **pH curves can be constructed by measuring pH changes during acid–base titrations.**
- **The K_a value of a weak acid can be determined using pH curves.**
- **The end point of an acid–base titration can be determined using an indicator. Indicators are weak acids.**
- **For an indicator to be suitable for a titration, the working range of the indicator should match pH range of equivalence.**
- **A buffer is a solution whose pH is resistant to change on the addition of relatively small quantity of an acid or a base.**

Unit 3 Questions

6

1 a) (i) Define pH.
(ii) Calculate the pH of a 0.10 M solution of hydrochloric acid. (2)
b) (i) Propanoic acid is a weak acid. Explain the term *weak acid*.
(ii) Write an equation to show the dissociation of propanoic acid (CH_3CH_2COOH) in water.
(iii) Write an expression for the acid dissociation constant, K_a, for propanoic acid.
(iv) Use this expression to calculate the pH of a 0.10 M solution of propanoic acid, given that its $K_a = 1.35 \times 10^{-5}$ mol dm^{-3} at 25°C. (7)
c) Why is the pH of 0.10 M HCl less than the pH of 0.10 M propanoic acid? (2)
d) What will be the effect on the K_a value of propanoic acid of increasing the temperature from 25°C to 45°C? Explain your answer. (3)

2 a) Hydrochloric acid is an example of a strong monoprotic acid. Explain the meaning of the terms *strong* and *monoprotic*. (2)
b) Write an equation to show the reaction between hydrochloric acid and sodium hydroxide. (1)
c) Calculate the pH of the solution formed when 30 cm^3 of 0.125 M NaOH are reacted with 25 cm^3 of 0.15 M HCl at 298 K. (7)

3 A solution of a strong acid, HA, has a pH value of –0.1.

a) Write an equation to show how HA behaves as a strong acid in water. (1)
b) Calculate the hydrogen ion concentration in this solution. (1)
c) Calculate the volume of 0.5 M NaOH required to completely neutralise 25 cm^3 of this acid. (3)

4 a) (i) Define the ionic product of water, K_w.
(ii) Give the units for this constant and its value at 25°C. (3)
b) (i) Use your answers to part a) to explain why the pH of pure water at 25°C has a value of 7.
(ii) Calculate the change in pH of this water if 5 cm^3 of 0.1 M nitric acid is added to 45 cm^3 of water. (7)
c) Explain why the pH of pure water increases as the temperature drops to 0°C. (3)

(5) A weak acid, HA, has a pK_a value of 5.45 at 298 K. 20 cm^3 of 0.1 M HA is titrated against 0.1 M NaOH.

a) Calculate the pH of 0.1 M HA. (4)
b) Calculate the pH of the solution after adding 30 cm^3 of alkali. (4)
c) Use your answers to a) and b) to sketch the pH curve for this titration. (4)
d) Use this pH curve to explain why phenolphthalein would be a suitable indicator for this titration. (2)

(6) $NH_3(g) + H_2O(l) \rightleftharpoons NH_4^+(aq) + OH^-(aq)$

a) Use the equation above to explain:
(i) the meaning of the terms *Brønsted–Lowry acid* and *Brønsted–Lowry base*.
(ii) why an aqueous solution of ammonia has a pH value greater than 7. (6)
b) At 298 K this ammonia solution contains 4.5×10^{-5} mol dm^{-3} of hydroxide ions; calculate its pH. (4)
c) Name a salt which produces a buffer solution when added to aqueous ammonia. (1)

(7) **a)** (i) Write an equation for the reaction between $HNO_3(aq)$ and HF(aq) showing nitric acid behaving as a Brønsted–Lowry acid.
(ii) Write an equation for the reaction between $HNO_3(aq)$ and $H_2SO_4(aq)$ showing nitric acid behaving as a Brønsted–Lowry base. (2)
b) What can be deduced from these equations about the relative strengths of HNO_3, H_2SO_4 and HF as acids? (1)
c) Calculate the pH of (i) 0.25 M nitric acid; (ii) 0.25 M sulphuric acid. (2)

(8) Hydrofluoric acid, HF, is a weak monoprotic acid. Its pK_a value is 3.45 at 298 K.

a) Explain the terms *weak* and *monoprotic*. (2)
b) Write an expression for the acid dissociation constant K_a for HF(aq). (2)
c) Calculate the pH of a 0.2 M solution of HF. (4)
d) 25 cm^3 of 0.2 M NaOH is added to 50 cm^3 of 0.2 M HF to form solution X. Deduce the pH of this solution. (2)
e) A further 10 cm^3 of 0.2 M NaOH is added to solution X. Calculate the pH of the solution so formed. (7)

(9) When aqueous solutions of ammonium sulphate and ammonia are mixed, a buffer solution is produced.

a) What is a buffer solution? (2)
b) Explain the buffer action of this mixture. (5)

1 Isomerism

At AS you studied several different types of isomerism in organic compounds. Isomerism occurs when two or more compounds have the same molecular formula but have different chemical or physical properties. It can be subdivided into structural isomerism and **stereoisomerism**. In this unit **optical isomerism** is introduced. This is a type of stereoisomerism that is particularly important in biological systems.

ISOMERISM
Occurs when two or more compounds have the same molecular formula but have different chemical or physical properties

Structural isomerism
Structural isomers have the same molecular formula but different structural formulae

Chain isomers
Occur when the atoms in the carbon chain are arrranged differently

Position isomers
Occur within the same homologous series when the functional group is on a different carbon atom

Functional group isomers
Occur when the compounds have a different functional group

Stereoisomerism
Stereoisomers have the same molecular and structural formulae but differ in the spatial orientation of one or more atoms

Geometrical isomers
Occur in alkenes due to the restricted rotation about the carbon–carbon double bond

Optical isomers
Occur in molecules which contain an asymmetric carbon atom (chiral centre)

Figure 1 *A summary of the different types of isomerism*

Structural isomerism

Structural isomers have the same molecular formula but have different structural formulae. The different types of structural isomers are shown in Figure 1 and some examples of each are given in Figure 2 (overleaf).

Chain isomers of C_5H_{12}

pentane

2 – methylbutane

2,2 – dimethylpropane

Chain isomers of C_3H_7COOH

butanoic acid

2 – methylpropanoic acid

Position isomers of C_3H_7OH

propan–1–ol

propan–2–ol

Position isomers of $C_7H_7NO_2$

2 – nitromethylbenzene

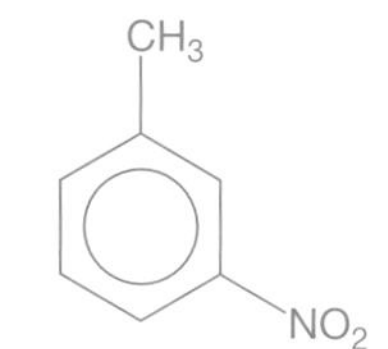

3 – nitromethylbenzene

4 – nitromethylbenzene

Functional group isomers of C_3H_6O

propanal

propanone

Two of the functional group isomers of $C_3H_6O_2$

propanoic acid

methyl ethanoate (see page 74)

Figure 2 *Examples of structural isomers*

1 **The isomers of pentene illustrate both chain and position isomerism. Draw out and name the five isomers.**

2 **Draw the structures of the isomers with molecular formula C_7H_7Cl**

Stereoisomerism

Stereoisomers have the same molecular formula and structural formula but differ in the spatial orientation of one or more atoms. Geometrical isomerism and optical isomerism are the two types of stereoisomerism.

Geometrical isomerism

This occurs in alkenes due to the restricted rotation about the carbon–carbon double bond giving rise to *cis* and *trans* isomers.

trans but-2-ene | *cis* but-2-ene

Figure 3 *Geometrical isomers of but-2-ene*

Viewed along the carbon–carbon double bond both methyl groups are on the same side in the cis isomer but are on opposite sides in the *trans* isomer. The necessary condition for an alkene to exhibit geometrical isomerism is that each of the carbon atoms joined by the double bond has two *different* groups attached. Notice that 2-methylpropene, which is a structural isomer of but-2-ene, has the same group on each carbon atom and thus does not have geometrical isomers.

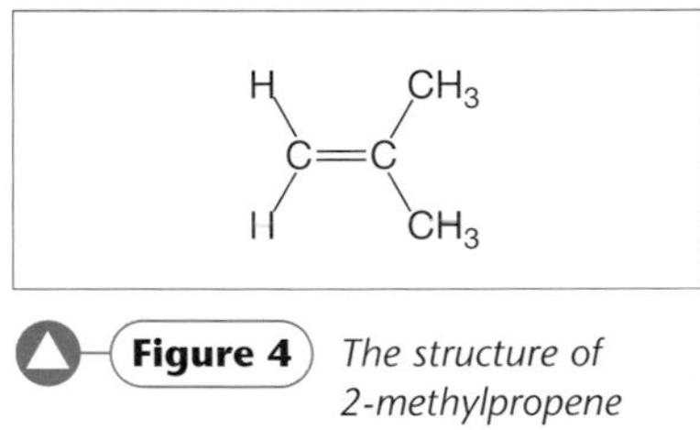

Figure 4 *The structure of 2-methylpropene*

3 Look again at the isomers of pentene that you have drawn. Identify which of these exhibit geometrical isomerism.

Key Ideas 57 – 59

- **Structural isomers have the same molecular formula but have different structural formula.**
- **Chain isomers, position isomers and functional group isomers are different types of structural isomers.**
- **Stereoisomers have the same molecular and structural formula but one or more of the atoms has a different spatial orientation.**
- **Geometric isomers occur when a compound has restricted rotation about a particular bond, usually a carbon carbon double bond.**
- **Geometric isomers are stereoisomers which exist in *cis* and *trans* forms.**

2 Optical isomerism

Optical isomerism is a type of stereoisomerism that is particularly important in biological systems. This is because enzymes, which control the reactions in the cell, are stereospecific. They will only 'recognise' one type of isomer.

Optical isomerism arises in organic molecules that contain at least one carbon atom attached to four different groups.

Optical activity

This occurs when a carbon atom has four different atoms or groups of atoms attached to it. This results in an **asymmetric** carbon atom or **chiral** centre.

Figure 1 *Diagram to represent a chiral centre*

When a molecule has a chiral centre there are two non-superimposable isomers that are mirror images of each other.

Figure 2 *Optical isomers are mirror images*

It is important when drawing optical isomers that their 3D shape is considered. Drawn flat they appear to be superimposable. The effect is best seen by making molecular models. 2-hydroxypropanoic acid (lactic acid) is an example of a compound that exhibits optical isomerism. Its formula is $CH_3CH(OH)COOH$

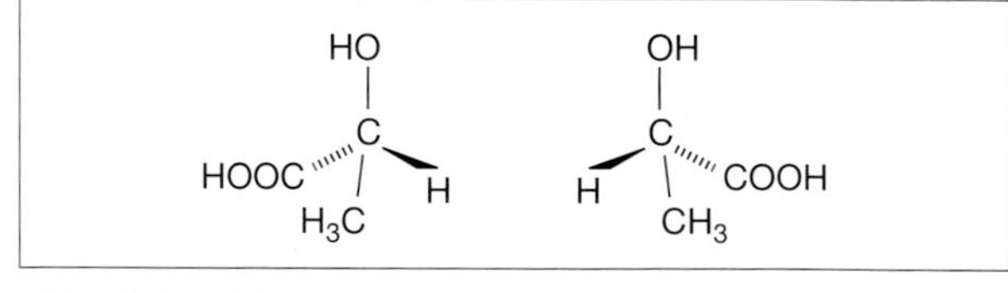

Figure 3 *3D structures of 2-hydroxypropanoic acid*

Q

4 Which one of the following compounds can exist as optical isomers?

a) $CH_3CHCHCH_3$ **b)** $CH_3CH(Cl)CH_2CH_3$
c) $CH_3CH(OH)CH_3$

The two optical isomers are called **enantiomers**. They have *identical* chemical and physical properties except for their effect on **plane polarised light**.

Plane polarised light is formed when light passes through a polaroid filter which only allows light in one plane to pass through it. The effect of optical isomers on plane polarised light can be demonstrated using a polarimeter.

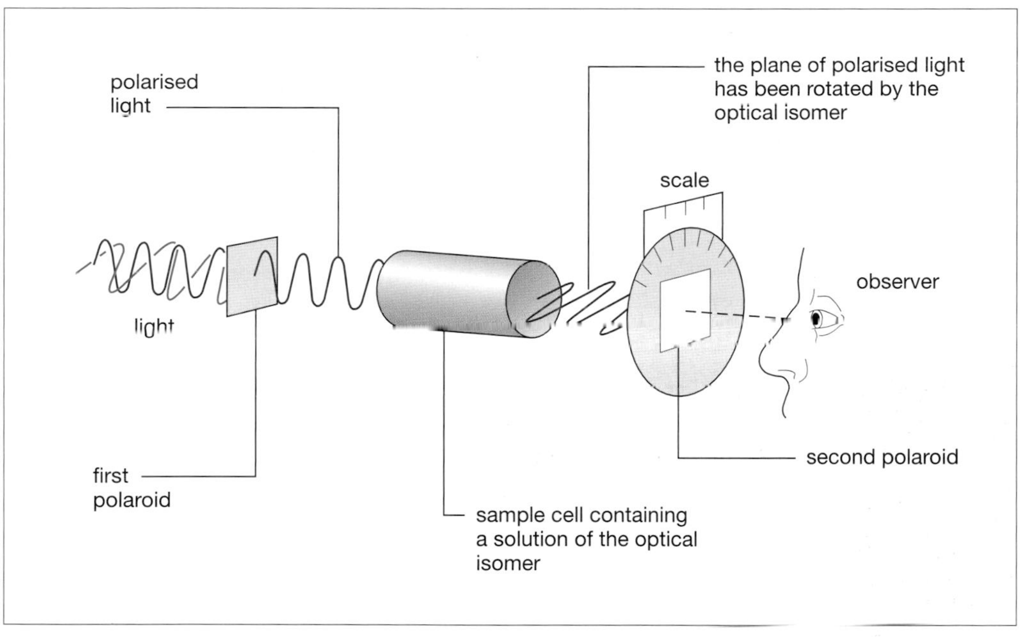

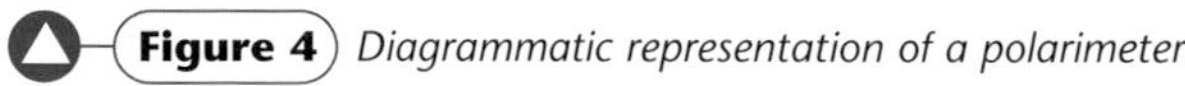

Figure 4 *Diagrammatic representation of a polarimeter*

When plane polarised light passes through *separate* solutions of the enantiomers they rotate the plane of the light in opposite directions. One enantiomer will rotate the light to the right (or clockwise). This is called the dextro-enantiomer and its name is prefixed with (+). The other isomer will rotate the light to the left (or anticlockwise). This is called the laevo-enantiomer (–).

When *equal* quantities of the two optical isomers are present as a mixture they appear to be optically inactive since the effect of one isomer cancels the effect of the other. A mixture containing equal quantities of the two enantiomers is called a **racemic mixture** or a **racemate**. When a compound capable of showing optical activity is synthesised in the laboratory a racemate is almost invariably made, e.g. the synthesis of lactic acid (see page 69).

Chirality in nature

When an optically active compound is synthesised in a biological system then only one of its enantiomers is formed. This is because biological systems involve enzymes which are **stereospecific** in their action. Enzymes are themselves optically active. They can only react with one optical form of a compound (substrate) and can only produce one of the optical isomers of the product. For example, only the (+)isomer of glucose is absorbed by the human body. The (–)isomer passes through the body unchanged.

Although enantiomers show identical properties in most laboratory reactions, they behave very differently with other chiral compounds in nature. Enantiomers can have different smells and tastes since our sense receptors are chiral protein molecules. Carvone is a naturally-occurring chemical with two enantiomers. These are shown below. One isomer tastes of caraway seeds while the other has a spearmint flavour.

(–)carvone: spearmint flavour (+)carvone: caraway flavour

Figure 5 *The enantiomers of carvone*

5 **Explain why the compound $CH_3CH(NH_2)COOH$**

a) can exist as enantiomers

b) occurs in nature as only the (–)isomer?

6 **How could you differentiate between the two optical isomers of 2-hydroxypropanoic acid?**

In the case of optically active drugs, very often only one of the isomers produces an effect on the body, although the patient may be given a racemic mixture, which is more economical to produce since the enantiomers have not undergone a costly separation.

This was true of the drug **thalidomide**, which was first used, apparently successfully for most people, in the early 1960s as a sedative. But it was prescribed to over 15,000 pregnant women worldwide as a treatment for nausea with some devastating results. The (+)isomer was indeed an effective drug but the (–)isomer was teratogenic (meaning 'monster forming'), affecting the development of the unborn foetus and resulting in babies being born with deformed limbs. Thalidomide was banned from general use in 1962, although it is still used in some countries to treat leprosy.

About 80% of optically active drugs are now marked as single enantiomer, which is safer and more effective than the racemate. Unfortunately this may not have helped in the case of thalidomide, since it is known that the (+) isomer can change into the (–) isomer in the body.

Key Ideas 60 – 62

- **Optical isomers contain an asymmetrical carbon atom (chiral) centre.**
- **The optical isomers that are called enantiomers are 3D mirror images of each other.**
- **Optical isomers can be distinguished by their effect on plane polarised light. The isomers rotate plane polarised light in opposite directions.**
- **A mixture of equal amounts of the two optical isomers is called a racemic mixture or racemate.**
- **A racemic mixture appears optically inactive, since the two isomers have opposite effects on plane polarised light, resulting in no overall rotation.**

Unit 4 Questions

3

1 a) (i) Write out and name the two structural isomers of molecular formula C_4H_{10}. (2)

(ii) How will the boiling points of these two isomers differ? Explain your answer. (3)

b) When 2-bromopentane undergoes an elimination reaction with ethanolic potassium hydroxide a mixture of isomeric alkenes results. Give the structures of these three alkenes. (6)

2 Tartaric acid is a weak acid used commercially in baking powder. Its IUPAC name is 2,3-dihydroxybutanedioic acid.

a) Draw out the structure of this molecule. (2)

b) Explain why this compound can exist as optical isomers. (2)

3 a) Give the structures of the four structural isomers represented by the molecular formula C_4H_9Br. (4)

b) Choose one of these isomers and outline the mechanism by which it can be converted to a primary amine. (4)

4 a) (i) What type of isomerism is shown by 2-hydroxypropanoic acid (lactic acid)?

(ii) What structural feature of the molecule is responsible for the isomerism?

(iii) Draw out the structures of the isomers and discuss how they are related to each other. (5)

b) After exercise lactic acid builds up in the muscle cells of the body and causes fatigue. What will be the difference between this lactic acid and that prepared in the laboratory? (3)

5 The molecular formula C_4H_8 represents four different isomers of butene.

a) Draw the structures of the two geometrical isomers of butene. (2)

b) Explain why the other two isomers do not exhibit geometrical isomerism. (2)

6 For each of the isomers A–F described below, identify a possible structure consistent with the chemical evidence given.

a) A and B have the molecular formula C_4H_8O. Isomer A precipitates silver from a warm solution of Tollen's reagent but B does not react. (2)

b) C and D have the molecular formula $C_4H_8O_2$. Isomer C produces effervescence when sodium carbonate is added. Isomer D has a sweet fruity smell. (2)

c) E and F have the molecular formula $C_4H_{10}O$. Isomer E turns warm acidified sodium dichromate(VI) solution from orange to green. F does not react. (2)

7 State the type of isomerism which occurs between the following pairs of compounds. In each case briefly justify your answer.

a) (3)

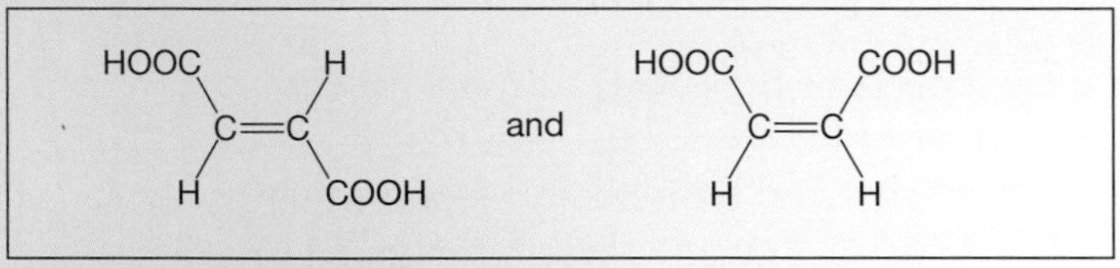

and

b) (3)

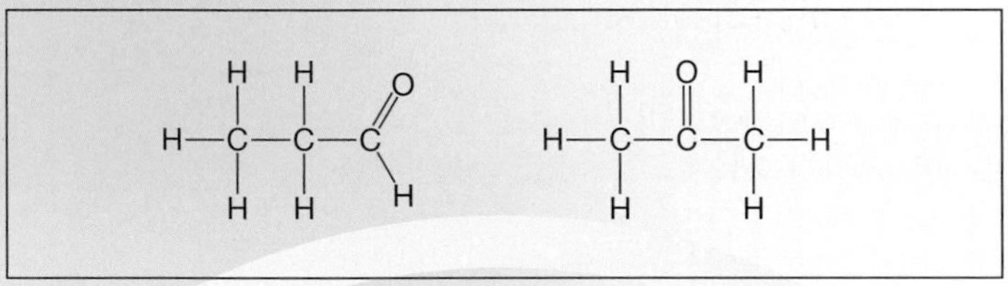

c) (3)

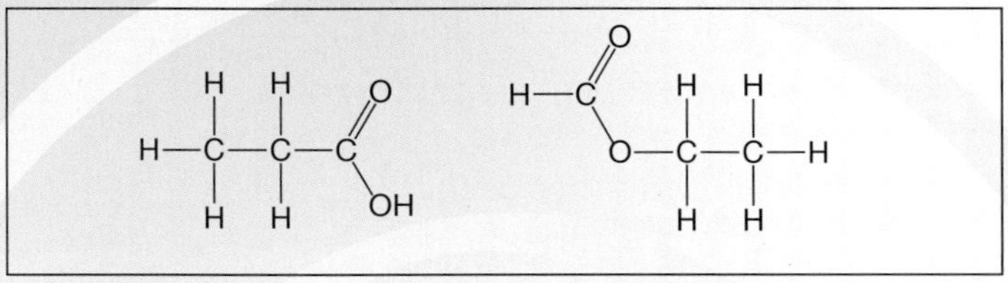

d) (3)

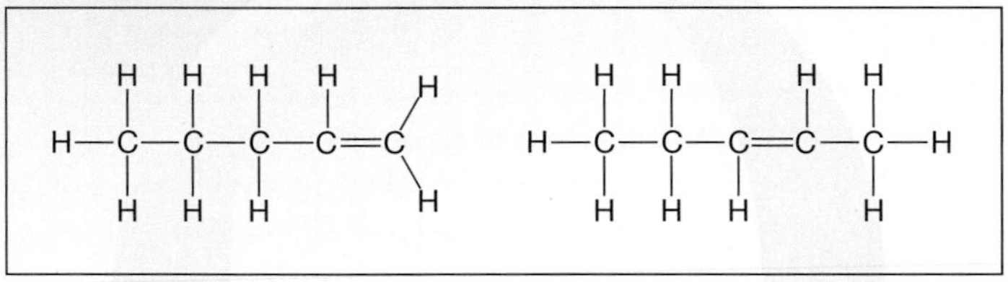

8 But-2-enal, $CH_3CH{=}CHCHO$, contains two functional groups which behave independently in most chemical reactions.

a) (i) Explain what is meant by the term *stereoisomerism*;
(ii) Write the structures for, and name the two stereoisomers of but-2-enal. (6)

b) Give the structures of the products formed when but-2-enal reacts with
(i) concentrated hydrogen bromide;
(ii) warm acidified potassium dichromate(VI)solution. (2)

The product formed in b) (i) shows a different type of stereoisomerism from but-2-enal.

c) Name this type of isomerism and show on your structure in b) (i) the feature of the molecule responsible for this type of isomerism. (2)

1 Carbonyl compounds

Aldehydes, ketones and carboxylic acids are three homologous series of organic compounds that were introduced in Module 3. They all contain the **carbonyl group** (–C=O). The carbonyl group occurs in a range of other organic compounds as well. These include esters, acyl chlorides and acid anhydrides, which are all derived from carboxylic acids. In this unit we will study some of the reactions of the carbonyl compounds.

The carbonyl group

The carbonyl group is the functional group in a range of organic molecules. Some examples are shown below:

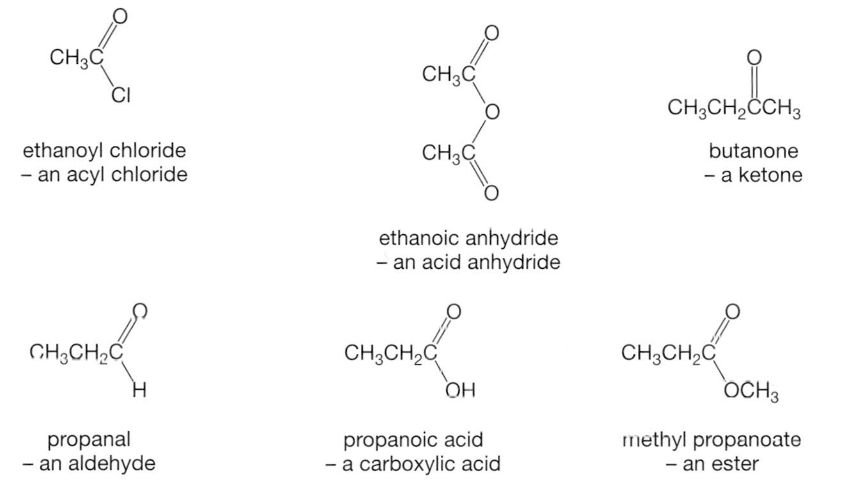

CH_3COCl
ethanoyl chloride
– an acyl chloride

$CH_3CO–O–COCH_3$
ethanoic anhydride
– an acid anhydride

$CH_3CH_2COCH_3$
butanone
– a ketone

CH_3CH_2CHO
propanal
– an aldehyde

CH_3CH_2COOH
propanoic acid
– a carboxylic acid

$CH_3CH_2COOCH_3$
methyl propanoate
– an ester

Figure 1 *The carbonyl group occurs in a range of organic compounds*

The carbon–oxygen bond is **polar** due to the difference in electronegativities between carbon and oxygen. The more electronegative oxygen atom draws the electrons in the double covalent bond towards itself and as a result there is a δ^+ charge on the carbon atom and a δ^- charge on the oxygen atom.

The δ^+ carbon atom is readily attacked by **nucleophiles** (species having a lone pair of electrons that attack an electron deficient carbon atom): see Figure 2.

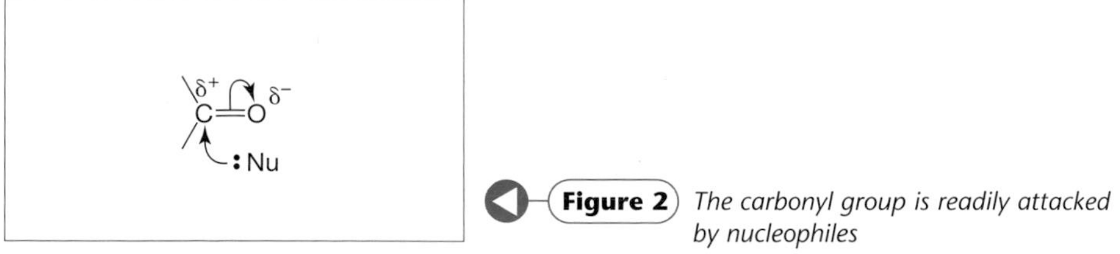

Figure 2 *The carbonyl group is readily attacked by nucleophiles*

Aldehydes and ketones

The aldehydes and ketones were studied in AS Chemistry as the oxidation products of alcohols using warm acidified potassium dichromate(VI) solution as the oxidising agent. [O] is used in these equations to represent the oxidising agent.

Aldehydes are formed by the oxidation of primary alcohols:

$$RCH_2OH + [O] \rightarrow RCHO + H_2O$$

e.g. $$\underset{\text{propan-1-ol}}{CH_3CH_2CH_2OH} + [O] \rightarrow \underset{\text{propanal}}{CH_3CH_2CHO} + H_2O$$

If an excess of the oxidising agent is used, then the aldehyde is oxidised to the corresponding carboxylic acid:

$$RCHO + [O] \rightarrow RCOOH$$

e.g. $$\underset{\text{ethanal}}{CH_3CHO} + [O] \rightarrow \underset{\text{ethanoic acid}}{CH_3COOH}$$

Ketones are formed by the oxidation of secondary alcohols:

$$RCH(OH)R' + [O] \rightarrow RCOR' + H_2O$$

e.g. $$\underset{\text{butan-2-ol}}{CH_3CH_2CH(OH)CH_3} + [O] \rightarrow \underset{\text{butanone}}{CH_3CH_2COCH_3} + H_2O$$

1 Draw the structures of all the oxidation products of the isomers of butanol (C_4H_9OH). Explain why one of these isomers does not undergo oxidation.

Tests to distinguish between aldehydes and ketones

A test to differentiate between these two types of compounds is based on the fact that aldehydes can be oxidised to form carboxylic acids whereas ketones are resistant to oxidation. Two different mild oxidising agents can be used.

Figure 3 *The 'silver mirror' test*

1 **Tollen's reagent** contains $[Ag(NH_3)_2]^+$ ions formed by dissolving silver nitrate in aqueous ammonia. When Tollen's reagent is heated with an aldehyde on a hot water bath the silver compound is reduced to metallic silver, which forms a silver mirror in the test-tube.

The aldehyde is oxidised to the corresponding carboxylic acid:

$$RCHO(aq) + [Ag(NH_3)_2]^+(aq) + H_2O(l) \rightarrow RCOOH(aq) + Ag(s) + 2NH_4^+(aq)$$

2 **Fehling's solution** contains aqueous copper(II) ions. When boiled with an aldehyde the copper(II) ions are reduced to copper(I) oxide, Cu_2O, which forms a brick-red precipitate. The aldehyde is oxidised to the corresponding carboxylic acid:

$$RCHO(aq) + 2Cu^{2+}(aq) + 4OH^{-}(aq) \rightarrow RCOOH(aq) + Cu_2O(s) + 2H_2O(l)$$

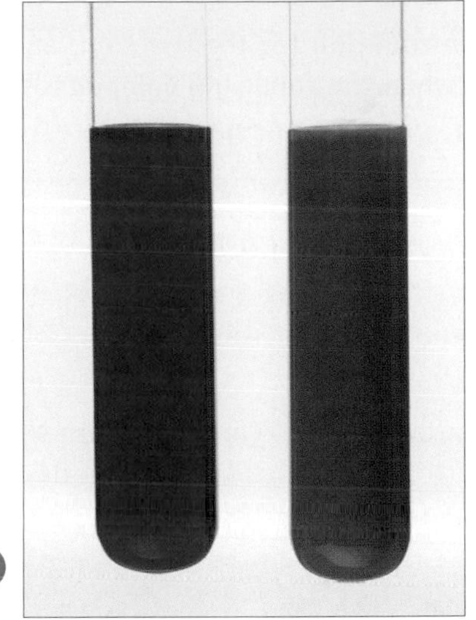

Figure 4 Fehling's solution before and after reaction with an aldehyde

Nucleophilic addition reactions

When the carbonyl group of an aldehyde or ketone is attacked by a nucleophile, an addition reaction occurs and the carbon–oxygen double bond becomes a single bond.

Figure 5 General nucleophilic addition mechanism

Reaction with $NaBH_4$

In AS we studied the reactions of aldehydes and ketones with sodium tetrahydridoborate(III), $NaBH_4$. These reactions are **reduction** reactions and the aldehydes and ketones are reduced to alcohols.

In the equations for these reactions we use [H] to represent the reducing agent

Aldehydes are reduced to primary alcohols:

$$RCHO + 2[H] \rightarrow RCH_2OH$$

e.g. $CH_3CHO + 2[H] \rightarrow CH_3CH_2OH$

ethanal → ethanol

Ketones are reduced to secondary alcohols

$$RCOR' + 2[H] \rightarrow RCH(OH)R'$$

e.g. $CH_3COCH_3 + 2[H] \rightarrow CH_3CH(OH)CH_3$

propanone → propan-2-ol

2 Write an equation for the reaction, and name the alcohols formed when the following compounds are reduced:

a) CH_3CH_2CHO b) $CH_3COCH_2CH_3$ c) $CH_3COCH_2CH(CH_3)_2$

In this unit the mechanism of the reaction is considered. $NaBH_4$ contains Na^+ and BH_4^-. The BH_4^- ion provides the **hydride ion**, H^-, which acts as the nucleophile in the reaction. Looking at the reduction of ethanal, the mechanism occurs in two steps:

The hydride ion attacks the δ^+ carbon atom and a pair of electrons in the carbon–oxygen double bond are transferred to the oxygen atom (Figure 6).

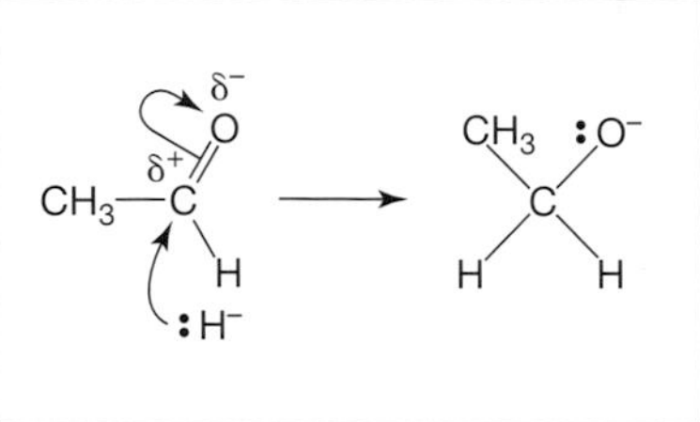

First step in the mechanism **Figure 6**

The intermediate produced then gains a proton from water, which is used as a solvent in the reaction (Figure 7).

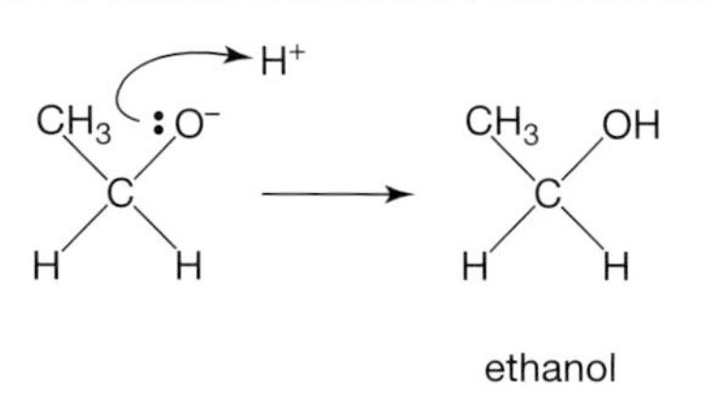

Second step in the mechanism **Figure 7**

The full mechanism is shown in Figure 8.

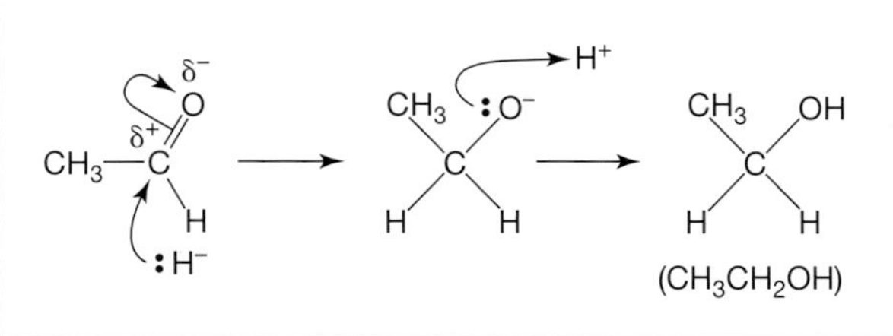

Nucleophilic addition **Figure 8**

The mechanism of the reaction with ketones is exactly the same:

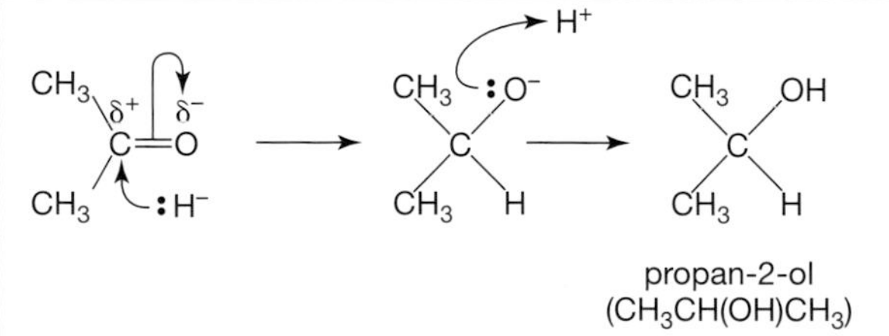

Full mechanism with propanone **Figure 9**

3 a) Explain why aldehydes and ketones undergo nucleophilic addition reactions.

b) Show the mechanism of the nucleophilic addition of the hydride ion to a molecule of butanone.

Reaction with HCN

Aldehydes and ketones undergo nucleophilic addition with HCN.

e.g. CH_3CHO + HCN → $CH_3CH(OH)CN$
ethanal — 2-hydroxypropanenitrile

The nucleophile in this reaction is the cyanide ion, CN^-. You will have studied the cyanide ion as a nucleophile when it attacks haloalkanes. The lone pair of electrons on the carbon atom in the cyanide ion attacks the δ^+ carbon atom on an aldehyde or ketone. The intermediate thus formed gains a proton from the solvent to form the final product:

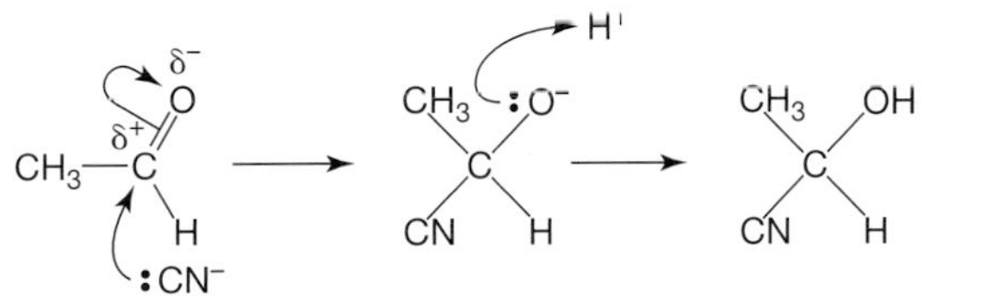

Figure 10 *Addition of HCN to ethanal*

The product of this reaction, 2-hydroxypropanenitrile, exhibits optical isomerism. Optical isomerism occurs when one or more of the carbon atoms in a molecule has four different groups of atoms attached. These carbon atoms are asymmetric and are called chiral centres. (see page 60).

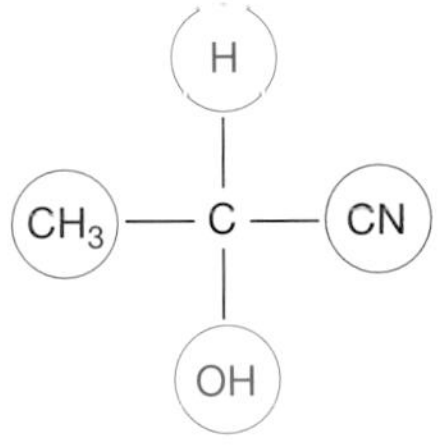

Figure 11 *Planar arrangement to show chiral centre in 2-hydroxypropanenitrile*

The nitrile group undergoes hydrolysis in acidic conditions to form a carboxylic acid group:

$CH_3CH(OH)CN$ + $2H_2O$ + HCl → $CH_3CH(OH)COOH$ + NH_4Cl
2-hydroxypropanenitrile — 2-hydroxypropanoic acid (lactic acid)

Lactic acid also exists as optical isomers but both lactic acid and 2-hydroxypropanenitrile synthesised in the laboratory will exist as racemates. In the nucleophilic attack of the cyanide ion on the ethanal molecule, the cyanide ion could attack the carbon atom equally from either side of the double bond resulting in an equimolar mixture of the (+) and (–) isomers. This mixture will therefore produce a racemic mixture of lactic acid on hydrolysis (Figure 12 overleaf).

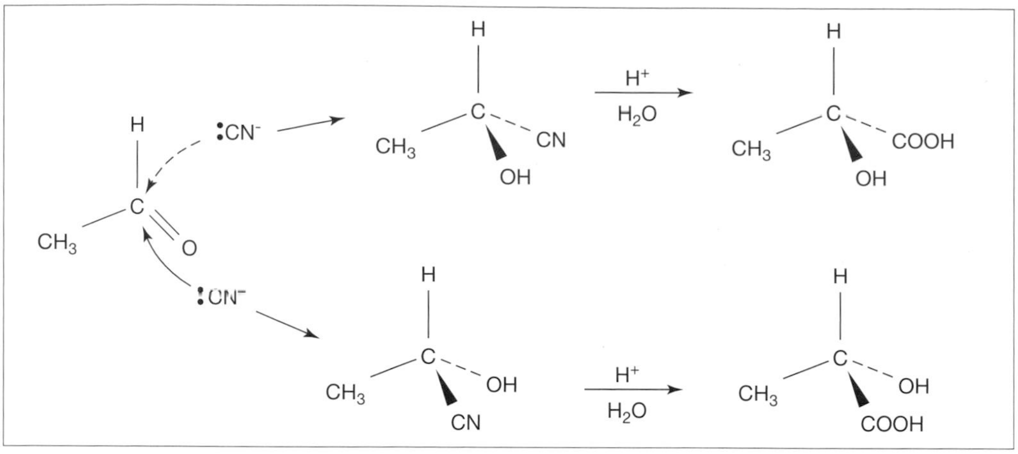

Figure 12 *The formation of a racemate*

The mechanism of the reaction of HCN with ketones is exactly the same as with aldehydes. For example:

$$CH_3COCH_3 + HCN \rightarrow (CH_3)_2C(OH)CN$$

2-hydroxy-2-methylpropanenitrile

4 Write out the mechanism for the above reaction.

If the ketone is symmetrical, for example CH_3COCH_3 or $CH_3CH_2COCH_2CH_3$, then the product is not optically active since there will not be a chiral centre present. When the ketone is asymmetrical, for example $CH_3COCH_2CH_3$, then the product will contain a chiral centre and will be optically active.

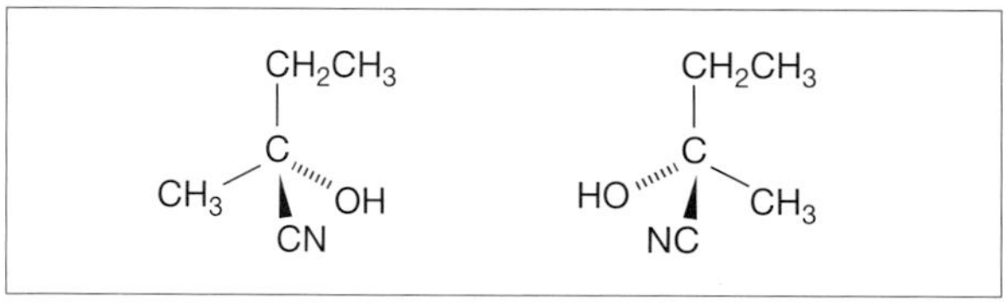

Figure 13 *Product from butanone showing the two mirror images*

5 Draw out and name the acid formed from the hydrolysis of 2-hydroxy-2-methylpropanenitrile. Can this acid show optical activity?

6 Write out a series of equations to show how 2-hydroxypropanoic acid can be synthesised from ethanol.

Key Ideas 65 – 70

- **The carbonyl group is polar and the δ^+ carbon atom is readily attacked by nucleophiles.**
- **Aldehydes and ketones undergo nucleophilic addition reactions with $NaBH_4$ and HCN.**

2 Carboxylic acids and esters

In AS Chemistry you met the carboxylic acids which were formed by oxidation of aldehydes using acidified potassium dichromate(VI). Reacting carboxylic acids with alcohols forms **esters**. These occur naturally as fats and oils. They are commonly used as solvents, plasticisers and food flavourings.

Carboxylic acids

Carboxylic acids are made in the laboratory by oxidising a primary alcohol or an aldehyde:

$$RCH_2OH + [O] \rightarrow RCHO + H_2O$$

e.g. $CH_3CH_2CH_2OH + [O] \rightarrow CH_3CH_2CHO + H_2O$
propan-1-ol → propanal

If an excess of the oxidising agent is used, then the aldehyde is oxidised to the corresponding carboxylic acid:

$$RCHO + [O] \rightarrow RCOOH$$

e.g. $CH_3CH_2CHO + [O] \rightarrow CH_3CH_2COOH$
propanal → propanoic acid

The notation [O] is used to represent the oxidising agent which in this case is usually warm acidified potassium dichromate(VI) solution.

Carboxylic acids contain the – COOH functional group (the carboxyl group)

ethanoic acid

benzene carboxylic acid (benzoic acid)

3-methylbutanoic acid

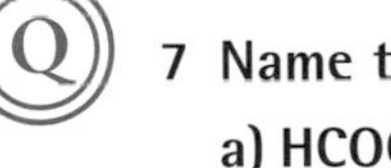

7 **Name the following acids**

a) HCOOH

b) $CH_3CH_2CH_2CH_2COOH$

c) $(CH_3)_2CHCH_2COOH$

d) $CH_3CH(CH_3)CH_2CH_2COOH$

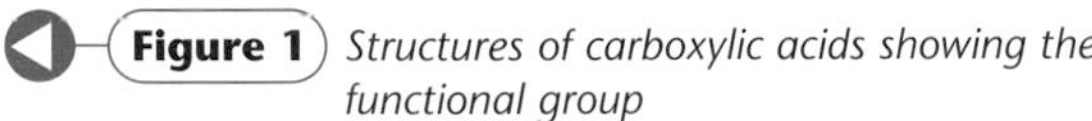

Figure 1 *Structures of carboxylic acids showing the functional group*

Reactions of carboxylic acids

1 Carboxylic acids are weak acids but they are stronger than carbonic acid and will therefore release carbon dioxide when reacted with carbonates or hydrogencarbonates (bicarbonates). This provides the basis of a test for carboxylic acids:

$$2RCOOH + Na_2CO_3 \rightarrow 2RCOO^-Na^+ + CO_2 + H_2O$$

e.g. $2CH_3COOH + Na_2CO_3 \rightarrow 2CH_3COO^-Na^+ + CO_2 + H_2O$
sodium ethanoate

2 Carboxylic acids will neutralise bases:

$$RCOOH + NaOH \rightarrow RCOO^-Na^+ + H_2O$$

e.g. $CH_3CH_2COOH + NaOH \rightarrow CH_3CH_2COO^-Na^+ + H_2O$

sodium propanoate

3 **Esterification**

Carboxylic acids react with alcohols in the presence of a strong acid, such as concentrated sulphuric acid (which acts as a catalyst in the reaction). The organic products of these reactions are called **esters**.

$$RCOOH + R'OH \rightarrow RCOOR' + H_2O$$

acid alcohol ester

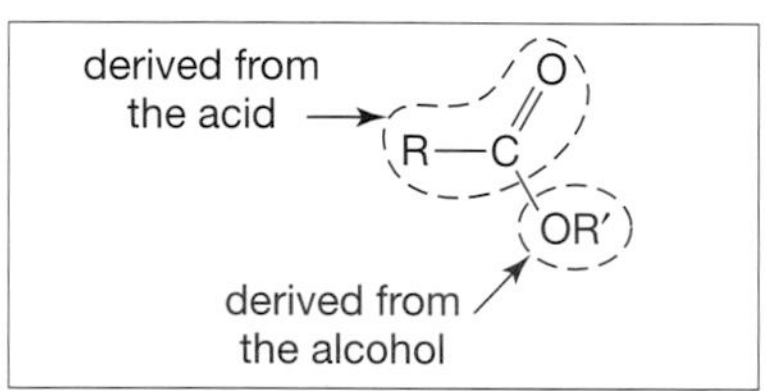

Figure 2 *General structure of an ester*

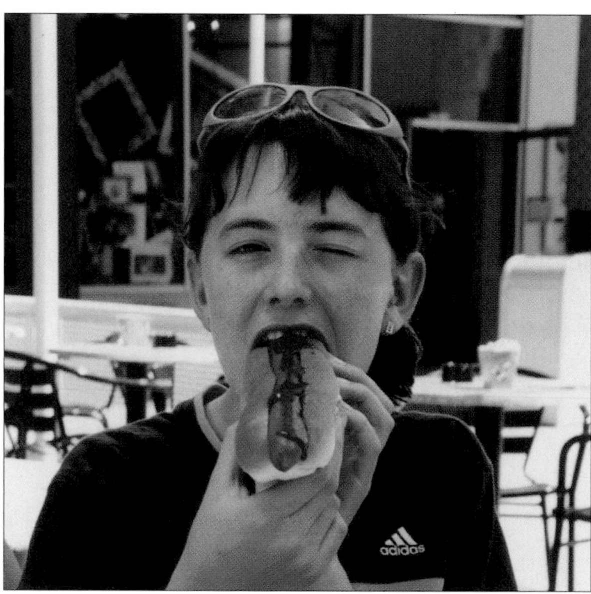

Figure 3 *Esters are used in food flavourings and wrapping.*

Esters have characteristic sweet smells and they are used as food flavourings (see Figure 5). They are also widely used as solvents and as plasticisers. Plasticisers are added to plastics to make them softer and more flexible, e.g. in children's toys. They have also been added to food wrapping film ('cling' film) but there are concerns that these additives may diffuse into fatty foods and cause harm.

Some examples of esterification reactions are given below:

$CH_3COOH + CH_3OH \rightarrow CH_3COOCH_3 + H_2O$

ethanoic acid methanol methyl ethanoate

$CH_3CH_2COOH + CH_3OH \rightarrow CH_3CH_2COOCH_3 + H_2O$

propanoic acid methanol methyl propanoate

$HCOOH + CH_3CH_2OH \rightarrow HCOOCH_2CH_3 + H_2O$

methanoic acid ethanol ethyl methanoate

The formation of an ester can be considered as a condensation reaction since it involves the elimination of water from the reactants:

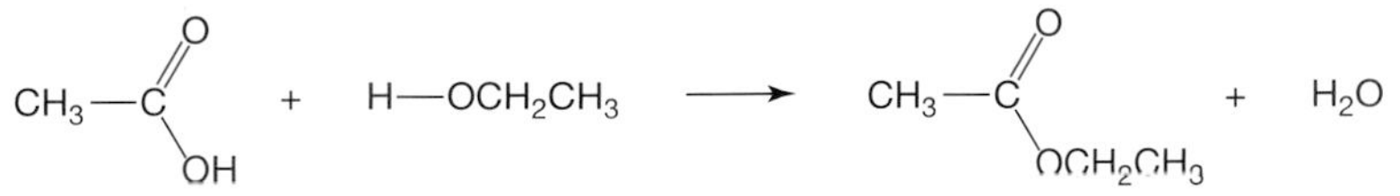

$$CH_3-C(=O)OH + H-OCH_2CH_3 \longrightarrow CH_3-C(=O)OCH_2CH_3 + H_2O$$

ethyl ethanoate

Figure 4 *The formation of an ester by loss of water*

Naming esters

The esters are named as substituted acids by changing the suffix from –oic to **–oate**. The alkyl group is derived from the alcohol. When writing the formula, the part of the molecule derived from the acid comes before the part of the molecule derived from the alcohol. This is shown in Table 1 below:

Name of alcohol	Name of carboxylic acid	Formula of ester	Name of ester
ethanol	methanoic acid	$HCOOCH_2CH_3$	ethyl methan**oate**
methanol	ethanoic acid	CH_3COOCH_3	methyl ethan**oate**
ethanol	ethanoic acid	$CH_3COOCH_2CH_3$	ethyl ethan**oate**
methanol	propanoic acid	$CH_3CH_2COOCH_3$	methyl propan**oate**

Table 1

8 Name and draw the structures for the following esters:

a) $CH_3CH_2CH_2COOCH_2CH_3$

b) $CH_3CH_2COOCH_2CH_2CH_3$

c) $CH_3CH_2CH_2COOCH_3$

9 Write equations for the formation of the following esters:

a) $CH_3CH_2COOCH_2CH_2CH_3$

b) $CH_3CH_2COOCH_2CH_3$

c) $HCOOCH_2CH_3$

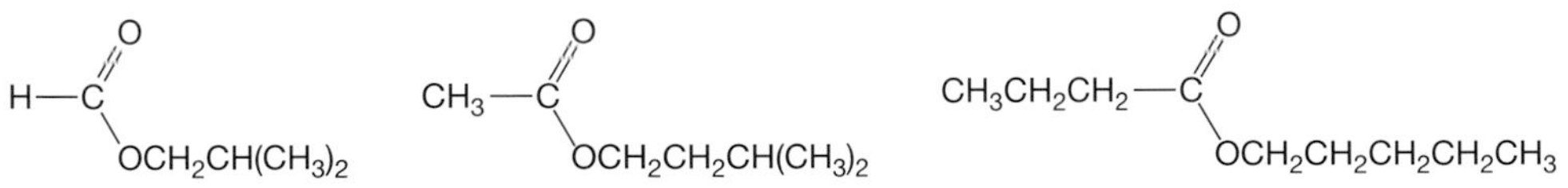

$H-C(=O)OCH_2CH(CH_3)_2$

methylpropyl methanoate (raspberry)

$CH_3-C(=O)OCH_2CH_2CH(CH_3)_2$

3 - methylbutyl ethanoate (bananas)

$CH_3CH_2CH_2-C(=O)OCH_2CH_2CH_2CH_2CH_3$

pentyl butanoate (strawberry)

Figure 5 *What gives fruits their smell?*

Isomerism in acids and esters

Esters and carboxylic acids are functional group isomers. Look, for example, at the molecular formula $C_3H_6O_2$. This can be propanoic acid, CH_3CH_2COOH, ethyl methanoate, $HCOOCH_2CH_3$ or methyl ethanoate, CH_3COOCH_3. The two esters are position isomers. The structures of these three isomers are shown in Figure 6.

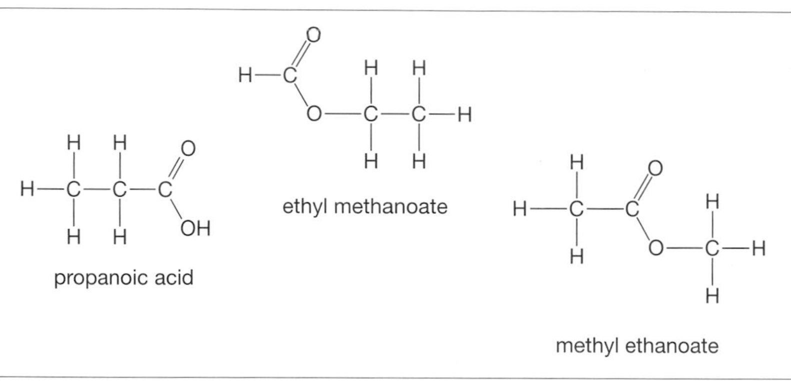

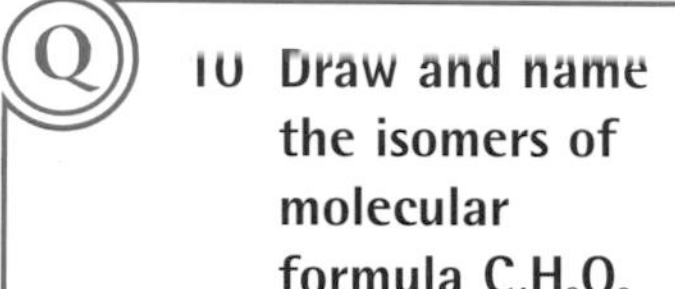

10 **Draw and name the isomers of molecular formula $C_4H_8O_2$**

Figure 6 *The isomers of $C_3H_6O_2$*

Hydrolysis of esters

Esters undergo hydrolysis in acid or alkaline solution. The hydrolysis in hot alkaline solution is usually preferred since the reaction is quicker. The alkaline hydrolysis of an ester produces an alcohol and the sodium salt of the carboxylic acid:

$$RCOOR' + NaOH \rightarrow RCOO^-Na^+ + R'OH$$

Some examples of hydrolysis are shown below:

$$\underset{\text{methyl ethanoate}}{CH_3COOCH_3} + NaOH \rightarrow \underset{\text{sodium ethanoate}}{CH_3COO^-Na^+} + \underset{\text{methanol}}{CH_3OH}$$

$$\underset{\text{ethyl methanoate}}{HCOOCH_2CH_3} + NaOH \rightarrow \underset{\text{sodium methanoate}}{HCOO^-Na^+} + \underset{\text{ethanol}}{CH_3CH_2OH}$$

$$\underset{\text{ethyl benzoate}}{C_6H_5COOCH_2CH_3} + NaOH \rightarrow \underset{\text{sodium benzoate}}{C_6H_5COO^-Na^+} + \underset{\text{ethanol}}{CH_3CH_2OH}$$

If an excess of dilute sulphuric or dilute hydrochloric acid is added to the sodium salt of a carboxylic acid then the carboxylic acid is reformed.

e.g. $C_6H_5COO^-Na^+ + HCl \rightarrow \underset{\text{benzoic acid}}{C_6H_5COOH} + NaCl$

11 **Give the name and structural formula of the acidic hydrolysis products of the following esters:**

a) $CH_3CH_2CH_2COOCH_2CH_3$

b) $CH_3CH_2COOCH_2CH_2CH_3$

c) $CH_3CH_2CH_2COOCH_3$

Triglycerides

Triglycerides are triesters of long–chain carboxylic acids (fatty acids) and propane-1,2,3-triol (glycerol).They occur naturally as fats and oils. Fats contain mainly the saturated acids – e.g. stearic acid, $CH_3(CH_2)_{16}COOH$ – whereas the acids in oils show some degree of unsaturation – e.g. oleic acid, which is a *cis* mono-unsaturated acid, $CH_3(CH_2)_7CH{=}CH(CH_2)_7COOH$.

Glycerol contains three alcohol groups and forms a triester with three carboxylic acid units. The 'R' groups of the triester may be the same or different.

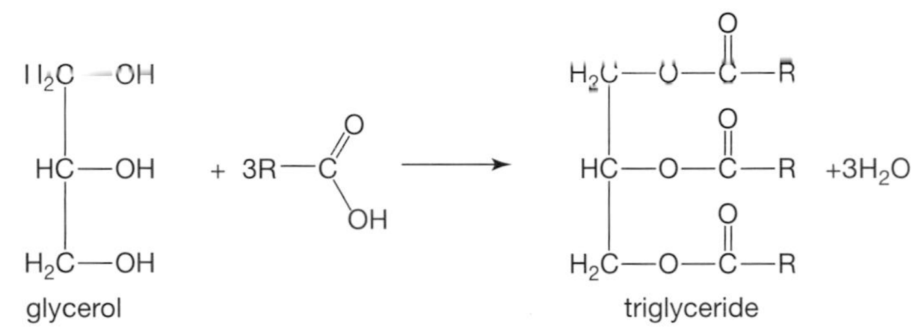

$$\text{glycerol } (H_2C{-}OH,\ HC{-}OH,\ H_2C{-}OH) + 3R{-}COOH \longrightarrow \text{triglyceride } (H_2C{-}O{-}CO{-}R,\ HC{-}O{-}CO{-}R,\ H_2C{-}O{-}CO{-}R) + 3H_2O$$

Figure 7 *The formation of a triglyceride.*

Triglycerides can be hydrolysed using a hot sodium hydroxide solution to form glycerol (a useful solvent) and the sodium salts of the long–chain carboxylic acids. These sodium salts (e.g. sodium stearate) are used in the manufacture of soap.

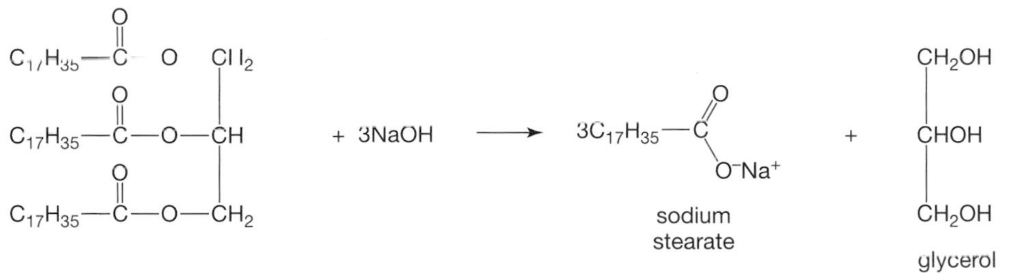

$$(C_{17}H_{35}COO)_3C_3H_5 + 3NaOH \longrightarrow 3C_{17}H_{35}COO^-Na^+ \text{ (sodium stearate)} + CH_2OH{-}CHOH{-}CH_2OH \text{ (glycerol)}$$

Figure 8 *The hydrolysis of a triglyceride*

Key Ideas 71 – 75

- **Carboxylic acids are formed by the oxidation of aldehydes and primary alcohols.**
- **Carboxylic acids are weak acids. Carbon dioxide is produced when they react with a carbonate or hydrogencarbonate.**
- **Esterification involves the reaction of a carboxylic acid with an alcohol to form an ester in the presence of concentrated sulphuric acid.**
- **Triglycerides are naturally occurring esters which can be hydrolysed to produce glycerol and long–chain fatty acids (used to make soap).**

3 Acyl chlorides and acid anhydrides

Acyl chlorides and acid anhydrides are derivatives of carboxylic acids. In acyl chlorides the –OH group of the acid is replaced by a chlorine atom and in acid anhydrides the –OH group is replaced by a RCOO– group. In both cases the resulting molecules are more reactive than the corresponding acid.

The chemistry of the acid derivatives

Acyl chlorides contain the —COCl functional group. The polarity of this functional group arises from the fact that both oxygen and chlorine are more electronegative than carbon. The δ^+ carbon atom is therefore readily attacked by nucleophiles (see page 78).

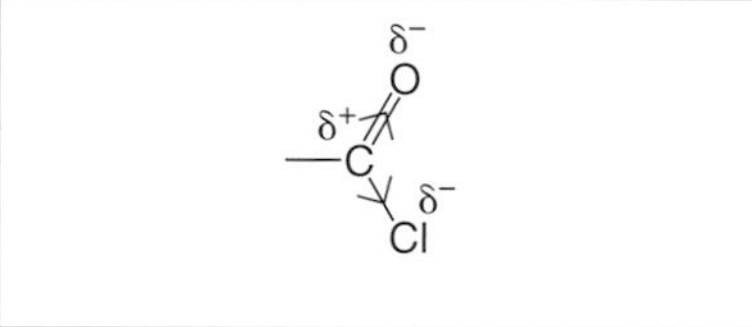

Figure 1 The structure of the acyl group showing polarity

The acyl chlorides are named after the corresponding carboxylic acid e.g. CH_3COCl, derived from ethanoic acid is called ethan**oyl** chloride.

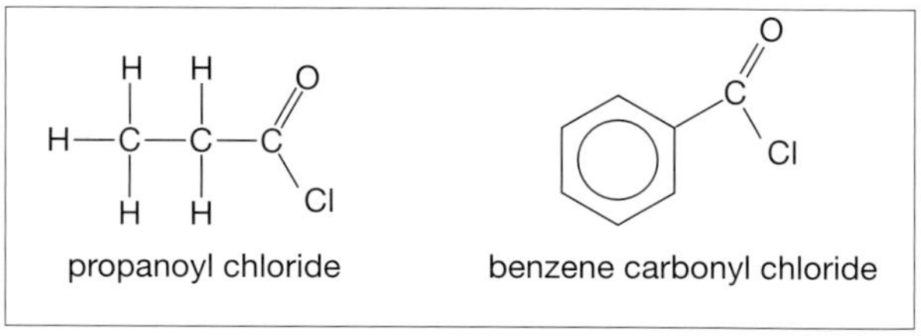

Figure 2 Some examples of acyl chlorides

Acid anhydrides are formed when two molecules of an acid join together with the elimination of water. An example of an acid anhydride is ethanoic anhydride:

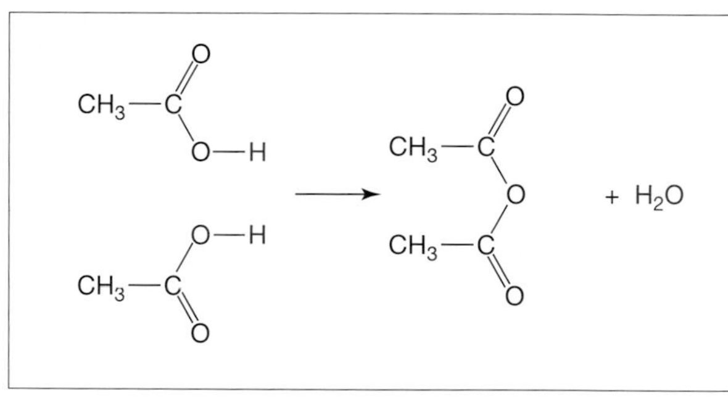

Figure 3 Formation of ethanoic anhydride

Reactions of the acid derivatives

Acyl chlorides and acid anhydrides react with **nucleophiles** such as water, alcohols, ammonia and amines.

e.g. $CH_3COCl + H_2O \rightarrow CH_3COOH + HCl$

$(CH_3CO)_2O + H_2O \rightarrow 2CH_3COOH$

Acyl chlorides react vigorously with water. If the top of a bottle of ethanoyl chloride is removed then fumes of hydrogen chloride are rapidly formed as the acyl chloride reacts with the moisture in air. In reactions involving acyl chlorides **anhydrous conditions** are therefore essential to prevent the hydrolysis reaction of the acyl chloride.

The reactions of acyl chlorides are summarised in Table 1 below:

		Nucleophile		Product 1	Product 2
acyl chloride RCOCl	+	water HO–H	→	carboxylic acid RCOOH	hydrogen chloride HCl
acyl chloride RCOCl	+	alcohol R′O II	→	ester RCOOR′	hydrogen chloride HCl
acyl chloride RCOCl	+	ammonia $H–NH_2$	→	acid amide $RCONH_2$	hydrogen chloride HCl
acyl chloride RCOCl	+	primary amine R′NH–H	→	*N*-substituted acid amide RCONHR′	hydrogen chloride HCl

The '*N*' in the name of a substituted amide stands for nitrogen. It indicates that the R′ group is attached to the nitrogen atom (see Figure 4 below).

Table 1 *Reactions of acyl chlorides*

When R = CH_3 the molecule is ethanoyl chloride. Its reactions are shown below:

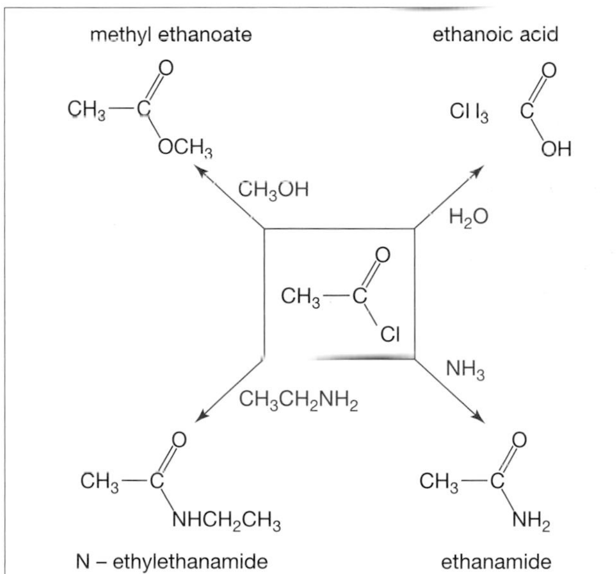

Figure 4 *The reactions of ethanoyl chloride*

Q

12 Write balanced equations to show the following reactions:

a) Propanoyl chloride + ethanol

b) Butanoyl chloride + ammonia

c) Ethanoyl chloride + methylamine.

Name the organic products in each case.

The reactions of acid anhydrides with these various nucleophiles form product 1 as shown in Table 1, but product 2 is *always* a carboxylic acid. Some examples of the reactions of ethanoic anhydride are shown below:

$$(CH_3CO)_2O + CH_3CH_2OH \rightarrow CH_3COOCH_2CH_3 + CH_3COOH$$

ethyl ethanoate

$$(CH_3CO)_2O + NH_3 \rightarrow CH_3CONH_2 + CH_3COOH$$

ethanamide

$$(CH_3CO)_2O + CH_3NH_2 \rightarrow CH_3CONHCH_3 + CH_3COOH$$

N-methylethanamide

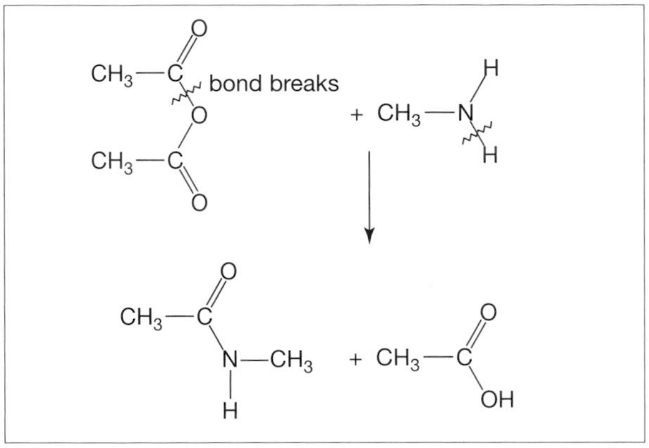

Figure 5 *The formation of N-methylethanamide*

Addition–elimination reactions of acyl chlorides

The reactions described above are all **nucleophilic addition–elimination** reactions. The reactions with nucleophiles occur very readily; no heat or catalysts are required. The reaction occurs in two steps:

1 The addition step

A nucleophile, e.g. H_2O, attacks the δ^+ carbon atom and a pair of electrons in the carbon–oxygen double bond are transferred to the oxygen atom:

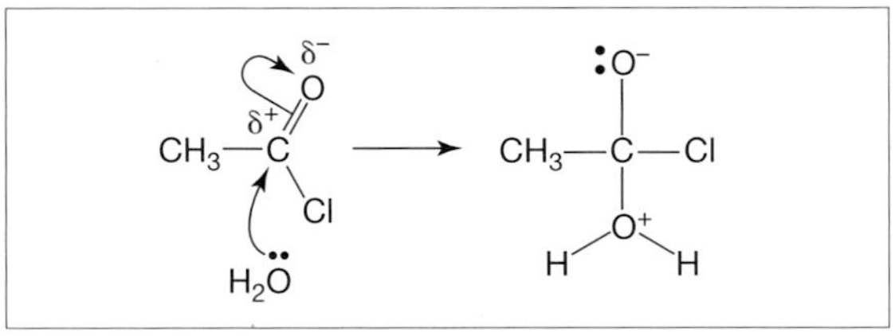

Figure 6 *The addition step*

2 The elimination step

In the second step the pair of electrons on the oxygen atom reform the double bond and the chlorine atom is eliminated. This reacts with a hydrogen atom on the protonated hydroxyl group to form HCl:

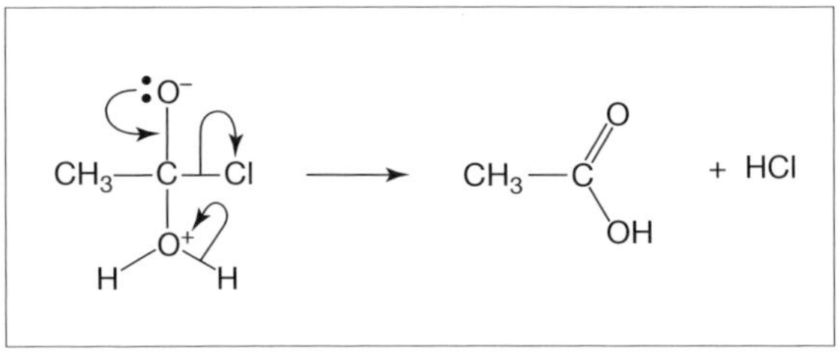

Figure 7 *The elimination step*

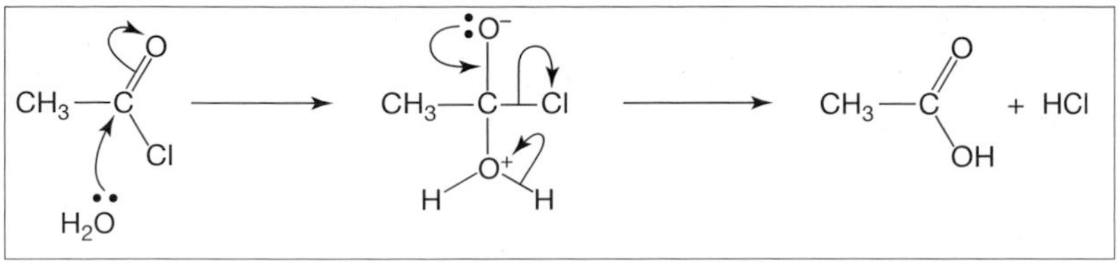

Figure 8 *The full mechanism*

Overall equation: $CH_3COCl + H_2O \rightarrow CH_3COOH + HCl$
ethanoyl chloride — ethanoic acid

The mechanism to show the formation of an ester

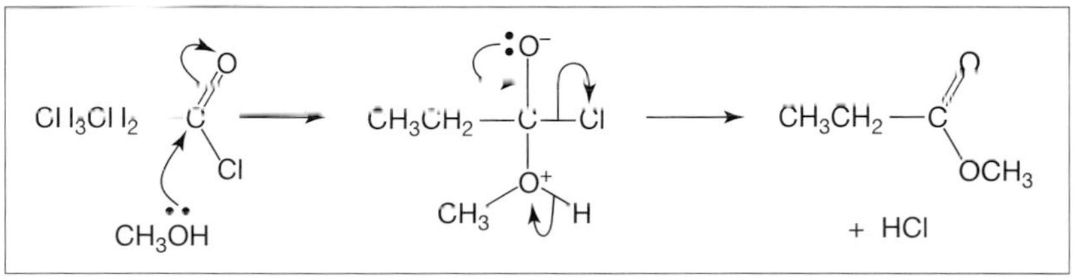

Figure 9

Overall equation:

$CH_3CH_2COCl + CH_3OH \rightarrow CH_3CH_2COOCH_3 + HCl$
propanoyl chloride — methyl propanoate

The mechanism to show the formation of an acid amide

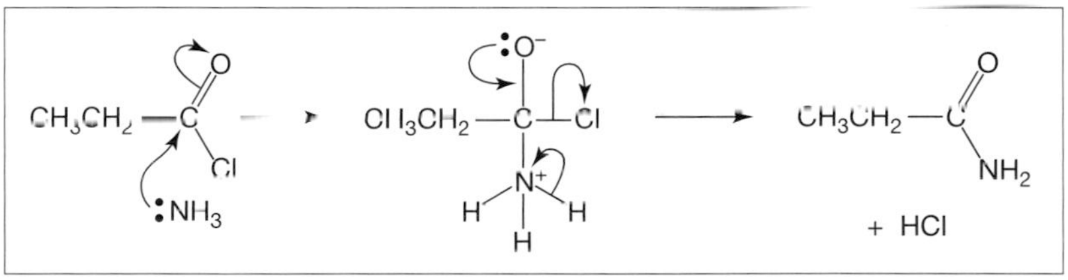

Figure 10

Overall equation:

$CH_3CH_2COCl + NH_3 \rightarrow CH_3CH_2CONH_2 + HCl$
propanoyl chloride — propanamide

13 Give the equations and outline the mechanisms for the formation of the following from the corresponding acyl chloride.

a) ethyl propanoate b) butanamide

The formation of *N*-phenylethanamide

CH_3COCl	+	$C_6H_5NH_2$	→	$CH_3CONHC_6H_5$	+	HCl
ethanoyl chloride		phenylamine		*N*-phenylethanamide		

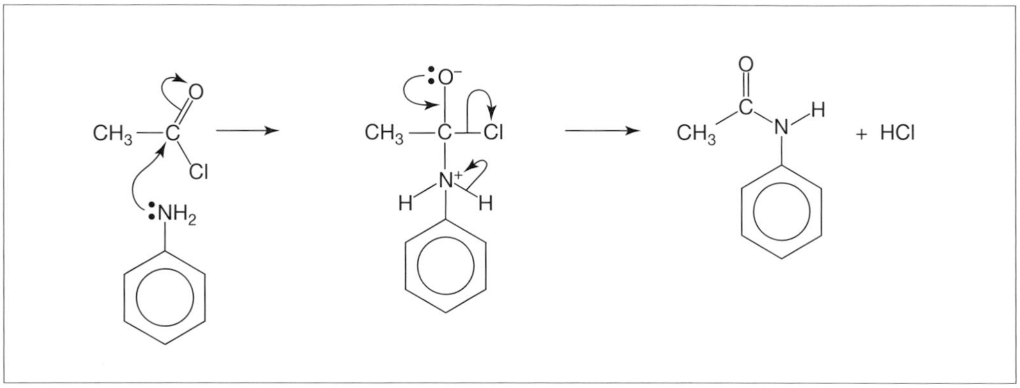

Figure 11 *Mechanism for the formation of a substituted amide*

Two commonly used drugs are paracetamol and aspirin. The product of the above reaction has a very similar structure to the drug paracetamol. The structure of both drugs is related to phenol (C_6H_5OH). Aspirin and paracetamol are sold as analgesics (painkillers) and both also have an anti-pyretic effect (they reduce body temperature). Paracetamol is perhaps a safer alternative to aspirin.

Paracetamol is manufactured by acylating 4-aminophenol, while aspirin is prepared by acylating 2-hydroxybenzoic acid. The –OH group in 2-hydroxybenzoic acid is esterified to form aspirin (see Figure 13).

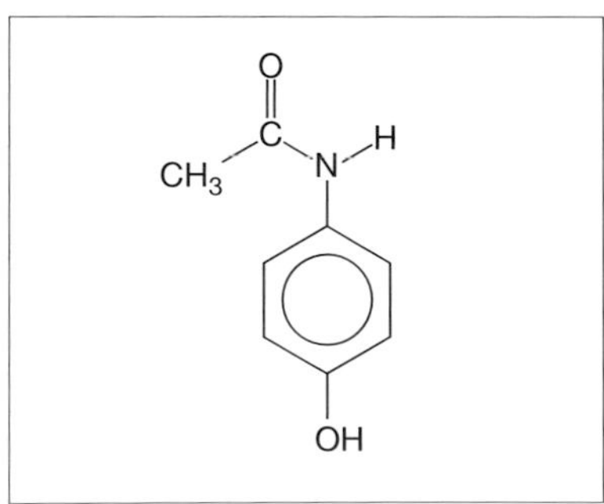

Figure 12 *The structure of paracetamol*

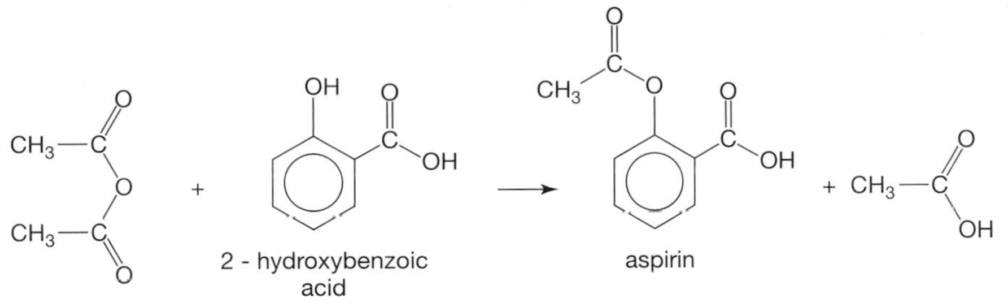

2 - hydroxybenzoic acid

aspirin

Figure 13 *The formation of aspirin*

Ethanoyl chloride or ethanoic anhydride could be used in this manufacture. However, ethanoic anhydride is preferred since it is cheaper, less corrosive and is less susceptible to hydrolysis.

14 Discuss the advantages and disadvantages of preparing an ester from a carboxylic acid or an acyl chloride.

15 Write an equation to show the acylation of 4-aminophenol to produce paracetamol.

Acyl chlorides will also react with benzene in the presence of aluminium chloride in an **electrophilic substitution** reaction to form an aromatic ketone. This is dealt with in the next unit.

Key Ideas 76 – 81

- **Acyl chlorides and acid anhydrides are carboxylic acid derivatives.**
- **They react with nucleophiles such as water, alcohols, ammonia and amines.**
- **The mechanism of these reactions is nucleophilic addition–elimination.**
- **This mechanism occurs in two stages. First the nucleophile is added, then, in the case of acyl chlorides, a molecule of HCl is eliminated.**
- **Ethanoic anhydride is the preferred acylating agent in the manufacture of aspirin since it is cheaper, less corrosive and is less susceptible to hydrolysis.**

Unit 5 Questions

4

1. An alcohol, A, undergoes the following reaction:

$$\underset{\textbf{A}}{C_4H_{10}O} \longrightarrow \underset{\textbf{B}}{C_4H_8O} \longrightarrow \underset{\textbf{C}}{C_5H_9NO}$$

a) Substance **B** is a ketone. Give its name and structure. (2)
b) Identify alcohol **A** by name or formula and justify your answer. (2)
c) (i) What type of reaction is involved in the conversion of **A** to **B**?
(ii) Give the reagent and conditions necessary for this conversion.
(iii) Write a balanced equation for the reaction. (4)
d) Substance **C** is optically active. Draw out the structure and identify the chiral centre. (2)
e) Name the mechanism involved in the conversion of **B** to **C**. (1)

2. **a)** Write equations for the reactions of ethanoyl chloride with (i) methylamine (ii) methanol. (2)
b) Name and outline the mechanism for the reaction occurring in a)(i). (5)

3. Compound **X**, C_3H_6O, precipitates silver metal when reacted with ammoniacal silver nitrate solution and reacts with HCN to produce **Y**, which is an equimolar mixture of two isomers.

a) Identify **X**. (1)
b) Draw the two isomers of **Y** and state how they could be distinguished experimentally. (4)
c) Name and outline the mechanism for the reaction between compound **X** and HCN. (4)

4. Compound **A** shows the following reactions:

- It liberates carbon dioxide from aqueous sodium carbonate.
- It reacts with ethanol in the presence of concentrated sulphuric acid to produce a fruity-smelling liquid **B**, $C_4H_8O_2$.
- Compound **A** is formed as the only product when compound **C** reacts with water.

a) Identify compounds **A**, **B** and **C** by name and show the structure of each. (6)
b) (i) Write an equation for the formation of compound B from compound **A**.
(ii) What is the role of concentrated sulphuric acid in this reaction? (2)
c) (i) Write an equation to show the reaction between compound **C** and ammonia.
(ii) Name the type of reaction occurring. (2)

5 Consider the following reaction scheme:

$$\underset{\mathbf{A}}{C_4H_{10}O} \xleftarrow{\text{step1}} \underset{\mathbf{B}}{C_4H_8O} \xrightarrow{\text{step 2}} \underset{\mathbf{C}}{C_5H_9NO} \xrightarrow{\text{step 3}} \underset{\mathbf{D}}{C_5H_{10}O_3}$$

a) (i) Given that **B** gives a positive result with Fehling's solution and
D is called 2-hydroxy, 3-methylbutanoic acid, identify **A–D** by writing out their structures.

(ii) What would you observe when **B** is tested with Fehling's solution?

(iii) Name one isomer of **B** which would also give a positive result with Fehling's solution and one isomer which does not react with Fehling's solution. (7)

b) Name the type of reaction occurring at each step. (3)

c) Name and outline the mechanism for step 1. (4)

6 The ester, methyl ethanoate, can be prepared from a carboxylic acid or an acyl chloride.

a) Write equations to show the formation of this ester by these two methods. (2)

b) State the conditions necessary for each of these reactions and comment on any important safety aspects. (5)

c) Outline the mechanism for the formation of the ester from the acyl chloride. (4)

d) Write an equation for the hydrolysis of the ester in alkaline conditions showing clearly the structures of the products of the reaction. (2)

7 Write an equation in each case to show how the following pairs of compounds react together. Name all of the organic reactants and products.

a) CH_3COCl and CH_3CH_2OH (4)

b) $(CH_3CO)_2O$ and CH_3OH (5)

c) CH_3CH_2COCl and NH_3 (3)

d) $(CH_3CO)_2O$ and $CH_3CH_2CH_2NH_2$ (4)

e) CH_3COCl and $C_6H_5NH_2$. (3)

8

$$CH_3COOH \xleftarrow{\text{step 1}} CH_3COCl \xrightarrow{\text{step 2}} CH_3COOCH_2CH_3$$

Ethanoyl chloride can be converted into ethanoic acid or ethyl ethanoate as shown above.

a) Give the reagent(s) and conditions necessary for each step. (3)

b) Compounds **X** and **Y** are isomers of ethyl ethanoate. **X** reacts with an aqueous solution of sodium carbonate to produce a gas which turns lime water chalky. **Y** reacts with aqueous solution of sodium hydroxide to produce propan-2-ol. On reduction **X** forms 2-methylpropanal.

Identify **X** and **Y** and write equations for the reactions described. (7)

1 Aromatics

The organic chemistry studied so far has been limited to aliphatic chemistry. This is the chemistry based on carbon chains. **Aromatic chemistry** is the study of compounds containing benzene rings. The name aromatic comes from the fact that many of these compounds have a distinctive smell (an aroma). This unit considers the unique structure of benzene and its reactions, which occur via an electrophilic substitution mechanism. Aromatics are important in the synthesis of many important synthetic compounds such as drugs, dyes, explosives and some plastics.

The structure of benzene

Faraday discovered benzene in 1825. However, working out its structure proved to be difficult. The empirical formula of benzene was found to be CH and its relative molecular mass 78. This gives a molecular formula of C_6H_6 which indicates that benzene is a highly unsaturated compound. But the properties of benzene did not suggest that it was unsaturated. In fact it was found to be fairly unreactive, unlike other unsaturated compounds such as the alkenes.

Several pieces of experimental evidence have been used to decide upon the structure of the benzene molecule.

When benzene is hydrogenated using hydrogen gas and a nickel catalyst, three moles of hydrogen react with each mole of benzene to form cyclohexane, C_6H_{12}

$$C_6H_6(g) + 3H_2(g) \rightarrow C_6H_{12}(g)$$

The structure of cyclohexane is shown below

Figure 1 *The structure of cyclohexane*

This reaction indicates that benzene is a **cyclic** compound and that it contains three carbon–carbon double bonds.

One interpretation, proposed by Kekulé in 1865, is that the benzene ring consists of alternative single and double carbon–carbon bonds.

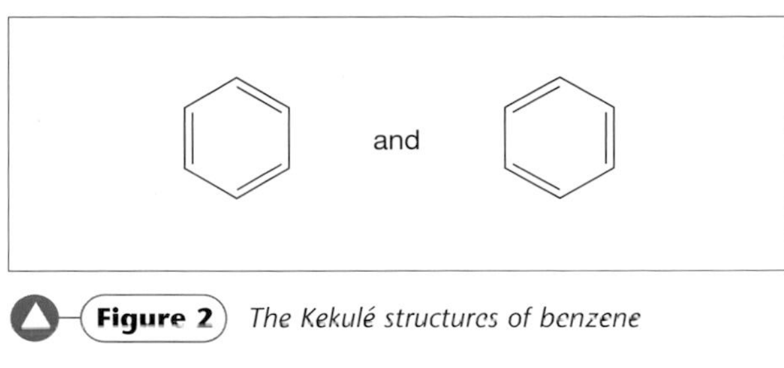

Figure 2 *The Kekulé structures of benzene*

This was the first time that it was even considered that carbon atoms could join together in rings rather than chains. Kekulé's idea came to him in a dream in which he visualised a snake biting its own tail and thus forming a ring. Although this was a massive breakthrough chemists working at the beginning of the 20th century found flaws with the Kekulé structures.

Problems with the Kekulé structures

1 If benzene is unsaturated it should undergo electrophilic addition reactions readily but it does not.

2 When benzene is chlorinated in the presence of an aluminium chloride catalyst to form 1,2-dichlorobenzene, $C_6H_4Cl_2$, only one structure can be formed; this indicates that all the hydrogen atoms in benzene are equivalent. From the Kekulé structures we would expect two different products as shown in Figure 3.

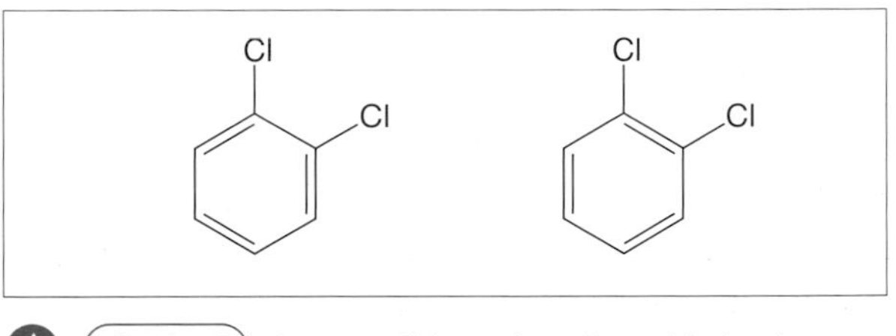

Figure 3 *Two possible products from chlorination of benzene*

3 Measurements from X-ray diffraction studies showed that the electron density around the carbon atoms is equal and that the carbon–carbon bond lengths are all equal and measure 0.140 nm (Figure 4).

In the Kekulé structure the bond lengths would be different, since single bonds are longer than double bonds and the areas of electron density would be concentrated around the double bonds. The bond length of 0.140 nm is in fact intermediate between a single and a double bond.

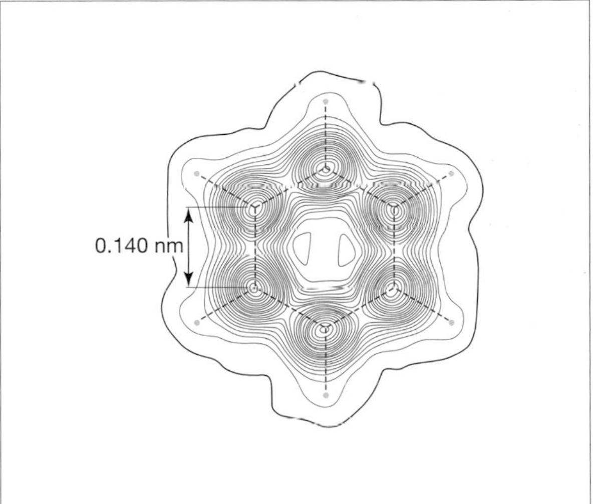

Electron density map of benzene **Figure 4**

4 The enthalpy of hydrogenation value for benzene provides further evidence that the Kekulé structures are incorrect (see overleaf).

Enthalpies of hydrogenation

When cyclohexene is hydrogenated, 120 kJ of energy are released.

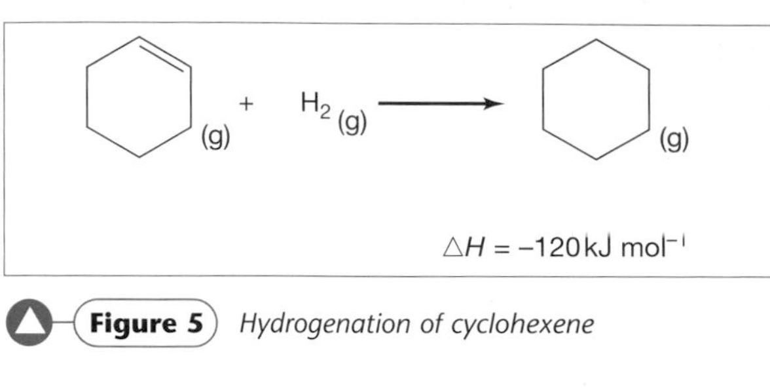

Figure 5 *Hydrogenation of cyclohexene*

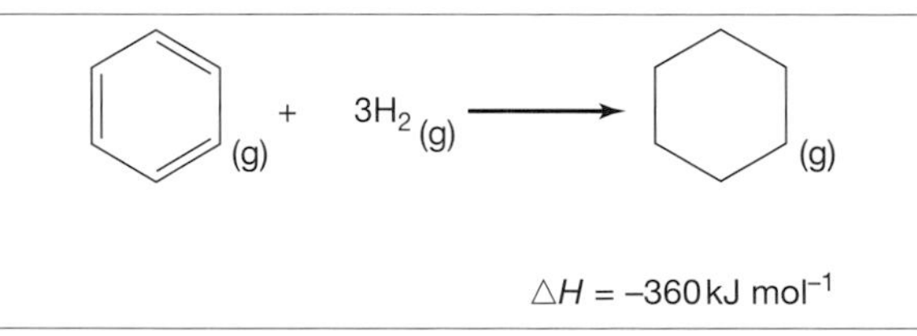

Figure 6

When benzene is hydrogenated, three moles of hydrogen gas react with one mole of benzene and the enthalpy of hydrogenation would be expected to be three times the value of that of cyclohexene, i.e. 360 kJ mol^{-1}.

However the observed value is only 208 kJ mol^{-1}. This is 152 kJ mol^{-1} less than expected. The energy needed to break the bonds in H_2(g) and the energy released when the carbon–hydrogen bonds are formed does not change. This indicates that more energy is required to break the 'double bonds' in benzene than to break three double bonds in an alkene. Benzene is therefore more stable than expected and less energy is released when benzene molecules are hydrogenated.

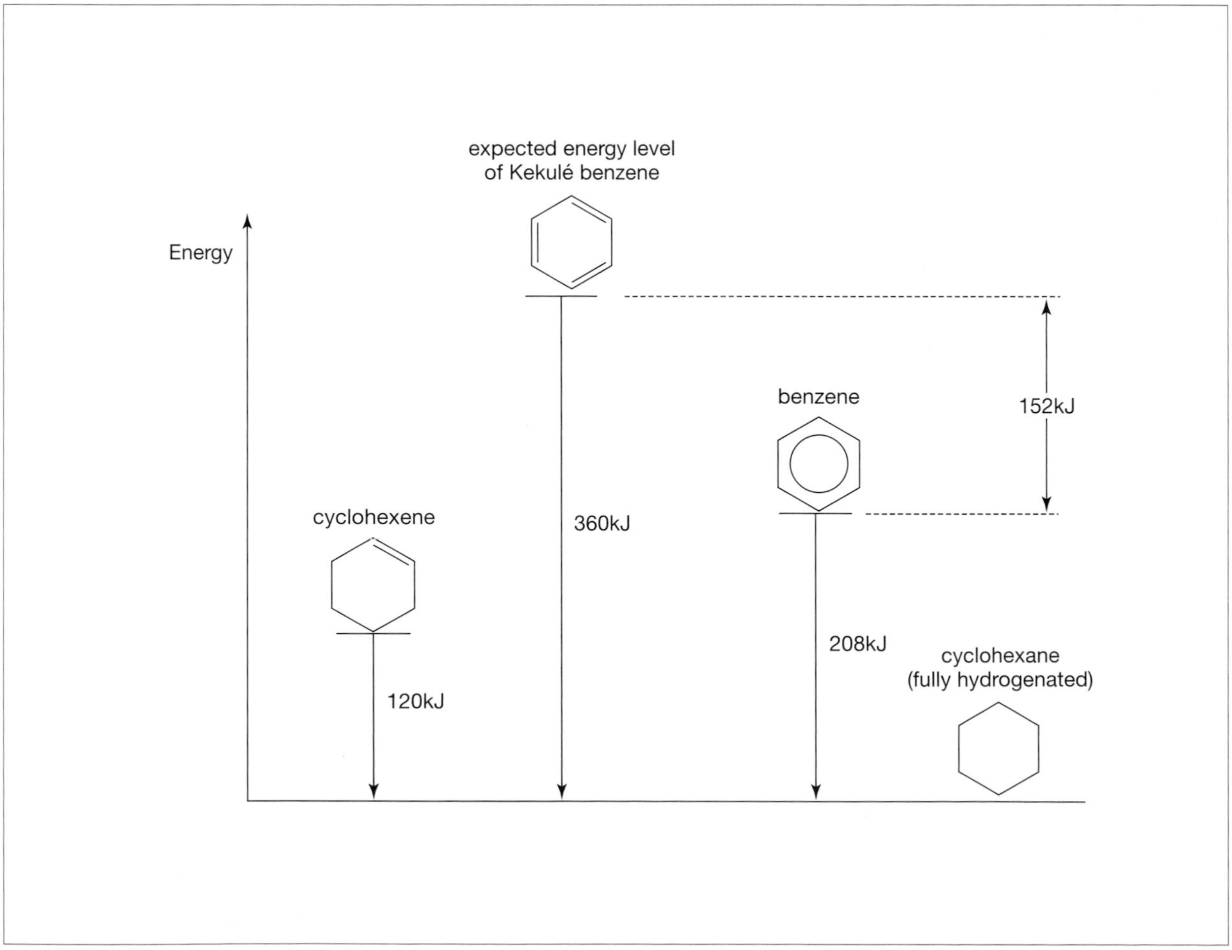

expected energy level of Kekulé benzene
Energy
benzene
152kJ
cyclohexene
360kJ
208kJ
cyclohexane (fully hydrogenated)
120kJ

Figure 7 *Energy level diagrams for hydrogenation of benzene and cyclohexene*

Interpretation of these data

The explanation for this extra stability in the benzene molecule is that the π electrons in the carbon–carbon double bonds are **delocalised** around the benzene ring. This delocalisation of electrons confers extra stability to the benzene molecule.

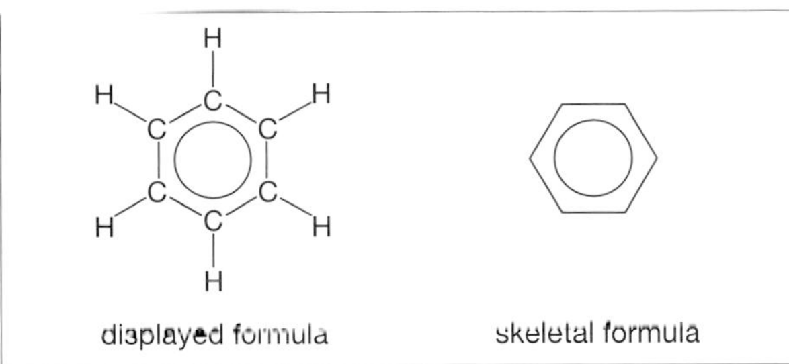

Figure 8 *Accepted structure of benzene*

The accepted structure of benzene is that the six carbon atoms have a planar hexagonal structure. Each carbon atom forms three bonds, one with a hydrogen atom and two with the adjacent carbon atoms in a trigonal planar arrangement. The fourth valency electron (2p) forms a π bond by overlap with the 2p electrons on the adjacent carbon atoms. This results in a 'ring' of delocalised π electrons above and below the plane of the benzene molecule.

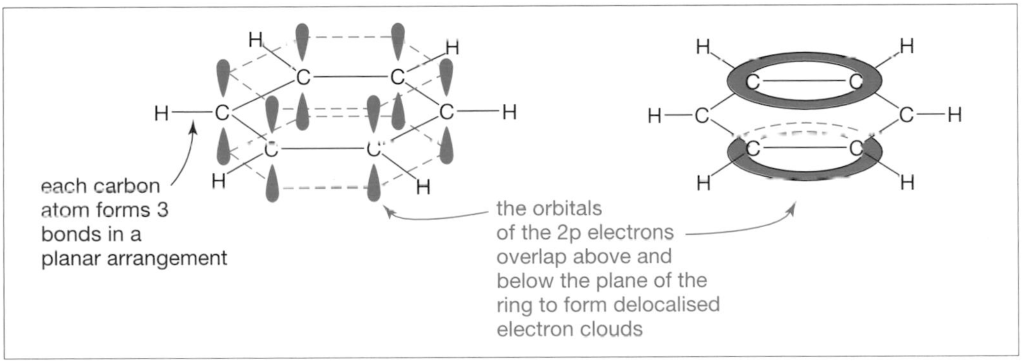

Figure 9 *Diagrams to show the formation of the delocalised electron structure of benzene*

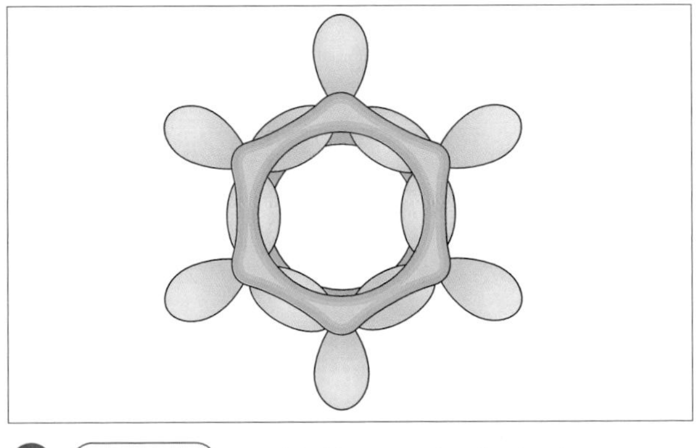

Figure 10 *Model of benzene showing its planar structure and a 'ring' of delocalised electrons*

Q

1. **What is the value of the bond angles in the benzene molecule?**
2. **Explain the difference between** *localised* **and** *delocalised* **electrons.**

Electrophilic substitution reactions

The region of high electron density above and below the plane of the molecule results in benzene being attacked by **electrophiles**. Due to the structure of benzene these reactions involve substitution rather than addition.

Mechanism of electrophilic substitution

The general mechanism of electrophilic substitution is in two parts:

1 Addition of the electrophile

A pair of electrons from the delocalised π electron system form a bond with the electrophile. This produces a highly unstable intermediate ion in which the delocalised ring is broken.

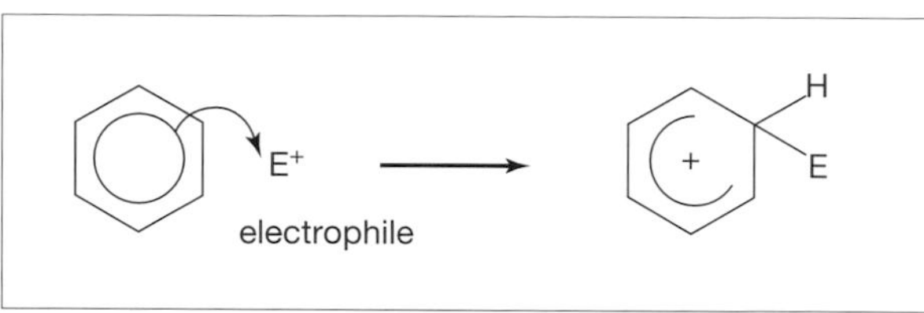

Figure 11 *Step 1 of the mechanism – the addition step*

2 Elimination

A hydrogen atom is easily lost from the intermediate ion to reform the delocalised π electron system in the organic product.

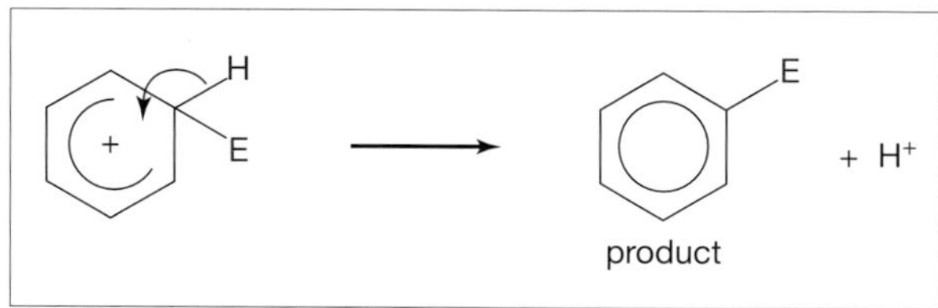

Figure 12 *Step 2 of the mechanism – the elimination step*

Notice that the mechanism involves addition of an electrophile followed by elimination of a hydrogen atom, resulting overall in a substitution reaction.

Benzene undergoes electrophilic substitution in preference to electrophilic addition since a substitution reaction retains the extra stability conferred by the delocalised electrons.

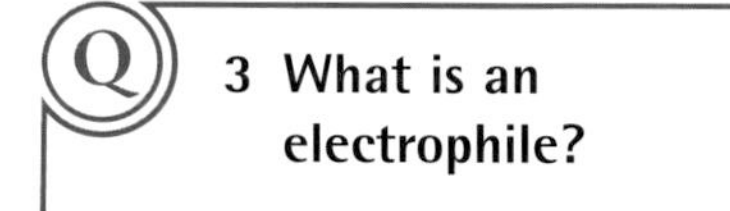

Q **3 What is an electrophile?**

Electrophilic substitution reactions of benzene are very important in synthesis as the specific examples below illustrate.

Nitration

Benzene reacts with a mixture of concentrated nitric acid and concentrated sulphuric acid at 50°C to form nitrobenzene:

$$C_6H_6 + HNO_3 \rightarrow C_6H_5NO_2 + H_2O$$

The mechanism of this reaction is electrophilic substitution. First, we need to look at the generation of the electrophile.

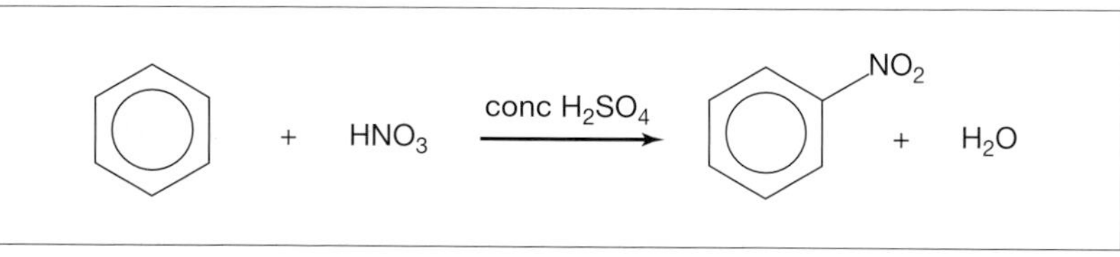

Figure 13 *The formation of nitrobenzene*

Concentrated sulphuric acid acts as a **homogeneous catalyst** (see page 233) in this reaction. Sulphuric acid is a stronger acid than nitric acid and protonates the nitric acid as shown in the equation below.

$$H_2SO_4 + HNO_3 \rightleftharpoons HSO_4^- + H_2NO_3^+$$

The protonated nitric acid then breaks down forming the **nitronium ion** NO_2^+

$$H_2NO_3^+ \rightarrow H_2O + \mathbf{NO_2^+}$$

The nitronium ion is the electrophile that attacks the benzene molecule.

The overall equation for the formation of the nitronium ion is:

$$2H_2SO_4 + HNO_3 \rightarrow 2HSO_4^- + H_3O^+ + NO_2^+$$

The mechanism of the reaction between the nitronium ion and benzene is shown in Figure 14.

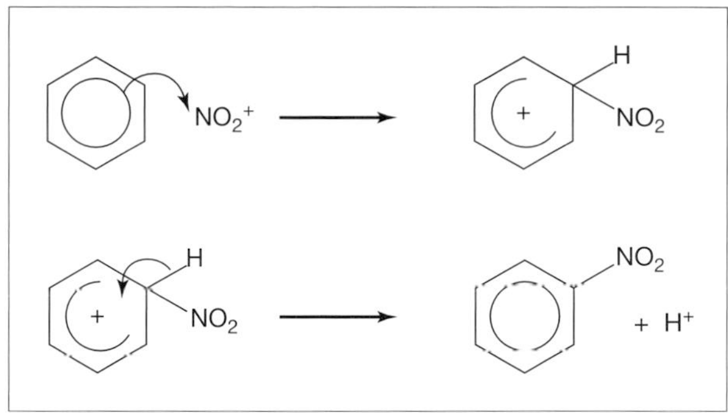

Figure 14 *The mechanism for nitration of benzene*

The importance of nitration in synthesis

Nitration of benzene and benzene derivatives is an important synthetic route used in the production of a large range of compounds. Nitrated benzene derivatives are used as explosives, e.g. TNT (trinitrotoluene).

From the structure of TNT you should see that its systematic name is methyl-2,4,6-trinitrobenzene. TNT is formed from methylbenzene by nitration. The presence of the methyl group, which is electron-releasing, makes the benzene ring more susceptible to attack by electrophiles. So rather than the substitution of one nitro group, three nitro groups are present in the product. Methylbenzene, like benzene, is an aromatic hydrocarbon. Aromatic hydrocarbons are called **arenes**.

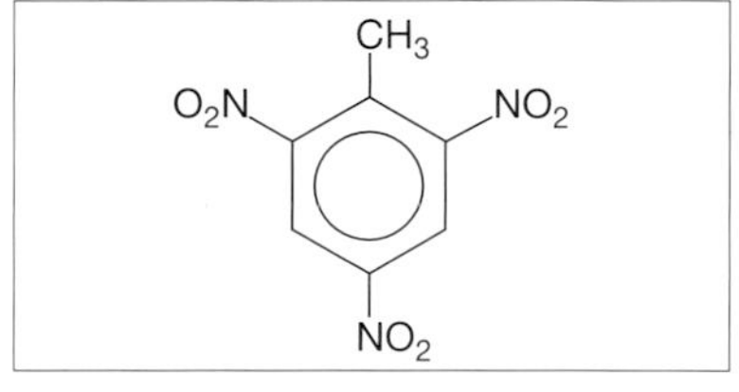

Figure 15 *The structure of TNT*

4 Outline the mechanism for the formation of methyl-4-nitrobenzene from methylbenzene.

The nitro- group in benzene derivatives can be reduced to produce aromatic amines. (see page 98) These aromatic amines are used to make synthetic dyes.

Friedel–Crafts reactions

Benzene will react with a haloalkane to form an alkylbenzene. It will also react with an acyl chloride to form an aromatic ketone. In both of these reactions aluminium chloride is used as a catalyst. The use of aluminium chloride requires anhydrous conditions to prevent a hydrolysis reaction between aluminium chloride and water (see page 184).

These reactions are called Friedel–Crafts reactions after the French chemist Charles Friedel and the American James Crafts who discovered these reactions in the late 1800s. These reactions are particularly useful in synthesis because they form a carbon bond with the benzene ring, thus producing a side chain.

Alkylation reactions

Benzene reacts with haloalkanes in the presence of an aluminium chloride catalyst to form an alkylbenzene:

$$C_6H_6 + RCl \rightarrow C_6H_5R + HCl$$

where R=alkyl group

Figure 16 *Formation of an alkylbenzene*

e.g. $C_6H_6 + CH_3CH_2Cl \rightarrow C_6H_5CH_2CH_3 + HCl$

chloroethane | ethylbenzene

The mechanism for alkylation is electrophilic substitution. Firstly the electrophile is generated using aluminium chloride. The electrophile is a **carbocation**.

Aluminium chloride has a vacant orbital and attracts a lone pair of electrons from the carbon–chlorine bond in the chloroalkane. The aluminium chloride is therefore acting as a **Lewis acid** (see page 213).

5 Why is it important that Friedel–Crafts reactions are carried out under anhydrous conditions?

$$R{-}Cl + AlCl_3 \longrightarrow R^+ + [AlCl_4]^-$$

electrophile

Figure 17 *Interaction of haloalkane with aluminium chloride showing generation of electrophile for Friedel–Crafts alkylation*

The mechanism of the reaction between benzene and the carbocation is shown below. The product is an arene.

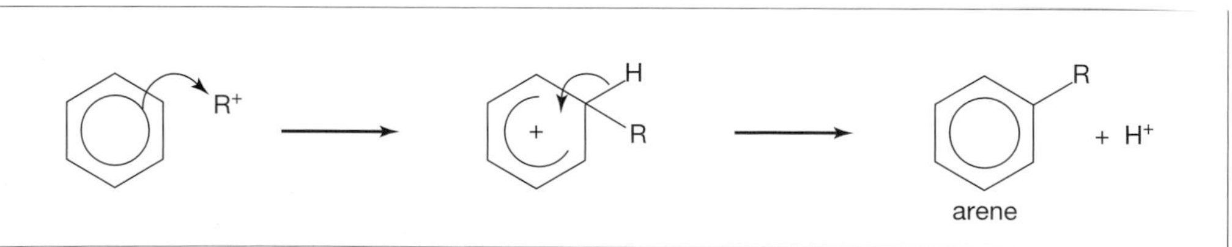

Figure 18 *The mechanism of alkylation*

The catalyst, $AlCl_3$, is regenerated as shown below:

$$H^+ + [AlCl_4]^- \rightarrow AlCl_3 + HCl$$

6 Outline the mechanism for the formation of ethylbenzene from benzene and chloroethane, showing clearly how the electrophile is generated.

Acylation reactions

Benzene reacts with acyl chlorides in the presence of an aluminium chloride catalyst to form an aromatic ketone.

$C_6H_6 + RCOCl \rightarrow C_6H_5COR + HCl$

Figure 19 *Formation of an aromatic ketone*

> **Q** **7 Draw out the structure of phenylethanone and its isomer phenylethanal**

e.g. $C_6H_6 + CH_3COCl \rightarrow C_6H_5COCH_3 + HCl$

ethanoyl chloride → phenylethanone

As in the alkylation reaction the aluminium chloride attracts a pair of electrons from the chlorine atom in the acyl chloride to produce the electrophile (an acylium ion):

Figure 20 *Interaction of acyl chloride with aluminium chloride producing an electrophile*

The electrophilic substitution mechanism of acylation is shown in Figure 21.

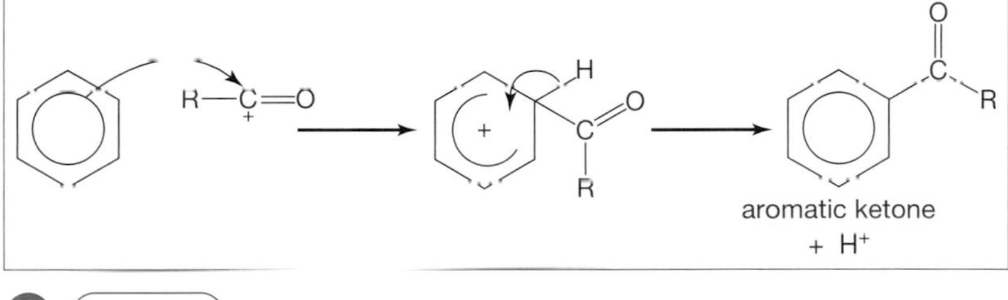

Figure 21 *Mechanism of acylation*

> **Q** **8 a) Outline the mechanism for the formation of phenylethanone from benzene and ethanoyl chloride.**
>
> **b) Explain the role of aluminium chloride in this reaction.**

Key Ideas 84 – 91

- **Delocalisation of electrons makes benzene a very stable molecule.**
- **Thermochemical data from the enthalpies of hydrogenation provide evidence for the structure of benzene.**
- **Aromatic hydrocarbons are called arenes. They undergo electrophilic substitution reactions, e.g. Friedel–Crafts reactions.**
- **Friedel–Crafts reactions are methods of alkylation and acylation.**
- **Electrophilic substitution reactions are important in synthesis**

2 The manufacture of polystyrene

Polystyrene is one of the polymers studied in Module 3. It is a good insulator and is used to make ceiling tiles, packaging materials and plastic cups. It is manufactured by **addition polymerisation** from the monomer, phenyethene.

Preparing the monomer

Ethylbenzene, $C_6H_5CH_2CH_3$, is an important intermediate in the manufacture of phenylethene (styrene), $C_6H_5CH{=}CH_2$.

Industrially ethylbenzene is manufactured by the reaction of benzene with **ethene** in the presence of hydrogen chloride and aluminium chloride.

This is a similar reaction to that of benzene with chloroethane and occurs via the same mechanism. Since chloroethane is manufactured from ethene it makes economic sense industrially to prepare ethylbenzene directly from ethene rather than make chloroethane and then react it with benzene.

The electrophile, which is a carbocation, is generated by the electrophilic addition of H^+ to ethene using HCl in the presence of $AlCl_3$:

9 Why is ethene used to generate the electrophile in this reaction, in preference to chloroethane?

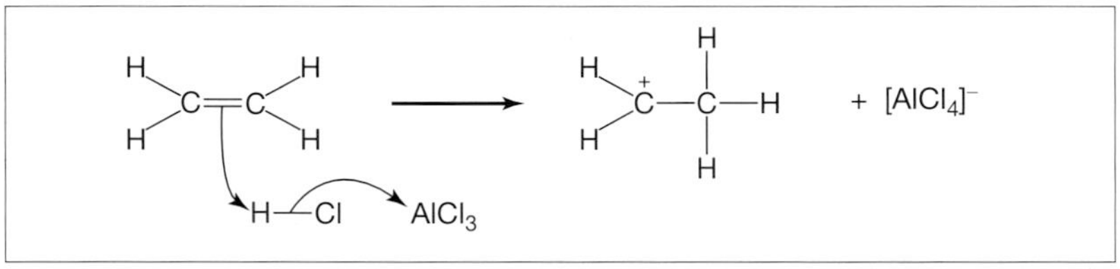

Figure 1 *Generation of the electrophile*

10 a) Write an equation to show the formation of chloroethane from ethene.

b) Name the mechanism of this reaction.

The electrophile then reacts with benzene via electrophilic substitution:

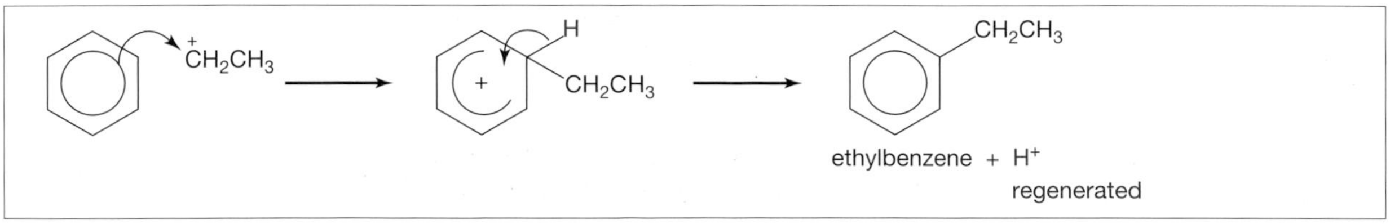

Figure 2 *Mechanism to show the formation of ethylbenzene*

Once the ethylbenzene has been produced it undergoes a catalytic dehydrogenation reaction to form phenylethene:

$$C_6H_5CH_2CH_3 \xrightarrow{Fe_2O_3} C_6H_5CH{=}CH_2 + H_2$$

Preparing the polymer

Phenylethene then undergoes **addition polymerisation** to form poly(phenylethene), at high pressure in the presence of a free-radical initiator.

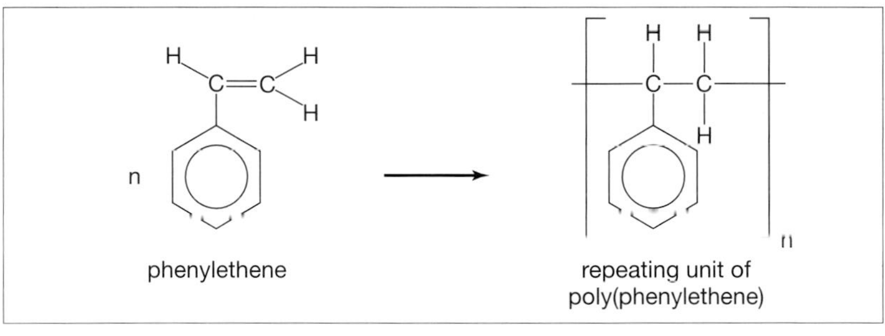

Figure 3 *The polymerisation reaction to form poly(phenylethene)*

11 Draw a flowchart to summarise the formation of poly(phenylethene) from ethene and benzene.

When benzene reacts with an **asymmetric** alkene such as propene, then two different alkybenzenes are formed. This is because when propene reacts with HCl and $AlCl_3$ two different electrophiles can be formed.

12 a) Give the formulae for these electrophiles and explain why one is more stable than the other.

(S)

b) Give the structures of the major and minor products of this reaction.

13 When benzene reacts with but-1-ene in the presence of HCl and $AlCl_3$ two different alkylated benzene derivatives, $C_6H_5CH_2CH_2CH_2CH_3$ and $C_6H_5CH(CH_3)CH_2CH_3$ are formed. Outline the mechanism for the formation of these two derivatives and explain why the branched side-chain product is formed in greater quantities.

Key Ideas 92 – 93

- Industrially ethylbenzene is manufactured from benzene and ethene.
- The reaction involves an electrophilic substitution mechanism.
- Ethylbenzene is an important intermediate in the production of polystyrene.
- If benzene reacts with an asymmetric alkene then two different alkylbenzenes are formed. The amount of each product depends on the stability of the carbocation intermediates.

Unit 6 Questions

3

① Benzene can be converted to phenylamine by the two-step process shown below:

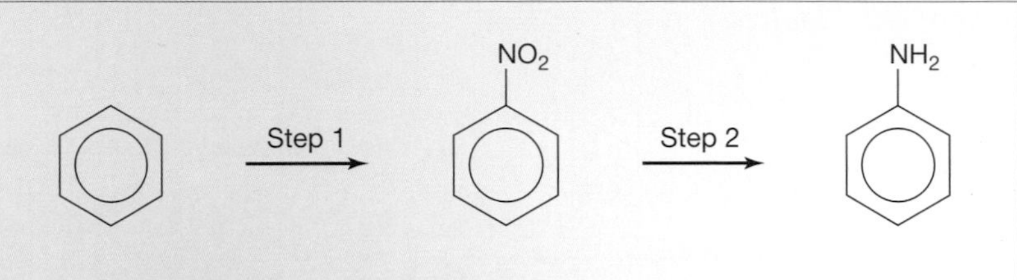

a) Give suitable reagents for each step. (3)
b) State the types of reactions occurring. (2)
c) Write equations for both reactions. (2)

② Friedel–Crafts reactions are examples of electrophilic substitution reactions. In these reactions aluminium chloride is used as a catalyst.

a) Outline the mechanism for the alkylation of benzene using chloroethane. (4)
b) Outline the mechanism for the acylation of benzene using ethanoyl chloride. (4)
c) Explain why these reactions require anhydrous conditions. (1)

③ Polystyrene is manufactured by addition polymerisation using phenylethene as the monomer.

a) Draw the repeating unit of this polymer. (1)
b) Phenylethene is manufactured from benzene in a two-stage process as shown in the reaction scheme below:

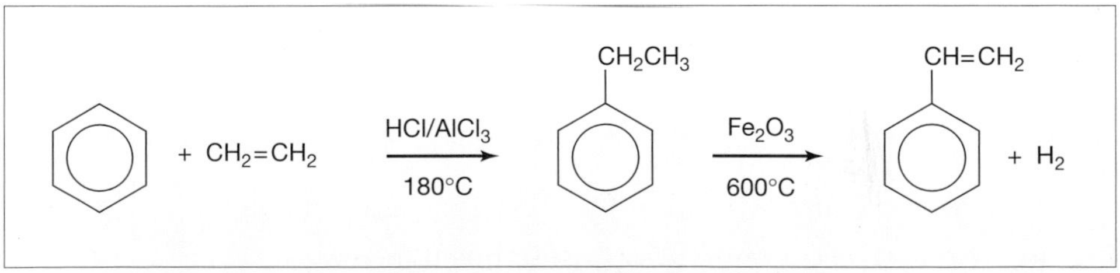

C_6H_6 + $CH_2{=}CH_2$ —$HCl/AlCl_3$, 180°C→ $C_6H_5CH_2CH_3$ —Fe_2O_3, 600°C→ $C_6H_5CH{=}CH_2$ + H_2

(i) Name the type of reaction occurring at each step.
(ii) Outline a mechanism for the first step, including the generation of the reactive intermediates.
(iii) Name an alternative organic reagent that could replace ethene in the first step. (8)

4 a) (i) What is a carbocation?
(ii) Give the structures of the two carbocations formed when propene is treated with $H^+(aq)$. (3)

b) (1-methylethyl)benzene ($C_6H_5CH(CH_3)_2$) is the major product from the reaction of benzene with propene in the presence of $AlCl_3$ and HCl.
(i) Explain, with an equation, the role of $AlCl_3$ and HCl in this reaction.
(ii) Explain why, in terms of the carbocation intermediates, (1-methylethyl)benzene is the major product of this reaction.
(iii) Give the structure of the minor product. (5)

5 a) What is an electrophile? (1)

b) Explain, in terms of its structure, why benzene undergoes electrophilic substitution reactions rather than electrophilic addition reactions. (4)

c) Outline the mechanism for the formation of ethylbenzene from benzene and bromoethane, including the generation of the electrophile. (4)

6 Benzene and cyclohexene can be hydrogenated using hydrogen and a nickel catalyst. The enthalpy changes for these reactions are shown in the table below.

Enthalpy of hydrogenation/kJ mol^{-1}	
cyclohexene	−120
benzene	−208

a) Write equations to show the hydrogenation of (i) cyclohexene; (ii) benzene. (2)

b) Explain why the value for the enthalpy of hydrogenation of benzene is less than originally expected. (3)

c) Describe a chemical test that could be used to distinguish between cyclohexene and benzene. (3)

7 The nitration of benzene is carried out at 50 °C using a mixture of concentrated nitric and sulphuric acids.

a) Name the nitrating species produced from this mixture of acids and write an equation for its formation. (2)

b) Name and outline the mechanism for this reaction. (4)

8 Benzene can be converted into an aromatic ketone as shown below:

O
C
CH_3

a) Name the aromatic ketone produced. (1)

b) Name the reagents necessary to bring about this conversion. (2)

c) Outline a mechanism for the reaction. (4)

1 Amines

Amines are a homologous series of organic molecules that contain a nitrogen atom. They are formed when haloalkanes undergo **nucleophilic substitution** reactions with ammonia. You met these reactions in AS chemistry. In this unit we look at how the amines are classified and study their reactions as Brønsted–Lowry bases and nucleophiles.

Nomenclature and classification

Amines are substituted ammonia compounds in which one or more of the hydrogen atoms has been replaced by alkyl or aryl groups (C_6H_5—) (see Figure 1).

The simplest amine is methylamine, CH_3NH_2. This is a **primary amine**. All primary amine molecules contain the **amino group** (—NH_2). They are named using the alkyl group prefix unless isomers exist, in which case the amino group is numbered and the prefix used is amino. Some examples of primary amines are shown in Figure 1.

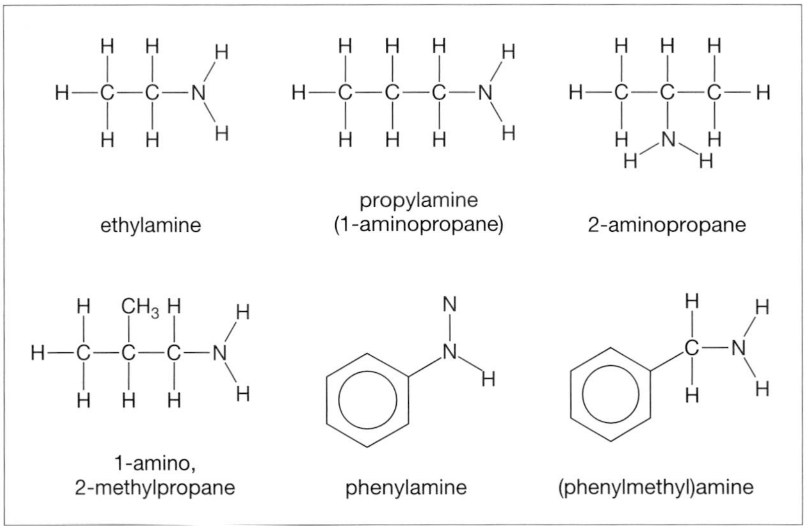

ethylamine

propylamine (1-aminopropane)

2-aminopropane

1-amino, 2-methylpropane

phenylamine

(phenylmethyl)amine

Figure 1 *Examples of primary amines*

Amines are classified as **primary**, **secondary** or **tertiary** depending upon the number of hydrogen atoms substituted. Primary amines contain one alkyl group or aryl group attached to the nitrogen atom. Secondary and tertiary amines contain two and three alkyl or aryl groups respectively. Their general formulae and some examples are shown in Figure 2.

1 Name the following primary amines
a) $CH_3CH(NH_2)CH_2$ **b)** $C_6H_5NH_2$
c) $CH_3CH_2CH(NH_2)CH_3$.

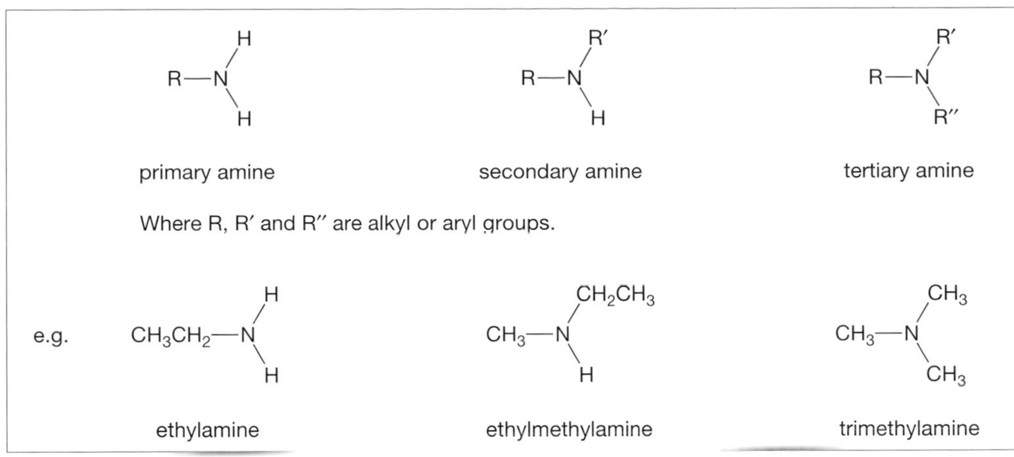

Figure 2 *Classification of amines*

2 Classify and name the following molecules

a) $CH_3CH_2CH_2NH_2$ b) $CH_3NHCH_2CH_2CH_3$ c) $CH_3CH(OH)CH_3$ d) $(CH_3)_3CCl$

Preparation of primary amines

1. From haloalkanes by nucleophilic substitution

The reactions of haloalkanes with ammonia were introduced in AS Chemistry. Halogen atoms have a greater electronegativity than carbon atoms and therefore haloalkanes have a polar carbon–halogen bond with a δ^+ carbon atom which is readily attacked by nucleophiles including ammonia, NH_3.

e.g. CH_3CH_2Br (bromoethane) + $2NH_3$ → $CH_3CH_2NH_2$ (ethylamine) + NH_4Br

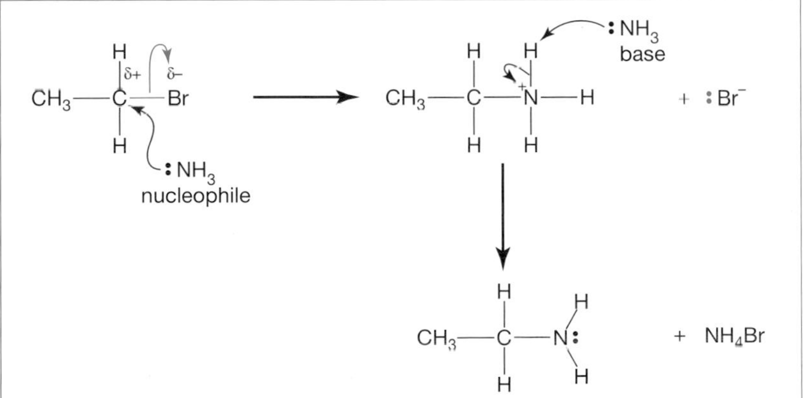

This reaction is carried out in the presence of excess ammonia.

Figure 3 *The formation of a primary amine by nucleophilic substitution*

The amine produced in this reaction contains a lone pair of electrons on the nitrogen atom. This means amines can act as nucleophiles (see page 101) and the reaction may continue. If excess ammonia is used then a primary amine is the major product. If excess of the haloalkane is used then successive substitution is more likely to occur.

3 Show the mechanism for the formation of 2-aminopropane from excess ammonia and an appropriate haloalkane.

Since successive substitution is possible in the reaction between ammonia and haloalkanes then product control is difficult. A more reliable method of producing a primary amine is by reduction.

2. By reduction

a) Amines can be formed by the reduction of **nitriles** using hydrogen in the presence of a nickel catalyst or $LiAlH_4$

$$RCN + 2H_2 \rightarrow RCH_2NH_2$$

or $$RCN + 4[H] \rightarrow RCH_2NH_2$$

where [H] can be used to represent the reducing agent. Notice in these reactions that the length of the hydrocarbon chain has increased.

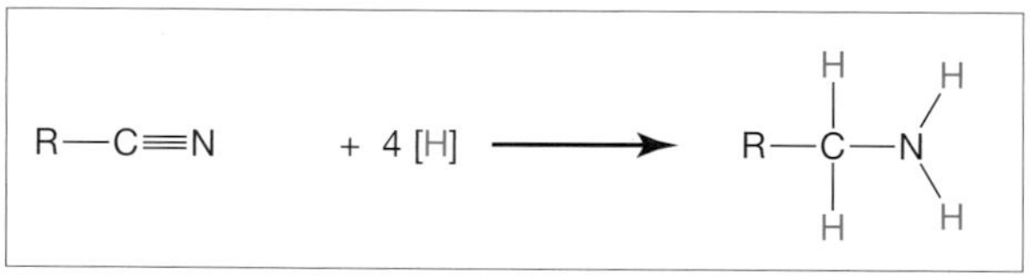

$$R{-}C{\equiv}N \quad + 4[H] \longrightarrow R{-}CH_2{-}NH_2$$

Figure 4 *Reduction of nitriles to primary amines*

e.g.

$$CH_3CN + 2H_2 \rightarrow CH_3CH_2NH_2$$
ethanenitrile → ethylamine

$$CH_3CH_2CN + 2H_2 \rightarrow CH_3CH_2CH_2NH_2$$
propanenitrile → 1-aminopropane

$$C_6H_5CN + 2H_2 \rightarrow C_6H_5CH_2NH_2$$
benzenecarbonitrile → (phenylmethyl)amine

b) Aryl amines are prepared by the reduction of **nitro derivatives**.

The reducing agent is a mixture of tin and concentrated hydrochloric acid or iron and concentrated hydrochloric acid.

$$RNO_2 + 6[H] \rightarrow RNH_2 + 2H_2O$$

e.g. $$C_6H_5NO_2 + 6[H] \rightarrow C_6H_5NH_2 + 2H_2O$$
nitrobenzene → phenylamine

The reduction can also be achieved using hydrogen gas and a nickel catalyst.

$$C_6H_5NO_2 + 3H_2 \rightarrow C_6H_5NH_2 + 2H_2O$$

Aryl amines are important in the production of synthetic dyes. These dyes, known as azo dyes, were the first synthetic dyes to be produced towards the end of the 19th century.

4 a) Give two ways of preparing propylamine.

b) Which of these two methods will produce a better yield of the required product? Explain your answer.

Properties of amines

Amines can behave as bases, nucleophiles and ligands. In each case these properties depend on the ability of the nitrogen atom in the amine molecule to donate its lone pair of electrons to another species.

- When amines act as bases the lone pair is donated to a proton.
- When amines act as nucleophiles the lone pair is donated to a δ^+ carbon atom.
- When amines act as ligands the lone pair is donated to a transition metal ion. This is dealt with in detail in Module 5 (see page 213).

Amines as Brønsted–Lowry bases

In this section the basic properties of the primary amines only are considered. Amines have a lone pair of electrons on the nitrogen atom and this allows them to accept a proton. Brønsted–Lowry bases are **proton acceptors**:

Figure 5 Amines as Brønsted–Lowry bases

$$RNH_2 + H^+ \rightleftharpoons RNH_3^+$$

In water the solution is alkaline due to the presence of hydroxide ions:

$$RNH_2 + H_2O \rightleftharpoons RNH_3^+ + OH^-$$

In dilute acid the amine dissolves due to the formation of the soluble ionic salt:

$$RNH_2 + HCl \rightleftharpoons RNH_3^+ + Cl^-$$

e.g. phenylamine, which is virtually insoluble in water, dissolves in excess dilute hydrochloric acid to form the salt, phenylammonium chloride. The insoluble amine is regenerated on addition of sodium hydroxide solution. This provides a method of purifying phenylamine.

5 Why do solutions of amines have pH values greater than 7?

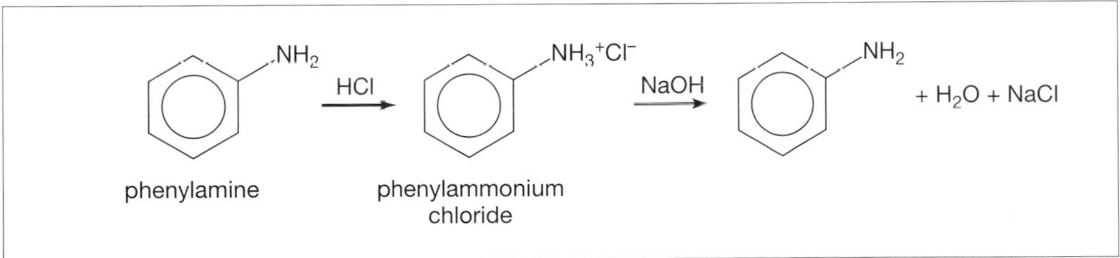

Figure 6 Phenylamine dissolves in dilute acid

Comparison of base strength

The strength of amines as bases depends upon the availability of the lone pair of electrons on the nitrogen atom, which is used to form the bond with a H^+ ion.

- Primary **aliphatic amines** are stronger bases than ammonia due to the presence of the alkyl group. The alkyl groups are electron-releasing relative to hydrogen and hence increase the availability of the lone pair. This effect increases with increasing chain length.

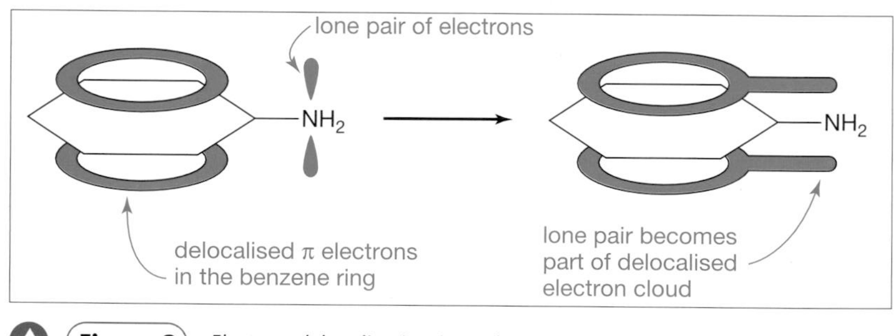

Figure 7 *The electron releasing effect of the alkyl groups in primary alphatic amines.*

- Aromatic **aryl amines** are weaker bases than ammonia since the lone pair of electrons on the nitrogen atom interact with the delocalised π electrons in the benzene ring. This means that the lone pair is less available for bonding with a H^+ ion.

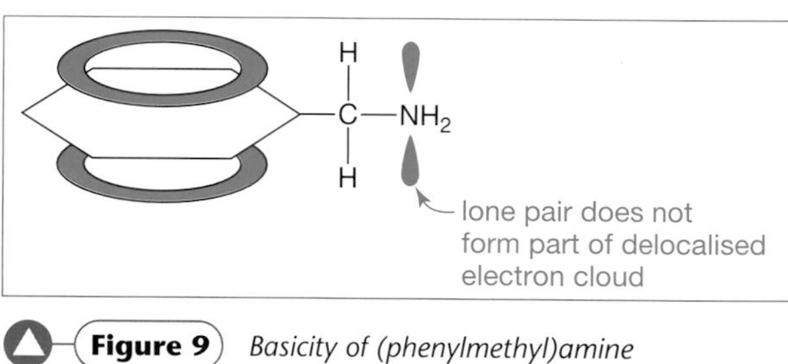

Figure 8 *Electron delocalisation in aryl amines*

- (Phenylmethyl)amine, $C_6H_5CH_2NH_2$ is an aromatic compound but the amine group is not directly attached to the benzene ring. This means that the lone pair of electrons on the nitrogen atom cannot interact with the delocalised electrons in the benzene ring. This results in the compound having a similar base strength to the aliphatic primary amines.

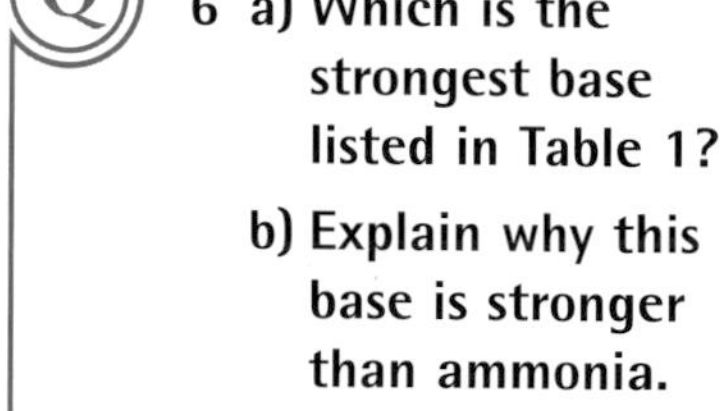

Figure 9 *Basicity of (phenylmethyl)amine*

The relative strengths of the primary amines can be compared by looking at the pK_a values in Table 1 below:

Name	Formula	pK_a
Ammonia	NH_3	9.25
Methylamine	CH_3NH_2	10.64
Ethylamine	$CH_3CH_2NH_2$	10.73
Propylamine	$CH_3CH_2CH_2NH_2$	10.84
Phenylamine	$C_6H_5NH_2$	4.62

The pK_a values are for the conjugate acid, RNH_3^+. The *stronger* the base the *weaker* the conjugate acid. Therefore a stronger base will have a *higher* pK_a value for its conjugate base.

Table 1 *pK_a values of amines*

Q

6 a) Which is the strongest base listed in Table 1?

b) Explain why this base is stronger than ammonia.

Amines as nucleophiles

1. With haloalkanes

Amines have a lone pair of electrons on the nitrogen atom which can be donated to a δ^+ carbon atom.

When ethylamine is produced from bromoethane according to the equation

$$CH_3CH_2Br + 2NH_3 \rightarrow CH_3CH_2NH_2 + NH_4Br$$

the primary amine produced has a lone pair of electrons on the nitrogen atom and can itself behave as a nucleophile. It will react with any unused bromoethane. This results in successive substitution occurring and the formation of a **secondary amine**.

$$CH_3CH_2Br + CH_3CH_2NH_2 \rightarrow \underset{\text{diethylamine}}{(CH_3CH_2)_2NH} + HBr$$

The mechanism of this reaction is nucleophilic substitution.

Since the secondary amine also contains a lone pair of electrons on the nitrogen atom it too can act as a nucleophile and further substitution is possible leading to the formation of **a tertiary amine** and ultimately a **quaternary ammonium salt**.

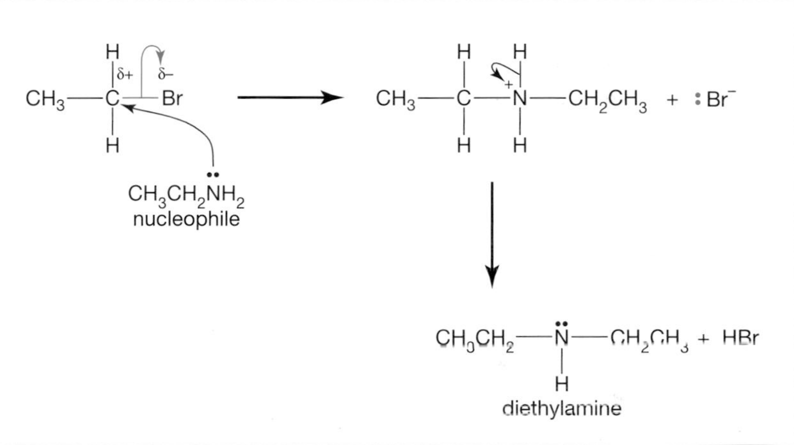

Figure 10 The formation of a secondary amine by nucleophilic substitution

$$CH_3CH_2Br + (CH_3CH_2)_2NH \rightarrow \underset{\text{triethylamine}}{(CH_3CH_2)_3N} + HBr$$

$$CH_3CH_2Br + (CH_3CH_2)_3N \rightarrow \underset{\text{quarternary ammonium salt}}{(CH_3CH_2)_4N^+Br^-}$$

The quaternary ammonium ion cannot behave as a nucleophile, since there is no longer a lone pair on the nitrogen atom.

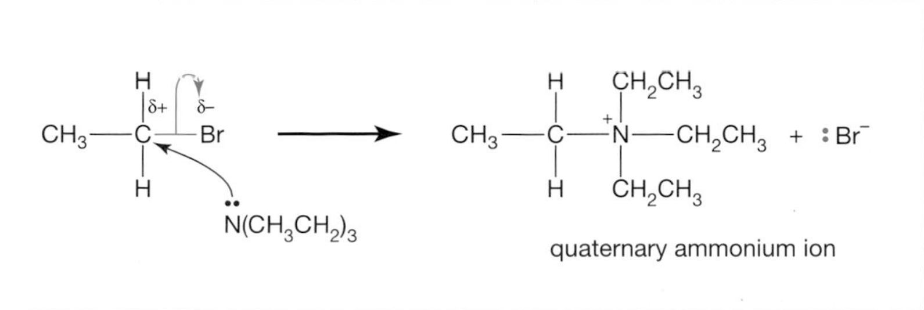

Figure 11 *The formation of a quaternary ammonium ion*

Figure 12 *Fabric conditioner*

Figure 13 *Hair conditioner*

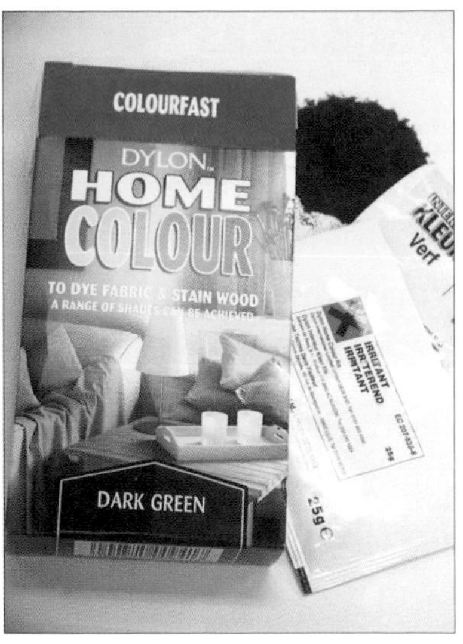

Figure 14 *Synthetic dyes*

Quaternary ammonium salts are used as cationic surfactants in fabric conditioners and hair products. They coat the surface of the cloth or hair with positive charges and reduce the static due to negatively charged electrons.

Aromatic aryl amines are important in the production of synthetic dyes, known as azo dyes. These were first produced towards the end of the 19th century.

Figure 15 *Lycra® clothing*

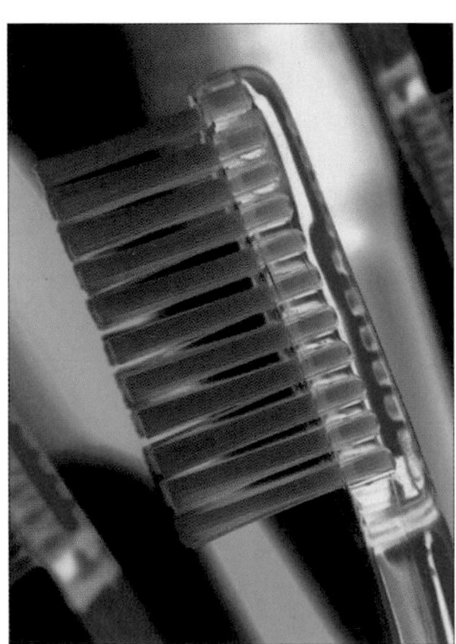

Figure 16 *Polyamide toothbrush*

Figure 17 *Polyamide carpet*

Amines are used to manufacture polymers, such as polyurethanes and polyamides. Polyurethanes are used for cavity wall insulation and in the production of elastomeric fibres such as Lycra R . Polyamides such as nylon are used to make fibres for a number of purposes, including fabrics, toothbrushes, carpets, as well as insulating cases for electrical equipment.

Amines are used to manufacture a whole range of drugs from tranquillisers like Librium, to painkillers, like pethidine.

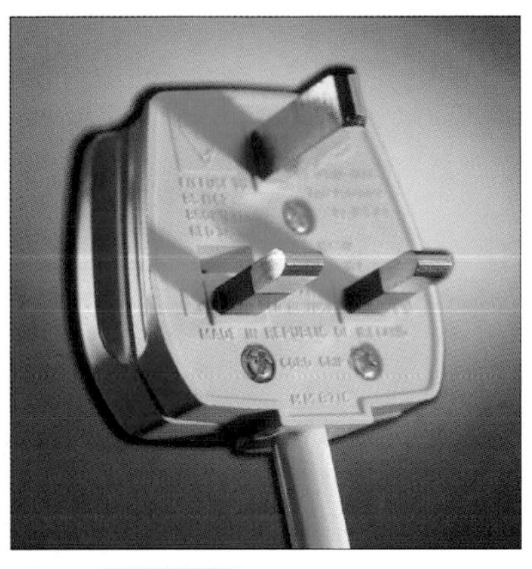

Figure 18 *Electrical equipment*

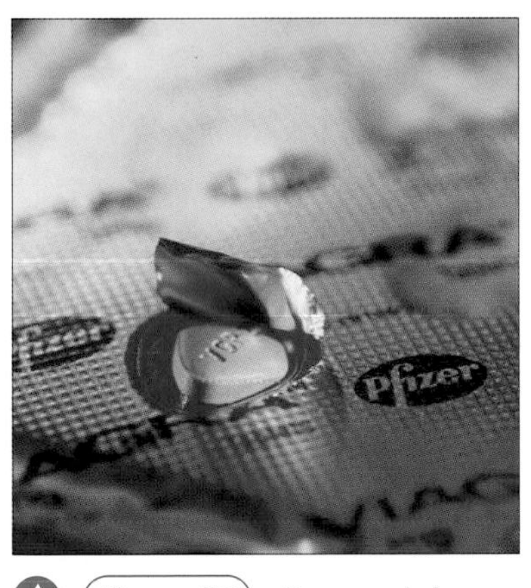

Figure 19 *Drugs made from amines*

> **Q** 7 Outline the mechanism for the formation of triethylamine from diethylamine.

2. With acyl chlorides and anhydrides

Primary amines react with acyl chlorides and acid anhydrides to form substituted amides (see page 77)

e.g. CH_3NH_2 + CH_3COCl (ethanoyl chloride) → $CH_3CONHCH_3$ (*N*-methylethanamide) + HCl

$CH_3CH_2NH_2$ + $(CH_3CO)_2O$ (ethanoic anhydride) → $CH_3CONHCH_2CH_3$ (*N*-ethylethanamide) + CH_3COOH

The mechanism of these reactions is nucleophilic addition–elimination where the amine is the nucleophile:

R—C(=O)Cl + R′–N̈H₂ ⟶ R—C(O⁻)(Cl)—N⁺(H)(H)R′ ⟶ R—C(=O)NHR′ + HCl

A substituted amide

Figure 20 *Nucleophilic addition–elimination*

Key Ideas 96 – 103

- **Amines are substituted ammonia compounds in which one or more of the hydrogen atoms have been replaced by an alkyl or aryl group.**
- **Amines are classified as primary, secondary and tertiary.**
- **Primary aliphatic amines can be prepared by nucleophilic substitution reactions of ammonia with haloalkanes and by the reduction of nitriles.**
- **Aromatic amines are prepared by the reduction of nitro-derivatives.**
- **Primary aliphatic amines are stronger bases than ammonia, but primary aromatic amines are weaker bases than ammonia.**
- **Amines are weak Brønsted–Lowry bases. Their strength as bases depends upon the availability of the lone pair of electrons on the nitrogen atom.**
- **Amines act as nucleophiles in their reactions with haloalkanes and acyl chlorides or acid anhydrides.**

Unit 7 Questions

1 a) (i) Write an equation for the reaction between ethylamine and ethanoyl chloride.
(ii) Name the type of reaction occurring in a)(i) and outline the mechanism of the reaction. (6)

b) Name another organic compound that will react with ethylamine to give the same product as that formed in a). (1)

2 Study the following reaction scheme:

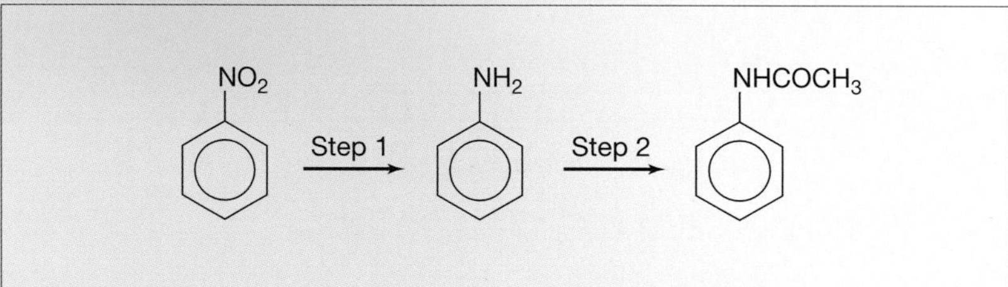

a) For each step
(i) Give the names of the reagents required for the reaction;
(ii) Name the type of reaction taking place. (5)

b) Outline a mechanism for step 2. (5)

3 a) Amines are classified as primary, secondary and tertiary. Give the structural formula of an isomer of each of these classes of amines for the compound C_3H_9N. (3)

b) Name the reactants and write equations to show the formation of the secondary amine you have drawn in a). (4)

c) (i) Give the general structure for a quaternary ammonium salt.
(ii) Give one use of quaternary ammonium salts. (2)

4 a) When ethylamine dissolves in water the following reaction occurs:
$CH_3CH_2NH_2 + H_2O \rightleftharpoons CH_3CH_2NH_3^+ + OH^-$
(i) Why is the solution formed alkaline?
(ii) What is the role of ethylamine in this reaction? Explain your answer.
(iii) If the $[OH^-]$ of this solution $= 4.8 \times 10^{-4}$ mol dm^{-3} calculate its pH at 298K. (7)

b) (i) Why is ethylamine a stronger base than ammonia?
(ii) Why is phenylamine a weaker base than ammonia? (6)

(5) Both compounds shown below can be used to prepare (phenylmethyl)amine.

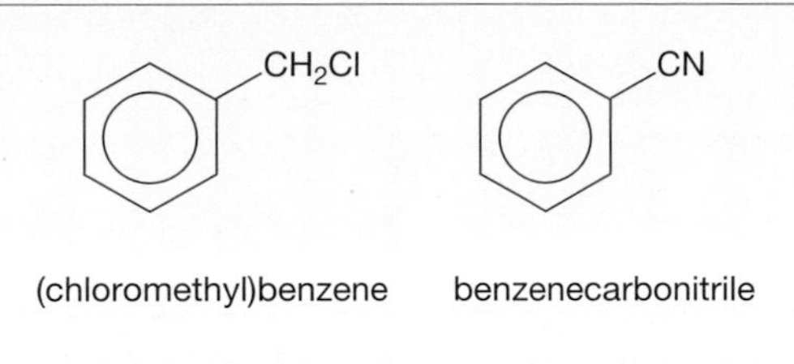

a) State the reagents required and write equations for these two preparations. (4)

b) Outline the mechanism for the formation of (phenylmethyl)amine from (chloromethyl)benzene. (4)

c) Both (phenylmethyl)amine and phenylamine are primary aromatic amines. Which is the stronger base? Explain your answer. (4)

d) Phenylamine is a colourless oily liquid, which is insoluble in water but readily dissolves in excess dilute hydrochloric acid.
Explain these observations. (3)

(6) When bromoethane reacts with excess ammonia, ethylamine is formed as the major product.

a) Write an equation for this reaction and outline the mechanism. (5)

When excess bromoethane reacts with ammonia there are three other products formed, one of which is a quaternary ammonium salt.

b) Write equations to show the formation of these other products. (3)

c) Suggest another method of preparation of ethylamine that does not involve the formation of by-products. (2)

(7) Write equations for the following conversions and in each case state the type of reaction occurring:

a) 2-chloropropane → 2-aminopropane (2)

b) propanenitrile → 1-aminopropane (2)

c) nitrobenzene → phenylamine (2)

d) ethylamine → diethylamine (2)

e) ethylamine → *N*-ethylethanamide (2)

(8) **a)** Write an equation for the reaction between methylamine and water to show the formation of its conjugate acid. (1)

b) Explain, with reference to its structure, why phenylamine is a weaker base than ammonia. (4)

c) Amines have a distinctive smell. On the addition of excess dilute hydrochloric acid the smell disappears but when aqueous sodium hydroxide is added to the resulting solution the smell returns.
Write equations to explain these observations for the amine, 1-aminopropane. (2)

1 Polymers

You studied polymers at GCSE and in AS Chemistry. **Polymers** are formed when many hundreds or thousands of smaller molecules called **monomers** join to form a long-chain molecule. Synthetic polymers are an integral part of modern life from plastics like PVC and Perspex® to fibres such as Terylene® and nylon. In this unit we also study proteins, which are natural polymers built up from monomers called **amino acids**.

Polymerisation

There are two different methods of manufacturing polymers, addition polymerisation and condensation polymerisation.

Addition polymers

These are formed from alkenes, usually by a free radical mechanism.

The reaction is carried out at high pressure, in the presence of an initiator which provides the free radicals needed to start the reaction. The simplest addition polymer is poly(ethene). A reminder of the polymerisation process is shown in Figure 1.

$$n\,H_2C{=}CH_2 \longrightarrow \left(-CH_2-CH_2- \right)_n$$

repeating unit

1 Give two uses for poly(ethene).

Figure 1 *Formation of poly(ethene)*

Addition polymers formed from alkenes are saturated compounds and are chemically unreactive. This is a useful property since they are not attacked by acids, bases or oxidising agents. Some examples of addition polymers and their uses are shown in Figure 2.

2 Give the systematic name for PVC and draw the structure of the monomer from which it is produced.

3 Name the polymer used to coat 'non-stick' pans.

Monomer	Name of polymer	Repeating unit for polymer	Examples of uses
$(CH_3)HC=CH_2$ propene	poly(propene)	$-[CH(CH_3)-CH_2]-$	Poly(propene) is used to make plastic pipes, chairs and wrapping film.
$(Cl)HC=CH_2$ chloropropene (vinyl chloride)	poly(chloroethene) (polyvinylchloride, PVC)	$-[CHCl-CH_2]-$	Poly(chloroethene) is used to make imitation leather, plastic pipes and floor tiles.
$(C_6H_5)HC=CH_2$ phenylethene (styrene)	poly(phenylethene) (polystyrene)	$-[CH(C_6H_5)-CH_2]-$	Poly(phenylethene) is used to make toys. Expanded poly(phenylethene) is used to make insulation tiles, packaging materials and plastic cups for hot drinks.
$F_2C=CF_2$ tetrafluoroethene	poly(tetrafluoroethene) (PTFE)	$-[CF_2-CF_2]-$	Poly(tetrafluoroethene) is used as a low-friction material in curtain rails, and as a non-stick surface on cooking utensils.
$H_2C=C(CH_3)COOCH_3$ methyl-2-methyl-propenoate	'perspex'	$-[CH_2-C(CH_3)(COOCH_3)]-$	Poly(methyl-2-methylpropenoate), or perspex, is used as a glass substitute in windows and lenses and for motorway road signs.

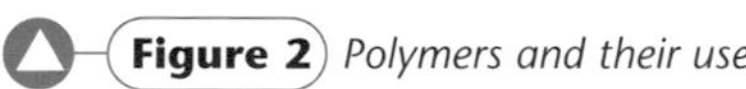
Figure 2 *Polymers and their uses*

Problems of disposal

The lack of chemical reactivity of these polymers does pose a problem of disposal after use. They are not **biodegradable** and if placed in rubbish dumps or in landfill sites they will not decay over the years.

What is the solution? Incineration of polymers could be a possible solution except that this produces greenhouse gases such as methane and other toxic gases; polyurethane foams burn to produce nitrogen dioxide and hydrogen cyanide.

Recycling of polymers is expensive but does offer an alternative solution instead of landfill and incineration.

Figure 3 *A landfill site*

Condensation polymers

Whereas addition polymers are formed from *one* unsaturated monomer condensation polymers are formed from two monomers with functional groups at *both* ends of the molecule. As they join a small molecule, usually water, is eliminated; hence the term 'condensation'.

There are two main types of condensation polymers, **polyesters** and **polyamides**. As these names suggest their structures are related to those of esters and amides.

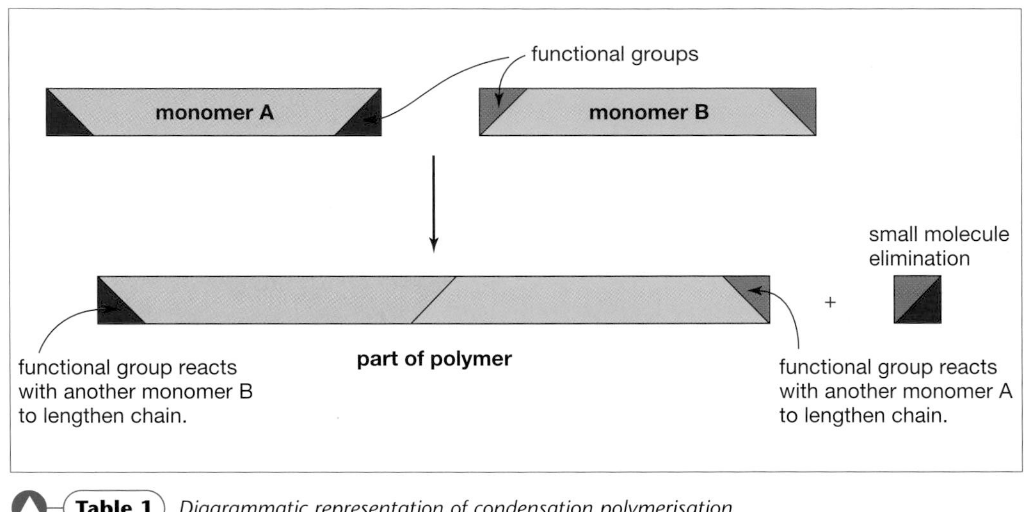

Table 1 *Diagrammatic representation of condensation polymerisation*

Polyesters

Esters can be formed by the reaction of a carboxylic acid and an alcohol:

$$RCOOH + R'OH \rightarrow RCOOR' + H_2O$$

If a **di**carboxylic acid and a **di**ol are reacted together then a long chain **polyester** can be formed.

One example of a commercial polyester is Terylene®, which is manufactured from benzene–1,4–dicarboxylic acid and ethane–1,2–diol:

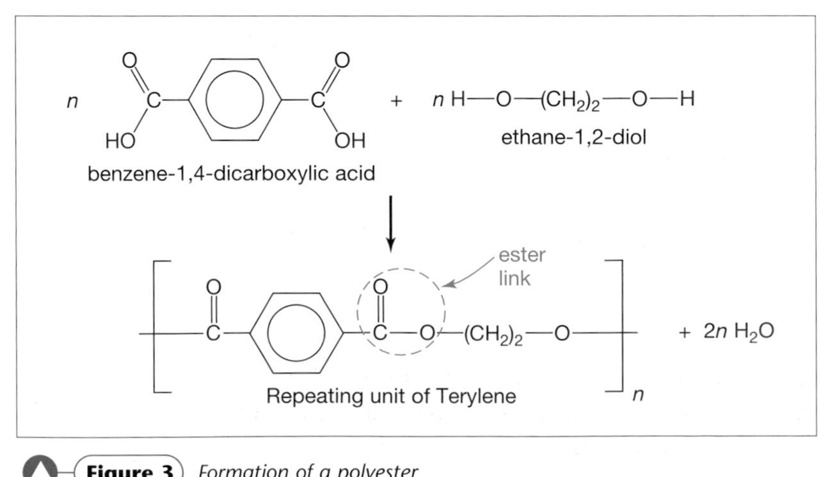

Figure 3 *Formation of a polyester*

Figure 4 *Drinks bottles made from PET*

Polyesters are not just used to make fibres; PET (polyethene terephthalate) was first used as a fibre under the trade name Dacron®. It is now used to make plastic bottles for fizzy drinks. Its properties are ideal for this purpose – it is light, strong, acid-resistant and doesn't smash on impact.

Polyamides

Substituted amides are formed by the reaction of a carboxylic acid and an amine:

$$RCOOH + R'NH_2 \rightarrow RCOONHR' + H_2O$$

When a **di**carboxylic acid and a **di**amine are reacted together then a chain reaction occurs leading to the formation of a long chain condensation polyamide. One polyamide is nylon–6,6 formed from the condensation reaction between hexanedioic acid and 1,6–diaminohexane:

4 Why do you think the acyl chloride, rather than the acid is used in this reaction?

5 Draw the repeating unit of a nylon made from pentanedioic acid and 1,4–diaminobutane.

There are many different polyamides called nylon. The name nylon-6,6 shows that the two monomers each contain six carbon atoms. Nylon-6,6 can be made in the laboratory using the acyl chloride of hexanedioic acid and 1,6-diaminohexane.

Esters and amides can be **hydrolysed** in acid and alkali solution. As a result polyester and polyamide condensation polymers will also react with acids and alkalis. This means that they are biodegradable.

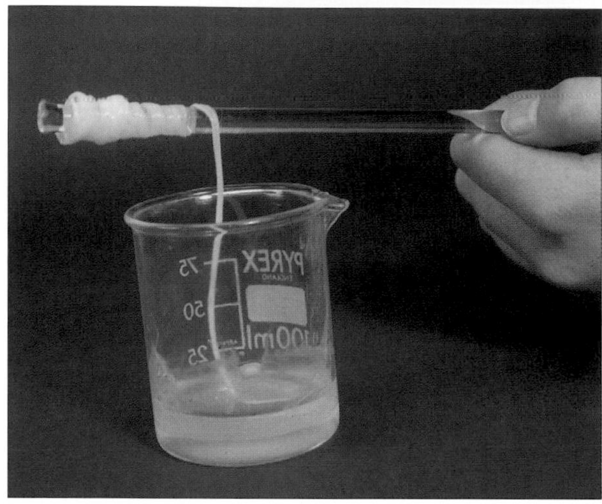

 **Figure 5** *The Nylon rope trick*

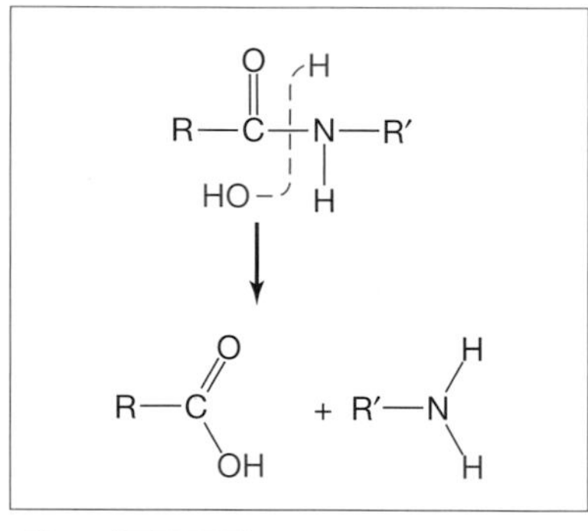

 **Figure 6** *Acid hydrolysis of a polyamide*

6 **Write an equation to show the hydrolysis of a part of a polyester molecule.**

7 **a) Give the repeating unit of the addition polymer that could be formed from *trans* butenedioic acid (HOOCCH=CHCOOH).**

b) Why would this polymer be identical to the addition polymer formed from the *cis* butenedioic acid?

8 **a) Give the repeating unit of a condensation polymer that could be formed between trans-butenedioic acid and 1,2-diaminoethane.**

b) Would this be the same or different from the polymer formed by reacting cis-butenedioic acid with 1,2-diaminoethane? Explain your answer.

Key Ideas 106 – 110

- Addition polymers are made from monomers containing a C=C bond
- Polyalkenes are non-biodegradable
- Condensation polymers are formed from two monomers; polyamides from a dicarboxylic acid and a diamine, polyesters from a dicarboxylic acid and a diol.
- Condensation polymers can be hydrolysed and are therefore biodegradable.

2 Amino acids

Amino acids are important molecules in biological systems. They contain an amine functional group and a carboxyl functional group. This means they are **bifunctional** compounds, having properties of both amines and carboxylic acids. Amino acids polymerise to form proteins.

The structure of amino acids

The general structural formula for amino acids is shown in Figure 1.

When the amino group is attached to the carbon atom next to the carboxyl group, the amino acids are classified as **α amino acids**.

The simplest α amino acid is aminoethanoic acid (glycine).

This is one of about twenty naturally occurring amino acids. Some other examples are shown in Figure 3. They are often called by their trivial names.

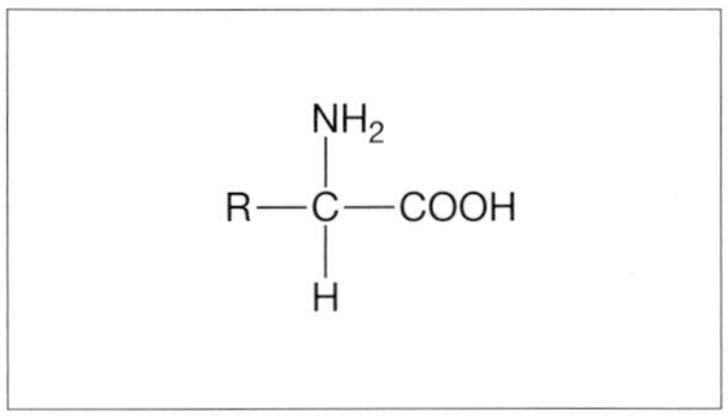

NH_2
R—C—COOH
H

Figure 1 *The general structural formula for amino acids*

NH_2
H—C—COOH
H

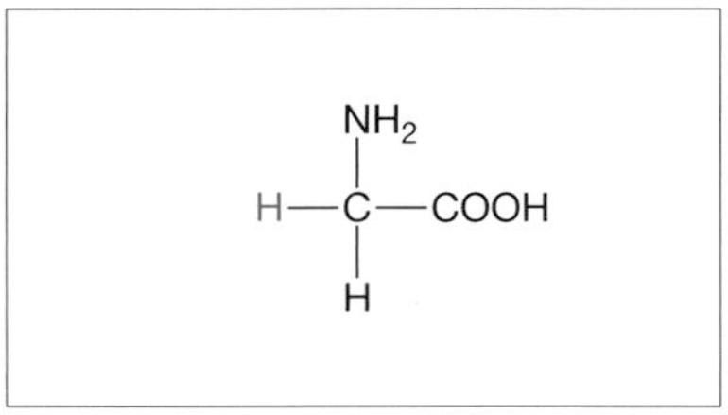

Figure 2 *The structure of glycine*

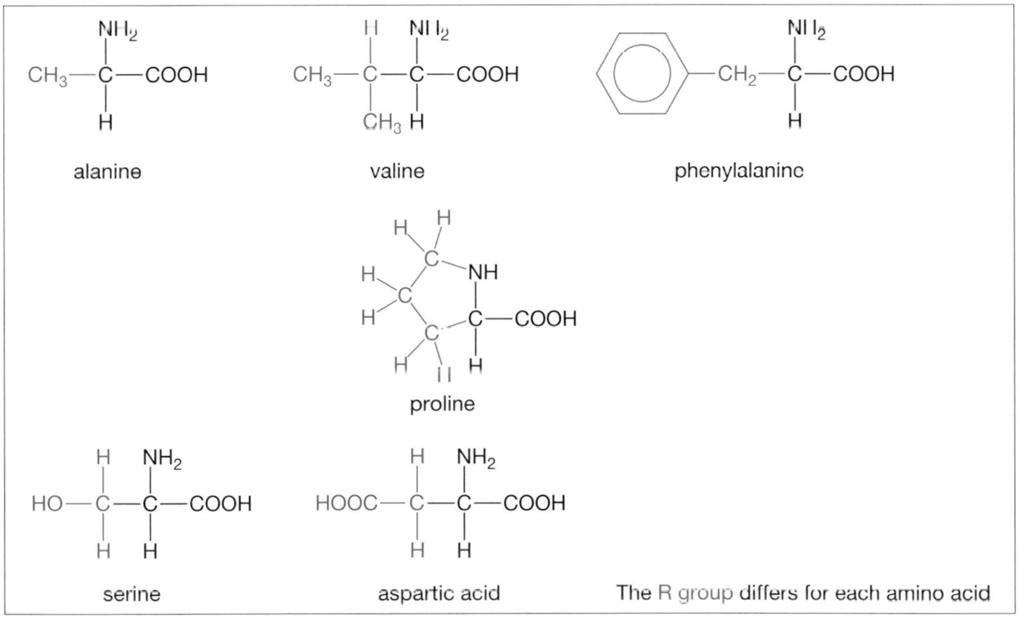

NH_2
CH_3—C—COOH
H
alanine

H NH_2
CH_3—C—C—COOH
CH_3 H
valine

NH_2
—CH_2—C—COOH
H
phenylalanine

H H
C—NH
H C H
H C—C—COOH
H H H
proline

H NH_2
HO—C—C—COOH
H H
serine

H NH_2
HOOC—C—C—COOH
H H
aspartic acid

The R group differs for each amino acid

Figure 3 *Examples of amino acids*

All amino acids contain the primary amine functional group apart from proline.

8 What class of amine is contained in the proline molecule?

9 Give the systematic name for serine.

Optical activity in amino acids

All the amino acids, except for glycine, have a **chiral centre**. This means that they are optically active (see page 60).

10 Draw the structure for valine and circle the chiral centre.

Amphoteric properties of amino acids

Since amino acids molecules contain a carboxylic acid and an amine group, they exhibit both acidic and basic properties:

As acids they donate protons to bases:

$$\underset{\text{acid}}{RCH(NH_2)COOH} + OH^- \rightarrow \underset{\text{conjugate base}}{RCH(NH_2)COO^-} + H_2O$$

As bases they accept protons:

$$\underset{\text{base}}{RCH(NH_2)COOH} + H^+ \rightarrow \underset{\text{conjugate acid}}{RCH(NH_3^+)COOH}$$

In the pure state amino acids are white crystalline solids, which easily dissolve in water and have high melting points, e.g. glycine melts at 290 °C. These observations do not match the general formula given in Figure 1. Hydrogen bonding between the hydrogen atoms of one molecule and the oxygen or nitrogen atoms of an adjacent molecule could not account for such high melting points.

In the pure state amino acids exist as **zwitterions**. The high melting points are due to the ionic bonds present.

Figure 4 *The structure of a zwitterion*

As the pH increases the $-NH_3^+$ group loses a proton i.e. it acts as an acid. If the pH is decreased the $-COO^-$ group gains a proton i.e. it acts as a base.

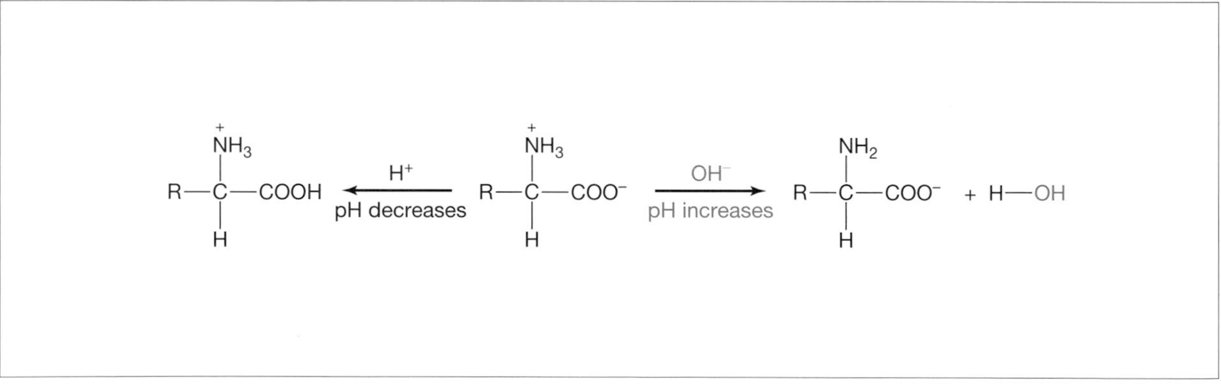

Figure 5 *The effect of changing pH on a zwitterion*

Notice from Figure 5 that zwitterions are behaving as buffers (see page 52)

11 Draw the zwitterion structure for alanine.

Polymerisation

Amino acids undergo condensation polymerisation to form polyamides. The linking unit between individual amino acids is called a **peptide link** and as a result the polymers are usually called **polypeptides**.

Two amino acid units form a dipeptide, three amino acid units form a tripeptide, many amino acid units form a polypeptide. In the body these condensation reactions are catalysed by enzymes.

Figure 6 *Formation of a dipeptide*

12 a) Draw the structure of the tripeptide, alanine–glycine–phenylalanine.

b) Explain how this tripeptide could become part of a longer chain.

Proteins

Long polypeptide chains form proteins. Proteins are important polymers in the body; muscles, skin and hair contain structural proteins, hormones and enzymes are complex proteins that control the body's metabolism.

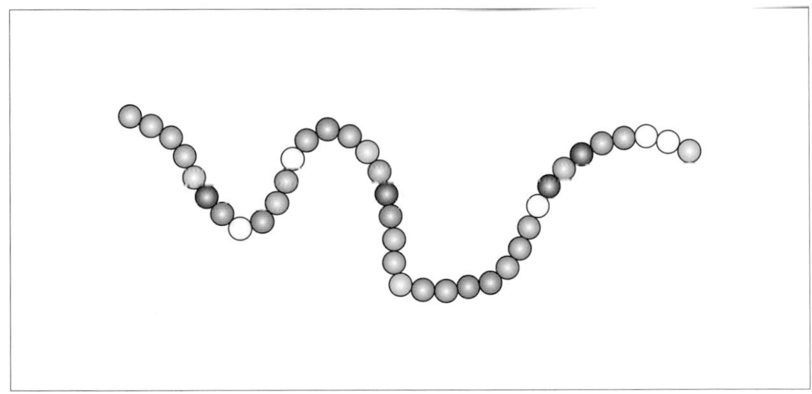

Figure 7 *Diagrammatic representation of the primary structure of a protein: each coloured 'bead' represents a different amino acid*

There are a massive number of combinations of the 20 amino acids that can combine together, via peptide links, to make proteins. The sequence of amino acids in a protein chain is called the **primary protein structure**. Different proteins contain a different sequence of amino acids and therefore have different primary structures. The hormone, insulin was the first protein to be sequenced around 1950. It was found to be 51 amino acid units (residues) in length and contained 17 different amino acids.

The peptide linkage readily undergoes hydrolysis. When a protein is hydrolysed the protein breaks down to form the constituent amino acids. The hydrolysis can be achieved in the laboratory by boiling the protein with acid or alkali.
In the body hydrolysis is catalysed by enzymes. The hydrolysis of proteins in food is called digestion.

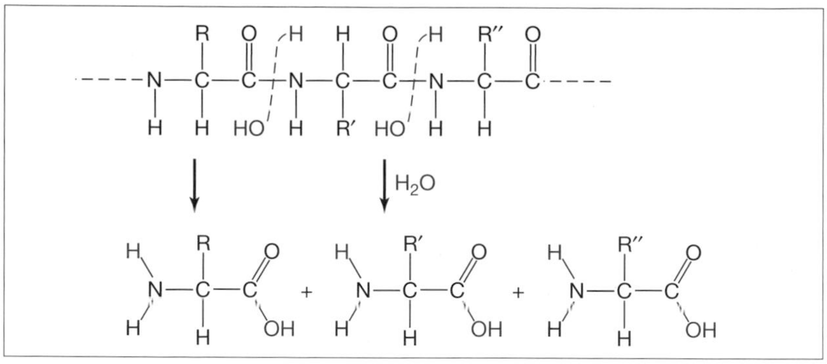

The amino acid chain in a protein is held in a particular shape by **hydrogen bonds** that form between the N–H group of one peptide link and the C=O group of another. There are two basic shapes which can result: the chain may be coiled into an α-helix or folded into a β-pleated sheet. These are called **secondary protein** structures.

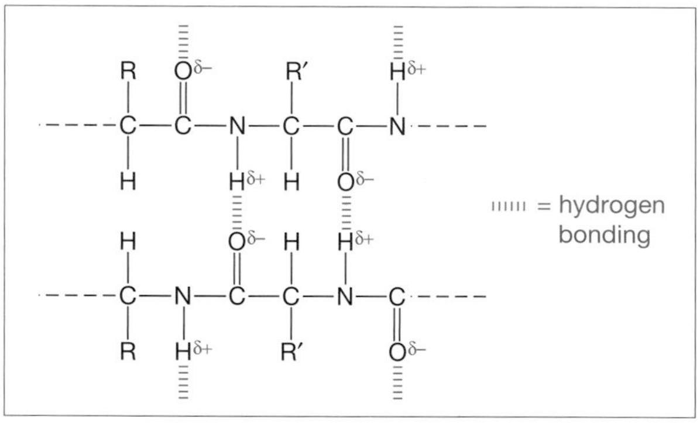

Figure 8 *Hydrolysis of a protein*

IIIIII = hydrogen bonding

Figure 9 *Hydrogen bonding between peptide links*

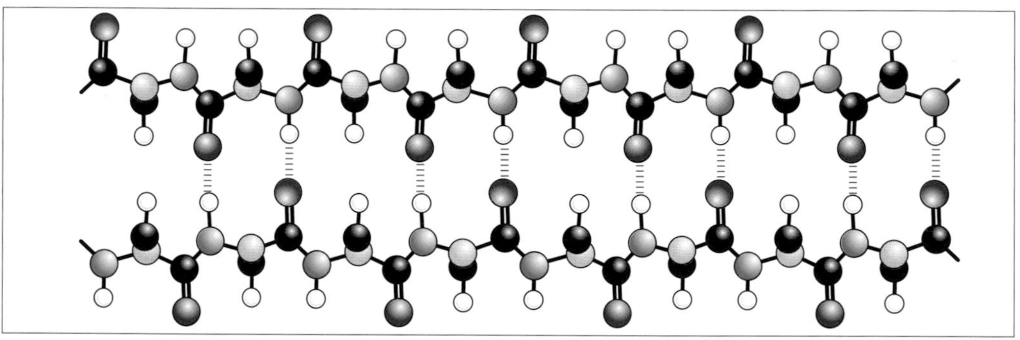

Figure 11 *Hydrogen bonding across two protein chains*

Key Ideas 111 – 114

- **Amino acids contain a carboxylic acid and an amine group so they exhibit both acidic and basic properties.**
- **Proteins are large polymers formed by condensation reactions of amino acids. They are sequences of amino acids joined by peptide links.**
- **Hydrogen bonding is important in protein structure.**

Unit 8 Questions

3

1. Write equations to show the formation of the following polymers, showing clearly the structures of the reactants and the repeating unit of the polymer:

   a) poly(choroethene) (2)
   b) Terylene® (4)
   c) nylon-6,6 (4)
   Explain why Terylene® and nylon-6,6 are described as *biodegradable*. (1)

2. The amino acid, phenylalanine, has the systematic name 2-amino-3-phenylpropanoic acid.

   a) Draw the structure of this amino acid (1)
   b) State the type of isomerism shown by phenylalanine and indicate how the two isomers can be distinguished. (2)
   c) (i) Explain why the melting point of phenylalanine (283°C) is much higher than that of 2-hydroxy-3-phenylpropanoic acid (124°C).
   (ii) A sample of phenylalanine was added to an excess of hydrochloric acid to form species **A**. When aqueous sodium hydroxide was slowly added to this solution, **A** was converted into species **B**. In the presence of excess NaOH(aq) **B** was converted into species **C**. Draw the structures of **A**, **B** and **C**. (6)

3. **a)** 'Amino acids show properties of acids and bases.' Using 2-aminoethanoic acid (glycine) as an example of an amino acid, write equations to illustrate this statement. (2)
   b) (i) Write an equation for the reaction between glycine and ethanoyl chloride.
   (ii) State the type of reaction taking place.
   (iii) Outline the mechanism for the reaction. (6)
   c) Glycine reacts with ethanol in the presence of concentrated sulphuric acid. Write an equation for this reaction. (1)

4. **a)** (i) Give the general structural formula for an α-amino acid.
   (ii) Using this general formula show how a polypeptide is formed. (3)
   b) What do the structures of polypeptides and polyamides, like nylon, have in common? (1)
   c) Oven cleaners contain sodium hydroxide. Explain why it would be unwise to use an oven cleaner with a nylon cloth. (2)

5 The cyclic compound **X** shown below contains a bond that resembles a peptide link.

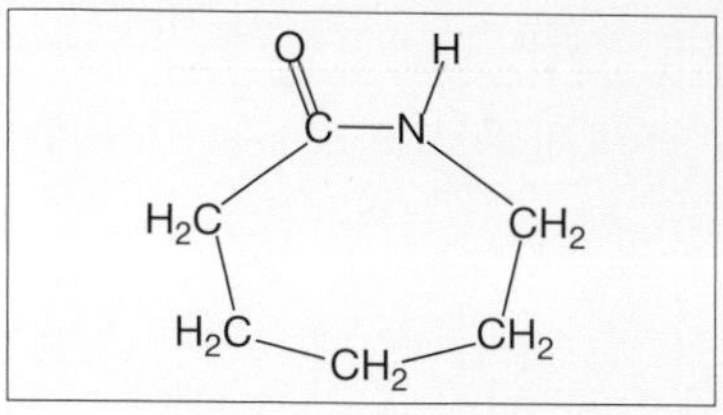

a) Draw out this structure and circle the peptide link. (1)
b) Deduce the structure of the product formed when **X** reacts with hot sodium hydroxide solution. (2)
c) When heated strongly the ring structure in **X** is broken and a polyamide called nylon-6 is formed. Deduce the repeating unit in nylon-6. (2)
d) Explain how polyamide chains can bind together to form strong fibres. (2)

6 The amino acid alanine, $CH_3CH(NH_2)COOH$, can be prepared from 2-bromopropanoic acid by reaction with a large excess of ammonia.

a) Write an equation for this reaction. (2)
b) Name the mechanism involved and explain why a large excess of ammonia is required (3)
c) Samples of natural and synthetic alanine behave differently when a solution of each is examined in plane polarised light. State and explain the difference. (4)
d) Name the polymers formed when amino acids undergo condensation polymerisation and draw the structure of the linkage formed between the amino acids. (2)

7 A section of an addition polymer chain is shown below:

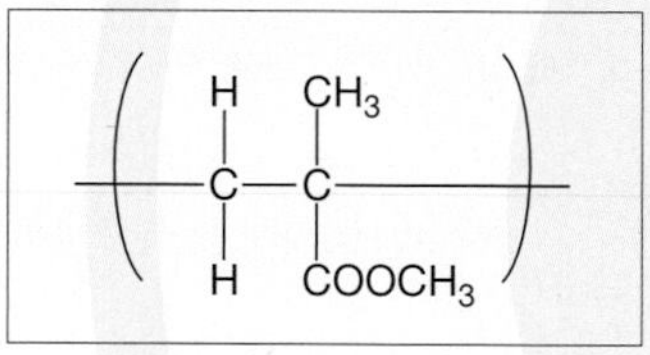

a) Draw the structure of the monomer from which this polymer has been synthesised. (1)
b) The monomer is a bifunctional molecule. Circle the functional groups on the structure you have drawn in a) and name the two homologous series that are represented in this molecule. (2)
c) Write an equation to show the acid hydrolysis of this monomer. (2)

8 In 1933 two British chemists working at ICI were trying to make a ketone using an aromatic aldehyde and ethene under very high pressure. They failed to make the ketone but instead produced a small amount of a high molecular mass solid, which was found to be a saturated hydrocarbon. What had these chemists discovered? Give the structure of the product and the type of reaction involved. (3)

1 Structure determination

In this unit we look at a range of instrumental techniques used in the determination of the structure of organic compounds which make the process of identification so much quicker and reliable than it once was. We are less interested in how the machines work than in interpretation of the **spectra** produced by the instruments. The spectra, in conjunction with chemical tests, can be used to determine the structure of organic compounds.

Mass spectrometry

The principles of the mass spectrometer were studied at AS level. You should be able to interpret mass spectra for *elements*. At A2 we study the mass spectra for *compounds*.

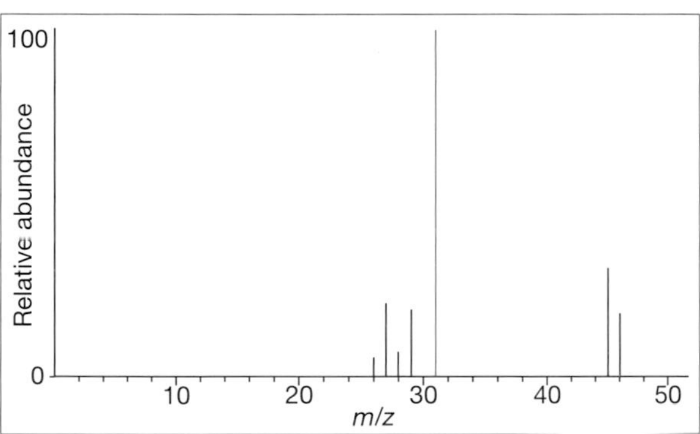

Figure 1 *Mass spectrum of an alcohol*

When a *gaseous* sample is placed in a mass spectrometer the electron gun can knock an electron from a molecule, forming a **molecular ion**:

$$M(g) \rightarrow M^{+\bullet}(g) + e^-$$

Notice that the molecular ion is also a free radical since it contains an unpaired electron. It can also be called a **radical cation**.

The molecular ion will **fragment** to produce smaller cations and free radicals. The ions form a complex pattern of peaks which make up the spectrum. (see Figure 1).

The peak with the highest *m/z* value will be caused by the molecular ion and, if the molecular ion is unipositive, then the *m/z* value of this peak equals the relative molecular mass of the compound (M_r)

The *m/z* value for the molecular ion peak = the M_r of the compound if the molecular ion is unipositive

The more stable ions produce the more intensive peaks. The most stable fragment forms the base peak. Other peak heights are given as a percentage of the base peak.

1 a) What is the relative molecular mass of the alcohol whose mass spectrum is shown in Figure 1?

b) How many fragments does the molecular ion form in this spectrum?

Fragmentation

Fragmentation occurs when a covalent bond in the molecular ion breaks. The weaker the bond the more likely it is to break. When a molecular ion fragments the reaction produces an ion and a free radical:

$$M^{+\bullet}(g) \rightarrow X^{+}(g) + Y^{\bullet}(g)$$

Only the *ions* are detected in the mass spectrometer. Some ions are common in many spectra because they are relatively stable. These include carbocations such as CH_3^+, $CH_3CH_2^+$ and acylium ions such as CH_3CO^+ and $CH_3CH_2CO^+$.

The *m/z* values of these and other common fragments are given in Table 1.

m/z peak value	Possible ion
15	CH_3^+
29	$CH_3CH_2^+$
31	CH_3O^+
43	$(CH_3)_2CH^+$ or CH_3CO^+
57	$CH_3CH_2CO^+$
77	$C_6H_5^+$

Table 1

The identification of the fragments in the mass spectrum can be used to help determine the structure of a compound and to distinguish between isomers. This is illustrated in the examples below. Note that any radicals formed do *not* produce a peak on the mass spectrum.

When writing fragmentation equations it important to show clearly that an ion and a free radical are formed.

For example:

$$CH_3CH_2COOH^{+\bullet} \rightarrow CH_3CH_2CO^{+} + OH^{\bullet}$$

$$CH_3CH_2COOH^{+\bullet} \rightarrow CH_3CH_2^{+} + COOH^{\bullet}$$

Worked examples

1 Look at the mass spectrum for compound X, which is a compound with the molecular formula C_3H_6O.

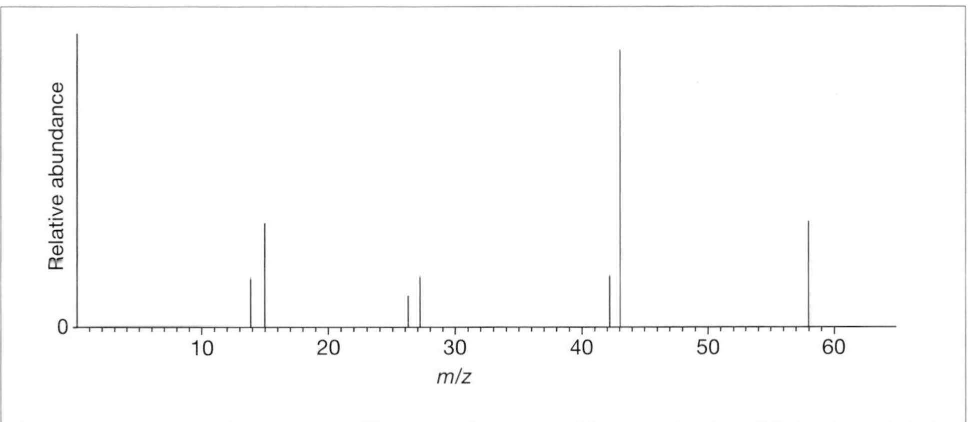

Figure 2 *The mass spectrum for compound X*

The M_r of this compound is 58 since the molecular ion peak is at 58. This confirms the molecular formula since (3 x 12) + (6 x 1) + 16 = 58

The base peak is at m/z = 43 which suggests CH_3CO^+ and the other dominant peak is at m/z = 15 which suggests CH_3^+

This information, which would be used in conjunction with other spectral evidence and functional group tests, leads to the identity of C_3H_6O as propanone.

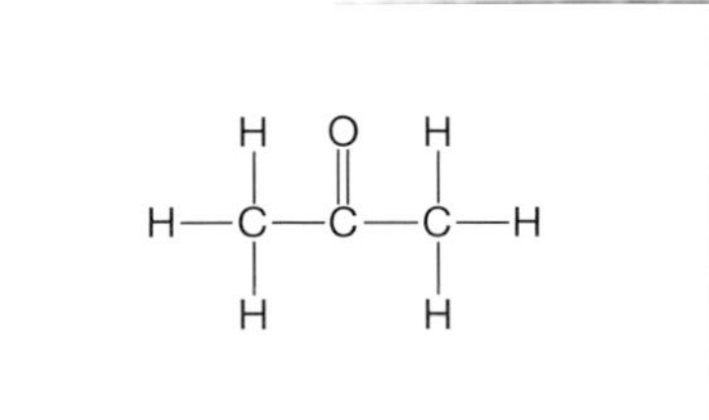

Figure 3 *Structure of propanone*

Fragmentation equations:

$$C_3H_6O^{+\bullet} \rightarrow \underset{m/z\ =\ 43}{CH_3CO^+} + CH_3^\bullet$$

$$C_3H_6O^{+\bullet} \rightarrow CH_3CO^\bullet + \underset{m/z\ =\ 15}{CH_3^+}$$

2 a) Draw the structural isomer of propanone and describe a chemical test you could use to distinguish between these two isomers.

b) Explain why this isomer of propanone will show a prominent peak at m/z = 29 in its mass spectrum.

2 Pentan-2-one and pentan-3-one have the same molecular ion peak (at *m/z* = 86) because they are isomers with the same molecular formula, but the fragmentation pattern is different.

For pentan-2-one:

$$CH_3CH_2CH_2COCH_3^{+\bullet} \rightarrow CH_3CH_2CH_2CO^+ + CH_3^{\bullet}$$
$m/z = 86$ → $m/z = 71$

$$CH_3CH_2CH_2COCH_3^{+\bullet} \rightarrow CH_3CH_2CH_2CO^{\bullet} + CH_3^+$$
$m/z = 86$ → $m/z = 15$

For pentan-3-one

$$CH_3CH_2COCH_2CH_3^{+\bullet} \rightarrow CH_3CH_2CO^+ + CH_3CH_2^{\bullet}$$
$m/z = 86$ → $m/z = 57$

$$CH_3CH_2COCH_2CH_3^{+\bullet} \rightarrow CH_3CH_2CO^{\bullet} + CH_3CH_2^+$$
$m/z = 29$

The two isomers can be distinguished by looking at the fragmentation patterns in their mass spectra. Pentan-2-one will have prominent peaks with *m/z* values of 15 and 71 whilst pentan-3-one will have prominent peaks with *m/z* values of 29 and 57.

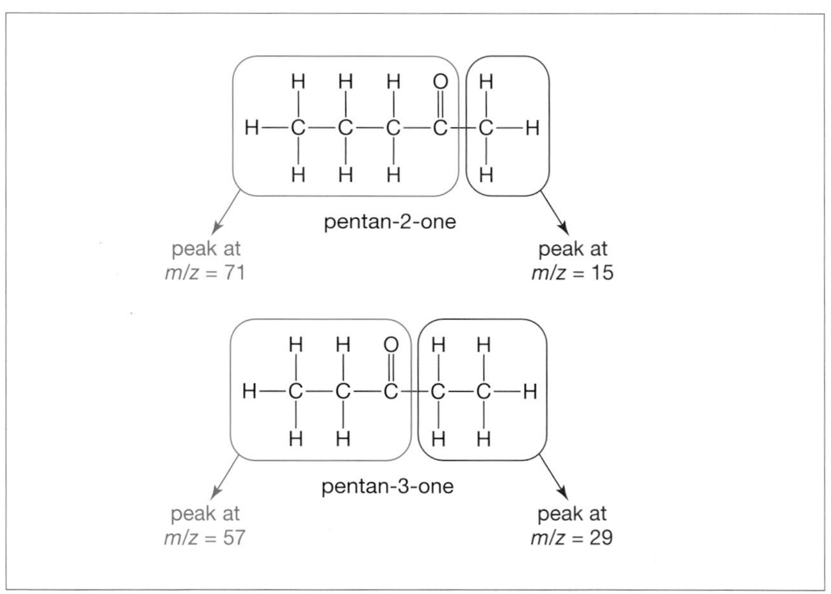

Figure 4 *Fragmentation in pentan-2-one and pentan-3-one*

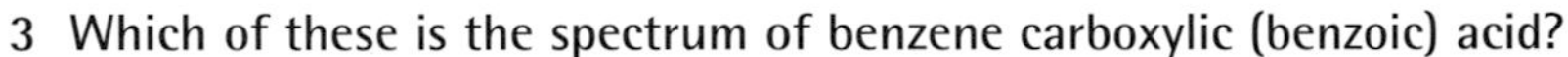

3 Which of these is the spectrum of benzene carboxylic (benzoic) acid?

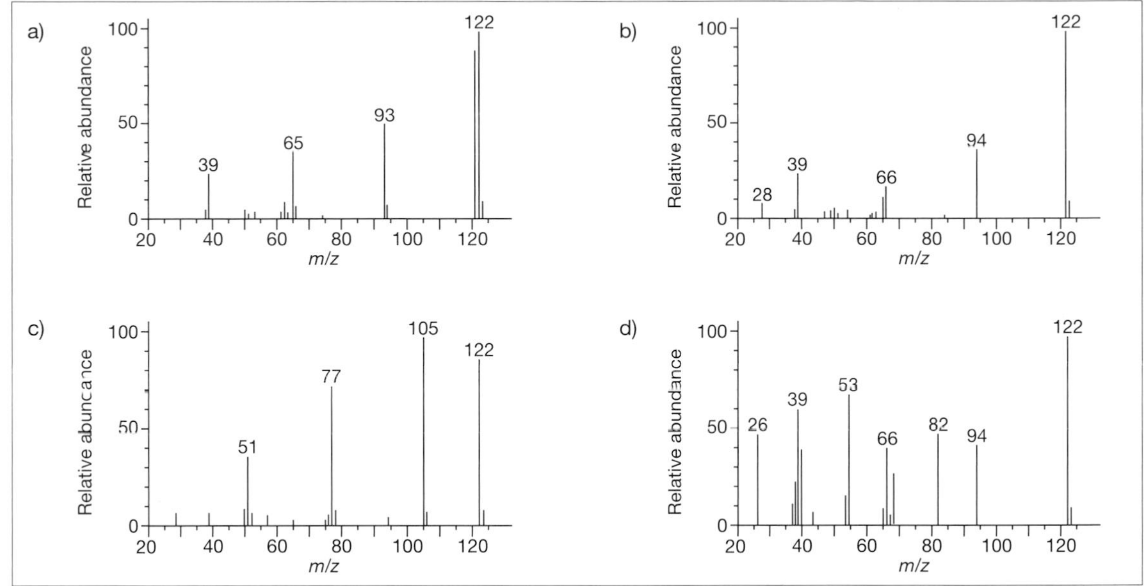

Figure 5 *Spectra of isomers of $C_7H_6O_2$*

Benzene carboxylic acid is an aromatic acid with the structure:

Figure 6

The correct spectrum is Figure 5c). The biggest clue on the mass spectrum is the peak at *m/z* = 77 which is due to the $C_6H_5^+$ ion. The base peak is due to $C_6H_5CO^+$, which is formed when the C–O bond breaks. It is not necessary to consider all the peaks but further evidence should be obtained for confirmation. Mass spectra data are rarely considered in isolation.

Notice, on the spectra for benzene carboxylic acid and its isomers, that there is a small peak to the right of the molecular ion peak at *m/z* = 123. This is due to the presence of **carbon–13** in these molecules. This isotope makes up about 1% of naturally occurring carbon. If there is one carbon atom in the molecule then this peak, known as the **M+1 peak**, is 1% of the height of the molecular ion peak. In Figure 5c) the relative height of the molecular ion peak for benzene carboxylic acid is 85. In benzene carboxylic acid there are seven carbon atoms per molecule so the height of the peak caused by the carbon-13 isotope is 7% of 85 = 5.95. So the height of the M+1 peak is a useful indication of the number of carbon atoms in the molecule. Some more examples, where isotopes are evident on the mass spectra, are discussed overleaf.

Spectra of haloalkanes

When a compound contains bromine or chlorine then the isotopes of bromine and chlorine will result in more than one molecular ion peak.

Bromine has two isotopes, ^{79}Br and ^{81}Br. These isotopes exist in equal quantities and compounds containing bromine will have two molecular ion peaks whose *m/z* values differ by two.

For example, bromoethane will have two molecular ion peaks $CH_3CH_2{}^{79}Br^{+\bullet}$ with a *m/z* value of 108 and $CH_3CH_2{}^{81}Br^{+\bullet}$ with a *m/z* value of 110.

With chlorine the two isotopes do not occur in equal quantities and hence the molecular ion peaks do not have the same heights. The natural abundance of the chlorine isotopes ^{35}Cl and ^{37}Cl is 3:1 and hence the height of the molecular ion peaks is in a ratio of 3:1.

If there are two atoms of chlorine in a molecule then there will be three molecular ions peaks.

For example with dichloromethane, CH_2Cl_2 there will peaks with *m/z* values of 84,86 and 88.The molecular ions responsible for these peaks are shown below:

$[H_2C({}^{35}Cl)({}^{35}Cl)]^{+\bullet}$ *m/z* = 84

$[H_2C({}^{35}Cl)({}^{37}Cl)]^{+\bullet}$ *m/z* = 86

$[H_2C({}^{37}Cl)({}^{37}Cl)]^{+\bullet}$ *m/z* = 88

Figure 7 *Structures of the molecular ions of dichloromethane*

3 **Study the mass spectrum for dichloroethene shown in Figure 8. Give the formulae of the species responsible for the peaks at *m/z* values of**

a) 96 b) 98 c) 100.

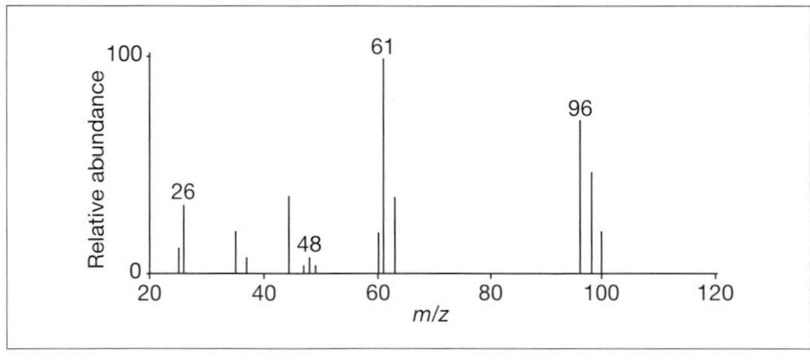

Figure 8 *The mass spectrum for dichloroethene*

4 **Dichloroethene can exist as stereoisomers. Draw the structures for the two stereoisomers of this compound.**

5 **Alkene A, C_4H_8, reacts with HBr to form compound B, C_4H_9Br. Suggest why the mass spectrum obtained for B has two identical peaks at *m/z* values of 136 and 138.**

The molecular formula from mass spectrometry

Historically the determination of the molecular formula of a compound would be a laborious process involving both qualitative analysis of the elements present and quantitative analysis of the percentage by mass of the elements present and M_r determination. High-resolution mass spectrometers can be used to find molecular formulae directly. These instruments can record precise *m/z* values to several decimal places and this allows us to identify compounds that have the same integral relative molecular masses.

When we use precise atomic masses then compounds with the same integral formula masses have slightly different relative molecular masses. For example cyclohexane, C_6H_{12}, and pent-3-enal, $CH_3CH{=}CHCH_2CHO$, both have an integral relative molecular mass of 84 but if we use precise atomic masses then the precise relative molecular masses are 84.09389 for cyclohexane and 84.05751 for pent-3-anal. Another example is shown in Table 2.

Formula	Actual mass
$C_4H_{10}O_4$	122.057903
$C_6H_4NO_2$	122.024201
$C_7H_6O_2$	122.036776
C_7H_8NO	122.060585
$C_8H_{10}O$	122.073161
C_9H_{14}	122.109545

Table 2 *Some formulae corresponding to nominal m/z = 122*

These are based on the following relative atomic masses:
C = 12.0000000; H = 1.0078246; N = 14.0030738; O = 15.9949141.

6 Compound C is an aromatic acid with an M_r value of 122.0367. Identify the molecular formula of compound C from Table 2.

Key Ideas 117 – 123

- **The relative molecular mass of a compound can be determined from the molecular ion peak on the mass spectrum.**
- **The molecular formula of a compound can be found directly from accurate M_r determinations.**
- **The fragmentation of the molecular ion produces a spectrum containing characteristic peaks for a particular compound.**
- **The more stable ions give rise to the highest peaks.**
- **The presence of isomers can be detected from the mass spectra.**

2 Infra-red spectroscopy

Infra-red spectroscopy is widely used to identify the functional groups present in organic compounds. Chemical bonds absorb infra-red radiation of specific frequencies so a particular bond can be matched to a particular absorption range on the infra-red spectrum. The range is quoted as the **wavenumber** which the reciprocal of wavelength.

Vibrations in molecules

In molecules the covalent bonds vibrate naturally. Infra-red radiation is absorbed by the bonds and the absorbed energy makes the bonds vibrate even more. They may stretch or bend. Different bonds absorb infra-red radiation of different frequencies. The frequency absorbed depends upon the bond energy and upon the masses of the atoms.

For infra-red radiation to be absorbed the vibrations must cause a change in the dipole moment of the molecule. In carbon dioxide the symmetrical stretching vibration causes no change in the dipole moment and therefore does not absorb infra-red radiation. But a change in dipole does occur for asymmetrical stretching and bending vibrations. The infra-red spectrum of carbon dioxide showing the absorptions for these two vibrations is shown in Figure 2.

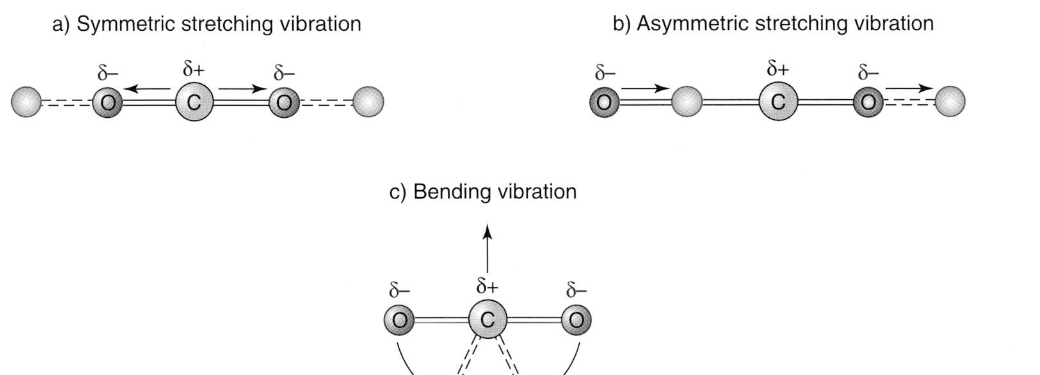

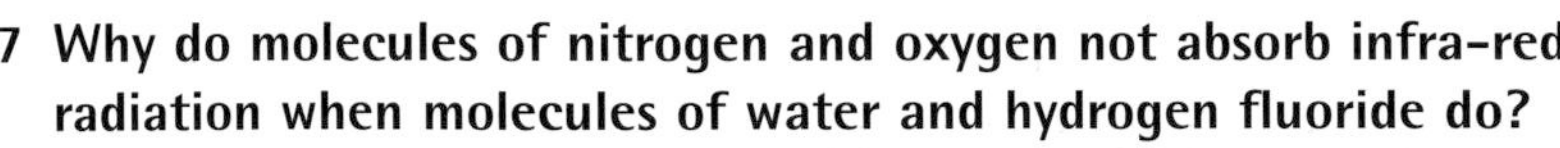
Figure 1 *Three types of vibration in carbon dioxide molecules*

Q

7 Why do molecules of nitrogen and oxygen not absorb infra-red radiation when molecules of water and hydrogen fluoride do?

8 How does the above discussion on carbon dioxide provide evidence that it is a 'greenhouse' gas?

The infra-red spectrometer

In an infra-red spectrometer a beam of infra-red light is split. One beam is passed through the organic sample, the other passes through a reference cell. The infra-red light transmitted through the organic sample is then compared with the second beam. (The compound must be dry since water will absorb infra-red radiation). The comparison then shows the percentage transmission of each of the infra-red frequencies when passed through the sample. When the infra-red radiation is absorbed by the bonds the transmission is reduced. This appears as a trough on the spectrum, usually referred to as an absorption (see Figure 2). Compare this to a mass spectrum or an n.m.r. spectrum where the spectra contain peaks.

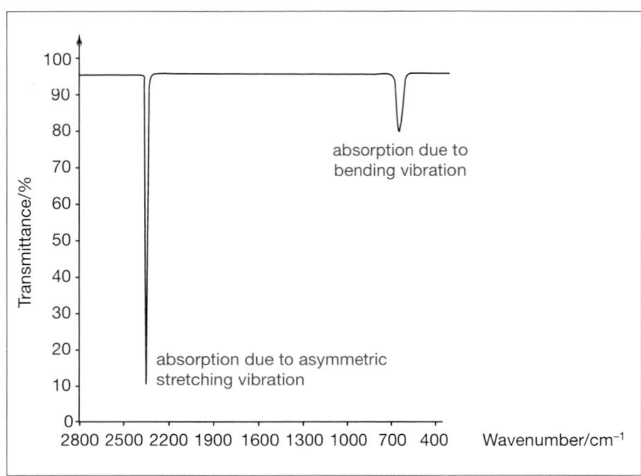

Figure 2 *Infra-red spectrum of carbon dioxide*

Interpreting infra-red spectra

A typical infra-red spectrum (see Figure 3) gives the percentage transmission of a range of infra-red frequencies. Wavenumbers, in cm^{-1}, are used rather than frequencies (frequency is inversely proportional to wavelength).

The absorptions in the infra-red spectrum show the presence of particular bonds in an organic molecule.

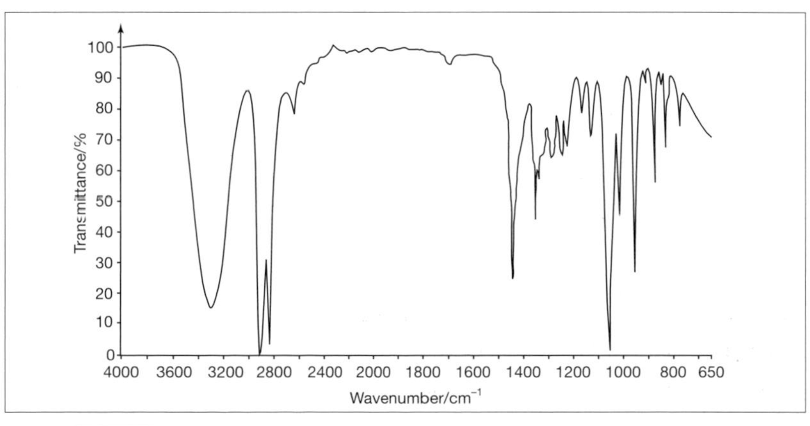

Figure 3 *A typical infra-red spectrum*

Some typical infra-red absorption values for bond stretching in organic molecules are shown in the table below:

Bond	Range/cm^{-1}	Examples
C=O	1680–1750	aldehydes, ketones, carboxylic acids, esters
C–H	2850–3300	most aliphatic organic molecules
O–H	3230–3550	alcohols
O–H	2500–3000	carboxylic acids
C–C	750–1100	alkanes
C=C	1620–1680	alkenes

Table 1

Using these data it can be seen that Figure 3 is the spectrum of an alcohol showing a typical broad absorption between 3200 and 3400 cm^{-1} due to the presence of the O–H group.

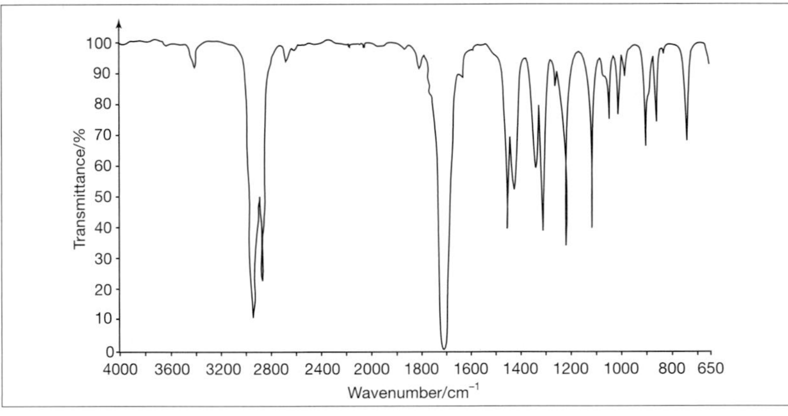

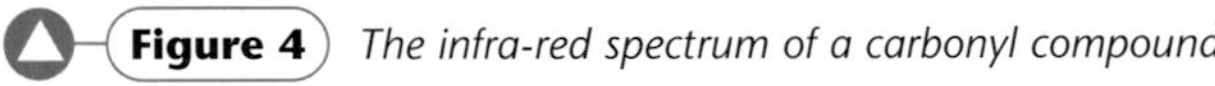
Figure 4 *The infra-red spectrum of a carbonyl compound*

In Figure 4 the strong sharp absorption at 1700 cm^{-1} is due to a carbonyl group (C=O) The compound is either an aldehyde or a ketone but this absorption doesn't distinguish between the two. Aldehydes and ketones can be distinguished from each other by simple chemical tests (see page 66) or using the fingerprint region of the spectrum.

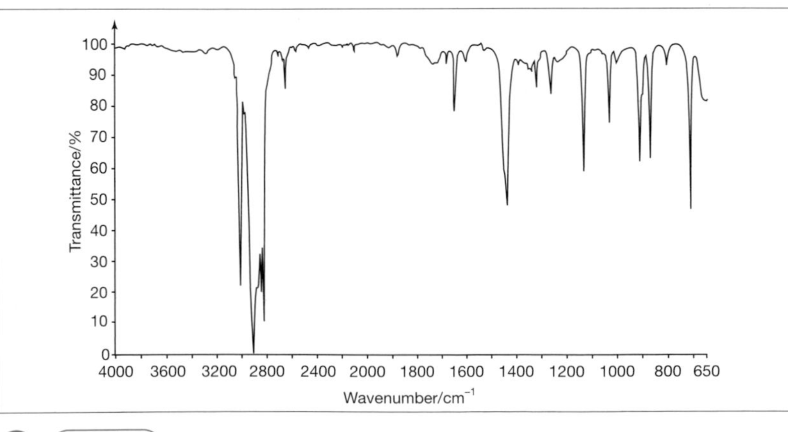

Figure 5 *The infra-red spectrum of an alkene*

In Figure 5 the dominant absorptions between 2800 and 3000 cm^{-1} will *not* identify the functional group. These absorptions are due to C–H bonds and you will notice these are present on all the spectra shown. On this spectrum the absorption which identifies the functional group of the alkene i.e. C=C is tiny and can be found between 1600 and 1700 cm^{-1}

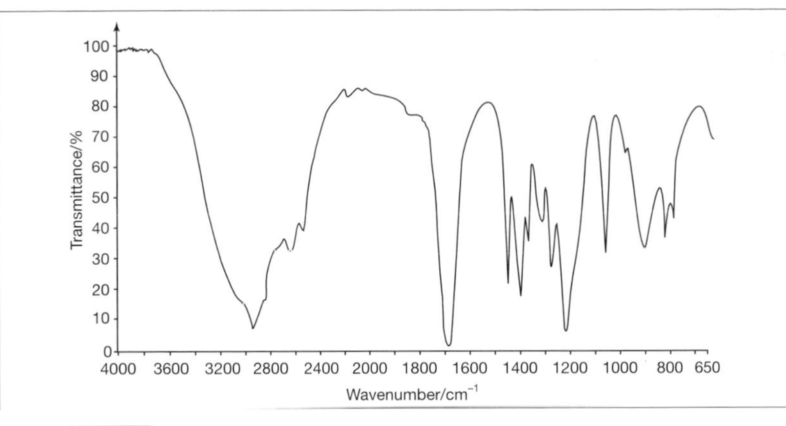

In Figure 6 there are two main absorptions to consider: the broad absorption which peaks at 3000 cm^{-1} is due to the O–H group in the acid and the sharp absorption at 1700 cm^{-1} is due to the carbonyl group which is also present.

Figure 6 *The infra-red spectrum of a carboxylic acid*

Comparing Figure 6 with Figures 3 and 4, the difference between alcohols, acids and aldehydes, and ketones becomes obvious. The absorption due to an O–H group is absent in Figure 4, and the absorption due to the C=O is absent in Figure 3. Sometimes the absence of a particular absorption is an important consideration.

9 Compound X of molecular formula $C_3H_6O_2$ has a sharp absorption at 1680 cm^{-1} in the infra-red, but no absorption due to an O–H bond is detected. To which homologous series does X belong? Suggest a structure for X given that its mass spectrum shows major peaks at *m/z* values of 31 and 43.

The fingerprint region

The 1500–400 cm^{-1} region in an i.r. spectrum is called the **fingerprint region**. Each compound produces a unique i.r. fingerprint pattern which can be seen from the four spectra shown above. The fingerprint is used to identify compounds by comparison of an unknown with the spectra of known compounds using a database. It can also be used to check the purity of a compound, since any small impurity present will produce additional peaks.

10 How could you distinguish between samples of 1-bromopropane and 2-bromopropane using the i.r. spectra of these compounds?

Key Ideas 124 – 127

- **Particular bonds in a compound absorb i.r. radiation at a particular frequency.**
- **This enables the functional groups of organic compounds to be identified from the absorption spectra.**
- **The fingerprint region of an i.r. spectrum is unique to a particular compound and can therefore be used for identification by comparison with spectra of known compounds.**

3 Proton nuclear magnetic resonance spectroscopy

Proton nuclear magnetic resonance spectroscopy (n.m.r.) uses the **magnetic** properties of certain **nuclei**, in this case those of hydrogen atoms, to investigate the structure of a compound. As the name suggests, the nucleus of a hydrogen atom, a **proton**, behaves like a tiny magnet. When energy is applied in the form of radio waves, the proton **resonates** between two different energy states. Hydrogen atoms in different environments within a molecule will resonate at different radio frequencies. This allows the identification of the different hydrogen atoms in the molecule.

The origin of the spectra

The nucleus of a hydrogen atom consists only of a proton. The nucleus has the property of spin. We are only concerned here with proton n.m.r., but the technique works for other atoms containing an odd **nucleon number** i.e. an odd number of protons plus neutrons, e.g. ^{13}C, ^{15}N, ^{19}F and ^{31}P.

When the hydrogen nucleus spins, it creates a small magnetic field. When a large external magnetic field is applied, the small magnetic field created by the spinning hydrogen nucleus can be aligned with or against the external magnetic field (B). This produces two different energy states. The alignment of the proton's magnetic field with the external magnetic field (α) is of lower energy than the alignment against the external magnetic field (β).

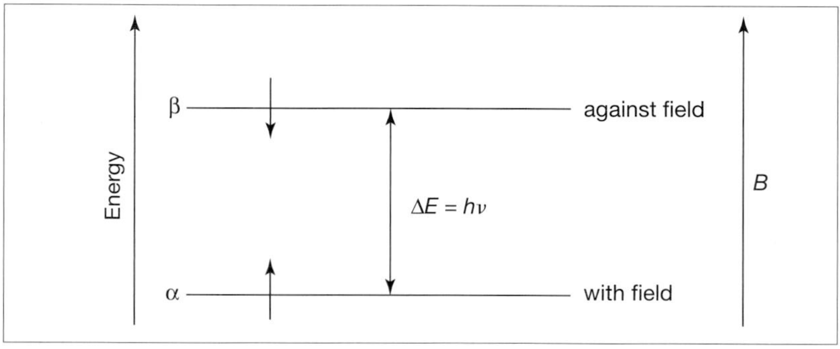

Figure 1 *Energy level diagram*

When radio waves of an appropriate frequency are applied the proton resonates between the two different energy states.

The frequency required to cause the proton to resonate depends upon the environment of the proton within the molecule and hence the environment of the hydrogen atom. Hydrogen atoms in different environments, called **non-equivalent** hydrogen atoms, will **resonate** at different radio frequencies. This allows the identification of the non-equivalent hydrogen atoms in a molecule.

Using the spectrometer

In practice, a sample of an organic compound is placed in a n.m.r. spectrometer with radio waves of a fixed frequency and the external magnetic field is varied to find the different resonance values in the sample. Proton n.m.r. spectra are recorded in solution so the sample is first dissolved in a solvent. This must be a proton-free solvent such as CCl_4 or a deuterated compound such as $CDCl_3$. Deutrated solvents contain ^2H (deuterium), which will not produce any absorptions to interfere with the spectra.

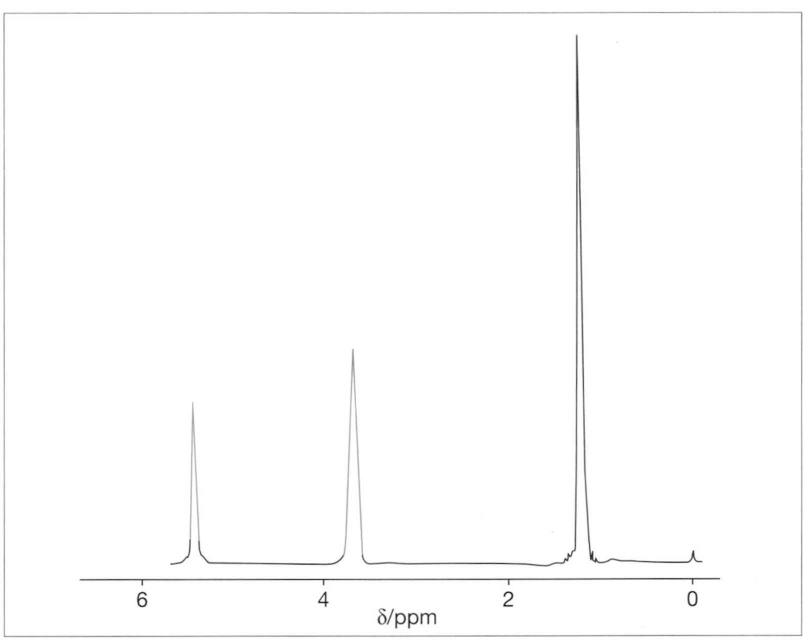

Figure 2 *Low-resolution proton n.m.r. spectrum for ethanol*

Interpreting proton n.m.r. spectra

A proton n.m.r. spectrum gives information about:

- the different non-equivalent hydrogen atoms (protons) present – each type produces a separate peak.
- the number of equivalent hydrogen atoms – the area under the peak.
- the local environment of the equivalent hydrogen atoms – the position of the peak.
- the number of non-equivalent adjacent hydrogen atoms – the splitting of a peak. This is only apparent when using high-resolution spectra (see page 131)

The number of peaks

This tells us how many different types of hydrogen atoms there are in the molecule.

The spectrum shown above in Figure 2 has three peaks because ethanol contains three types of non-equivalent protons.

It is useful when working through examples to indicate the different types of protons in different colours.

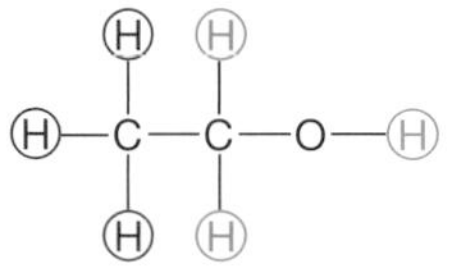

Figure 3 *The structure of ethanol*

Some other examples are shown in Table 1 overleaf.

11 Give the simplest ratio of peak areas for a) propane b) butanal.

The area under the peaks

For each peak the area is proportional to the number of hydrogens giving rise to that absorption. Since it is difficult to measure the area under the peak the information is either quoted as a ratio or shown as an integration trace (see page 129). For ethanol the peak ratios from left to right are 1: 2: 3 corresponding to HO: CH_2: CH_3

Name	Structure	No. of peaks
Ethane	H_3C-CH_3	1
Propanone	$H_3C-CO-CH_3$	1
Propane	$H_3C-CH_2-CH_3$	2
Butanal	$H_3C-CH_2-CH_2-CHO$	4

Table 1

Worked example

1 Draw the structures of the isomers of $C_4H_8O_2$ and indicate the number of peaks produced in the proton n.m.r. spectra for each of these compounds together with the ratio of the peak heights.

Answer

There are two carboxylic acids and four esters which match this formula:

Butanoic acid – $CH_3CH_2CH_2COOH$ – 4 peaks in a ratio 3:2:2:1

Methylpropanoic acid – $(CH_3)_2CHCOOH$ – 3 peaks in a ratio 6:1:1

Ethyl ethanoate – $CH_3COOCH_2CH_3$ – 3 peaks in a ratio 3:2:3

Methyl propanoate – $CH_3CH_2COOCH_3$ – 3 peaks in a ratio 3:2:3

Propyl methanoate – $HCOOCH_2CH_2CH_3$ – 4 peaks in a ratio 1:2:2:3

Methylethyl methanoate – $HCOOCH(CH_3)_2$ – 3 peaks in a ratio 1:1:6

Notice that the ratio total = 8. This is the number of hydrogen atoms in each molecule.

To further distinguish between these isomers it would be necessary to consider the position of the peaks (see page 129) or the splitting patterns (see page 131). Alternatively i.r. or mass spectra could be used. It is important to realise that evidence from a variety of sources may be necessary to confirm a structure.

12 How could you distinguish between 1-bromobutane and 2-bromobutane using low-resolution n.m.r?

Integration traces

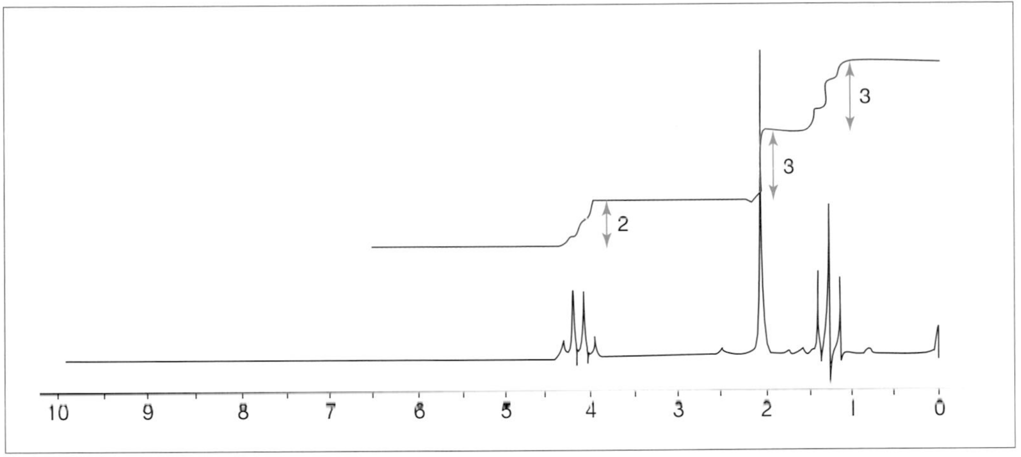

Figure 4 *High-resolution n.m.r. spectrum of ethyl ethanoate showing the integration trace*

Integration traces are usually drawn on **high-resolution spectra**.(see page 131) The spectrometer measures the relative areas under each peak electronically and produces an integration trace. The height of the steps in the integration trace is proportional to the number of hydrogen atoms associated with a particular peak. This is shown above on the high-resolution n.m.r. spectrum of ethyl ethanoate. The integration trace shows the ratio of peak heights to be 2:3:3.

Q

13 Ethoxyethane is isomeric with the four isomers of butanol.

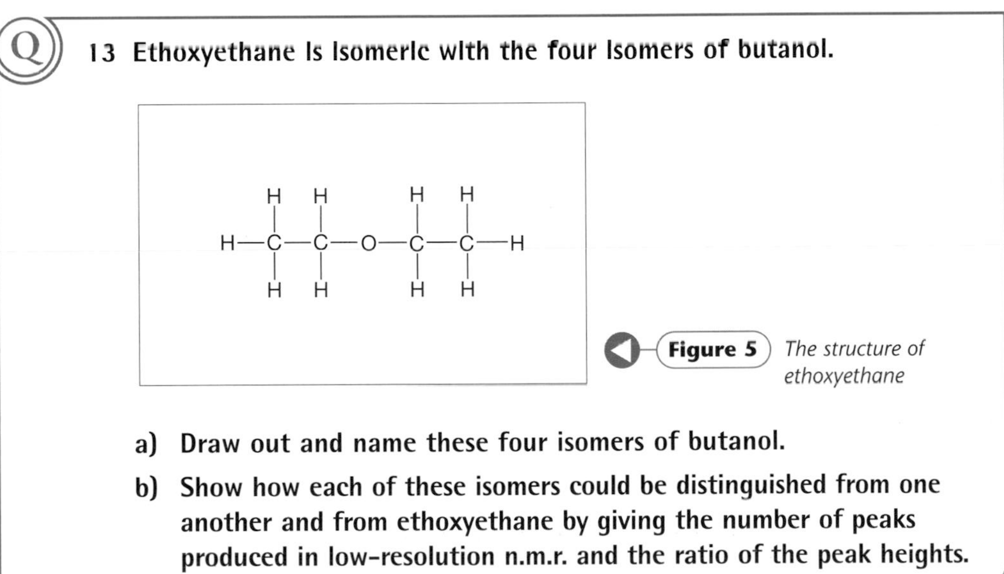

Figure 5 *The structure of ethoxyethane*

a) Draw out and name these four isomers of butanol.

b) Show how each of these isomers could be distinguished from one another and from ethoxyethane by giving the number of peaks produced in low-resolution n.m.r. and the ratio of the peak heights.

The position of the peaks

The horizontal axis of an n.m.r. spectrum is the **δ scale** (delta scale) of **chemical shifts** which is a number, from 0 to about 12.

The position of the peaks on this axis varies depending on the position of the hydrogen atoms within the molecule. Hydrogen atoms, in different parts of a molecule, are affected by the electrons in the adjacent covalent bonds.

The external magnetic field induces these electrons to circulate in such a way that they produce small local magnetic fields which oppose the external field. This means the total applied field is reduced and the proton is said to be **shielded**.

The extent of shielding depends on the electron density around the proton. The greater the electron density around the proton the greater the shielding, and the peak shifts to the right on the δ scale, since a higher external field must be applied to cause resonance.

The presence of an electronegative atom such as oxygen causes **deshielding** and the peak appears downfield towards the left. This can be seen on the spectrum for ethanol (see Figure 6) The proton attached to the oxygen atom in the O–H group is downfield compared to the other two peaks.

The result of shielding and deshielding is that non-equivalent hydrogen atoms cause resonance at very slightly different field strengths – **chemical shifts**. The differences are so small that they are measured in parts per million (ppm) relative to a standard, **tetramethylsilane**, $Si(CH_3)_4$.

Tetramethylsilane, TMS, is used as the reference peak because:

- it produces a single intense peak (all hydrogen atoms are equivalent)
- it is non-toxic and chemically inert
- it is upfield from nearly all peaks produced by hydrogen atoms.

By definition the chemical shift, δ, of TMS is zero.

All other peaks will have a chemical shift value in parts per million (ppm) relative to the TMS reference peak.

The table below shows the proton responsible for the peak over a small δ range and how the environment of the proton affects the δ value.

Type of proton	δ/ppm
RCH_3	0.7–1.2
R_2CH_2	1.2–1.4
R_3CH	1.4–1.6
$RCOCH_3$	2.1–2.6
$ROCH_3$	3.1–3.9
$RCOOCH_3$	3.7–4.1

Table 2 *Typical chemical shift data*

Chemical shift data are usually used in conjunction with peak splitting to identify compounds from high-resolution spectra (see the worked example on page 133.

Peak splitting

Using **high-resolution** proton n.m.r. some of the peaks are split into a number of smaller peaks.

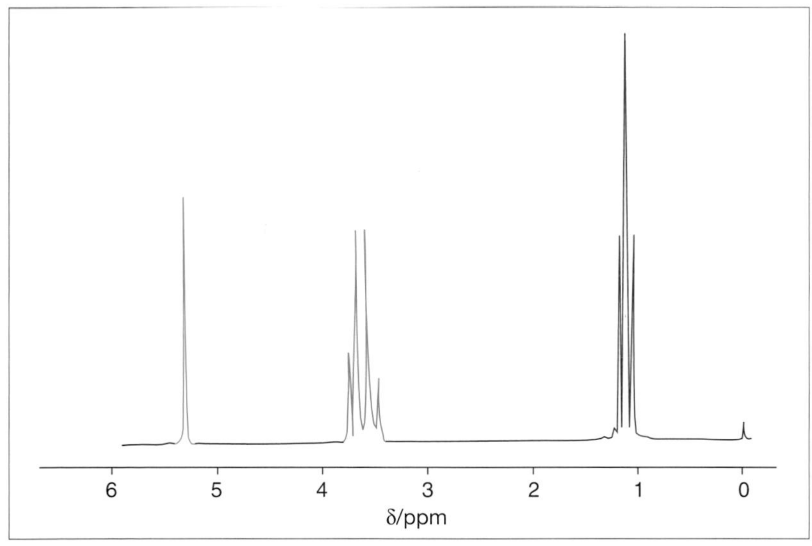

Figure 6 *High-resolution n.m.r. of ethanol*

Compare the high-resolution spectrum of ethanol above with the low-resolution spectrum on page 127. The peak at δ5.3 is unchanged. This is called a **singlet**. The peak at δ3.7 is now split into four smaller peaks. This is called a **quartet**. The peak at δ1.1 forms a **triplet**.

The splitting arises when **neighbouring** non-equivalent hydrogen atoms are present. Each of the neighbouring non-equivalent hydrogen atoms will create a small magnetic field that will affect the external magnetic field. The small magnetic fields caused by neighbouring hydrogen atoms can align with or against the external magnetic field resulting in small differences in the local magnetic field. This is called **spin–spin coupling**.

If there is one neighbouring non-equivalent hydrogen then the small magnetic field from this hydrogen can be aligned with or against the external field. This produces two slightly different magnetic fields around the proton. This results in the peak splitting to produce a pair of peaks called a **doublet**.

If there are two neighbouring non-equivalent hydrogen atoms then the magnetic field from each of these atoms can be aligned with or against the external magnetic field. This leads to three different possibilities:

Both aligned with the external field	↑↑
One aligned with and one aligned against the external field	↑↓ and ↓↑
Both aligned against the external field	↓↓

This lead to the peak splitting into three smaller peaks (a triplet) with a ratio of 1:2:1

When there are three neighbouring non-equivalent hydrogen atoms then there are four different ways that the coupling can occur:

All three aligned with the external field	↑↑↑
Two aligned with and one aligned against the external field	↑↑↓ ↑↓↑ ↓↑↑
One aligned with and two aligned against the external field	↓↓↑ ↓↑↓ ↑↓↓
All three aligned against the external field	↓↓↓

This produces a quartet of peaks in the ratio 1:3:3:1

The number of peaks formed by splitting is given by the **(n + 1) rule** where **n** is the number of non-equivalent **neighbouring** hydrogen atoms.

number of peaks = $n + 1$

Look again at the high-resolution spectrum of ethanol and at the structure of ethanol.

The singlet is caused by the single proton on the O–H group, which doesn't undergo coupling. The quartet is a result of the CH_2 group, which is directly linked to a methyl group, so the signal is split into four (3+1). The triplet is caused by the splitting of the CH_3 group peak by the CH_2 group (2+1).

Remember that the splitting of the peaks is caused by neighbouring protons, not by the protons themselves.

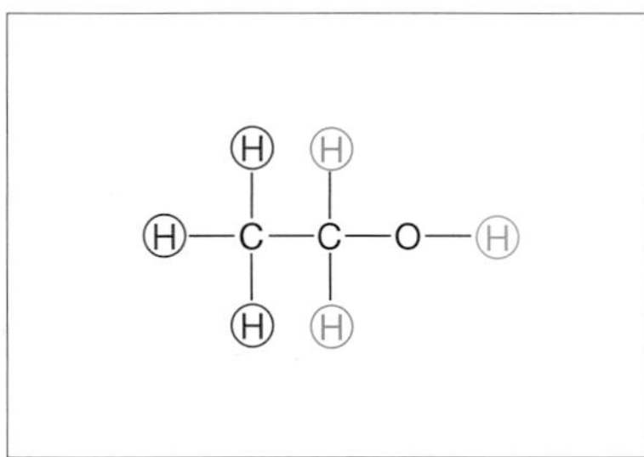

Figure 7 *The structure of ethanol*

A quartet and a triplet are common on high-resolution spectra. They indicate the presence of an **ethyl group** (CH_3CH_2). This is also evident in the spectrum of ethyl ethanoate (see page 129)

14 What compound is responsible for the signal at $\delta = 0$ on these spectra?

Worked example

2. The proton n.m.r. spectrum for compound X, $C_6H_{12}O_3$, is shown in Figure 8, together with some proton chemical shift data (Table 3).

The measured integration trace gives the ratio 0.6:3.6:1.2:1.8 for the peaks at δ 4.8, 3.4, 2.7 and 2.2 respectively. Deduce the structure of compound X.

Answer

a) **Look for the number of peaks** – there are 4 (excluding the one at zero which is the TMS peak) so there are 4 different types of protons.

b) **Look at the peak ratio** – this is given as 0.6:3.6:1.2:1.8 but the actual ratio must be in whole numbers i.e. 1:6:2:3. This is confirmed by adding the ratios together 1+6+2+3 = 12 i.e. the number of hydrogen atoms in compound X

c) **Look at the splitting pattern** – there is a singlet at δ3.4 and a singlet at δ2.2. The former is due to 6 equivalent hydrogen atoms, probably equivalent CH_3 groups, and the latter due to 3 equivalent hydrogen atoms, probably one CH_3 group. These groups are not coupled and therefore have no neighbouring protons. The peaks at δ2.7 and δ4.8 are split into a doublet and a triplet. This indicates coupling between two sets of protons in a ratio 2:1 and suggests the arrangement in compound X shown in Figure 9.

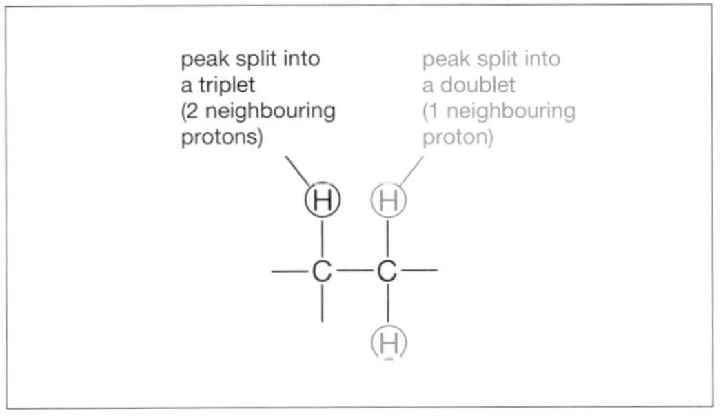

Figure 9

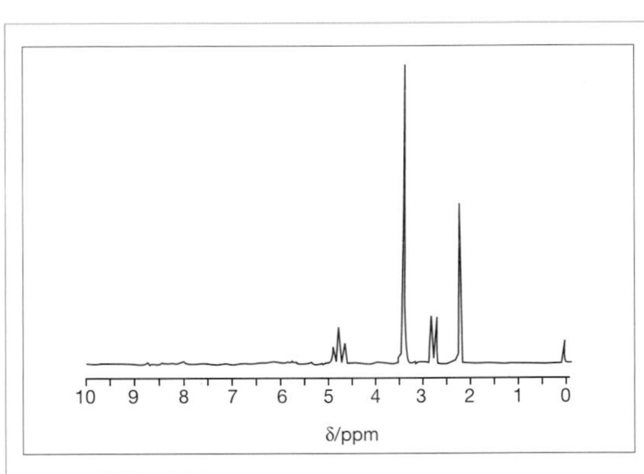

Figure 8

Proton chemical shift data	
Type of proton	δ/ppm
RCH_3	0.7-1.2
R_2CH_2	1.2-1.4
R_3CH	1.4-1.6
$RCOCH_3$	2.1-2.6
$ROCH_3$	3.3-3.9
$RCH(OR)_2$	4.4-5.0

Table 3

d) Look at the position of the peaks – the singlet at δ2.2 is caused by a proton of the type $RCOCH_3$. The singlet at δ3.4 is caused by a proton of the type $ROCH_3$. But we have already identified that there must be two of these groups present in the molecule. The triplet at δ4.8, which we have already identified as a single proton, is of the type $RCH(OR)_2$ where the $(OR)_2$ group must be $(OCH_3)_2$

Putting all this information together the structure of compound **X** must be:

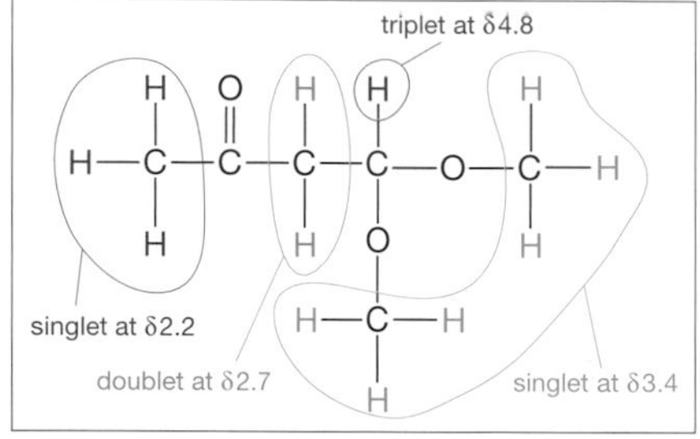

Figure 10

15 The n.m.r. spectrum of an alcohol Z, $C_5H_{12}O$, shows a triplet, a quartet and two singlets. The measured integration trace gives the ratio 0.9:0.45:2.7:1.35.

a) How many different types of protons are present in Z?

b) What is the ratio of the numbers of each type of proton?

c) Give a possible structure for alcohol Z which matches this information.

Key Ideas 126 – 136

- **Nuclear magnetic resonance gives information about the relative number and position of hydrogen atoms in a molecule.**
- **Spectra are obtained using samples dissolved in proton-free solvents.**
- **Tetramethylsilane (TMS) is used as a standard to calibrate the spectrometer.**
- **The number of peaks on the spectrum indicates the number of different types of hydrogen atoms present in the molecule.**
- **The area under the peaks is proportional to the number of equivalent hydrogen atoms present in the molecule. This can be calculated from the integration trace.**
- **Splitting of the peaks caused by spin–spin coupling indicates the number of neighbouring non-equivalent hydrogen atoms present in the molecule, using the *n*+1 rule.**
- **The position of the peaks gives clues as to the environment of each kind of hydrogen atom. The position is recorded as a number on the δ scale for recording chemical shift.**

Unit 9 Questions

4

The following infra-red spectra data may be used, where appropriate, in the answers to these questions:

Bond	Range/cm^{-1}	Examples
C=O	1680–1750	aldehydes, ketones, carboxylic acids, esters
C–H	2850–3300	most aliphatic organic molecules
O–H	3230–3550	alcohols
O–H	2500–3000	carboxylic acids
C–C	750–1100	alkanes
C=C	1620–1680	alkenes

1 **a)** The mass spectrum of ethanol has peaks at *m/z* values of 47, 46, 31 and 15.

(i) Which ions are responsible for these peaks?

(ii) Write equations for the formation of the ions with *m/z* values of 31 and 15. (7)

b) The infra-red spectrum of ethanol is shown below:

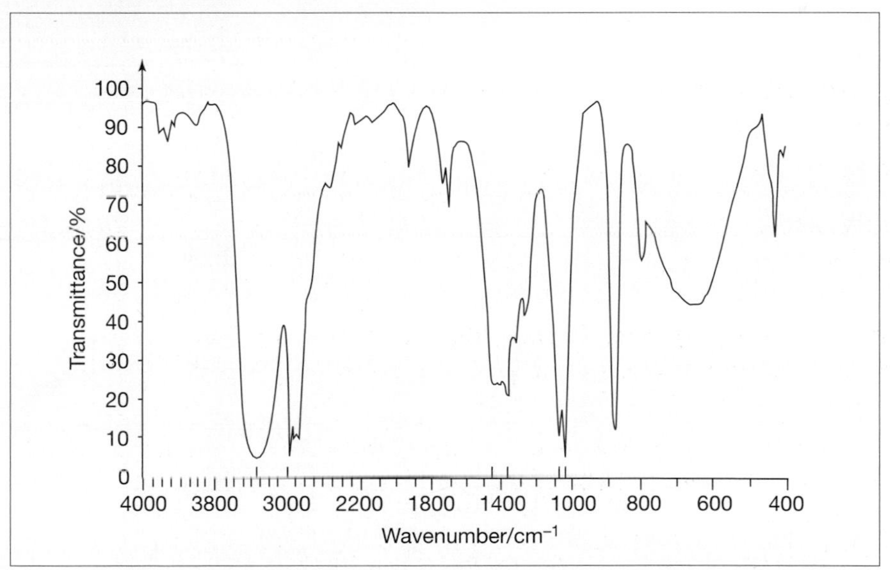

(i) What is the wavenumber of the absorption due to the –OH group?

(ii) What is the approximate range for the fingerprint region? How does this region of the spectrum enable a compound to be identified? (4)

c) Both ethanol and propanone show an absorption at 2950 cm^{-1} on their infra-red spectra.
   (i) Give the approximate wavenumber range for the absorption on the spectrum of propanone which would distinguish it from ethanol.
   (ii) Describe a chemical test that could be used to distinguish between ethanol and propanone. (4)

2 a) Explain why the mass spectrum of chloroethane has a peak at $m/z = 64$ and another peak at $m/z = 66$ which is about one-third the height of the $m/z = 64$ peak. (4)

b) The mass spectrum of chloroethane also shows a prominent peak at $m/z = 29$. Which ion is responsible for this peak? Write an equation for its formation. (3)

3 Compounds **A** and **B** are structural isomers with the following composition by mass: carbon 60%; hydrogen 13.3%; oxygen 26.6%.

a) Calculate the empirical formula for these isomers. (2)

b) Both compounds give a peak with an m/z value of 60 in their mass spectra.
   (i) What is the molecular formula for **A** and **B**?
   (ii) Why do both compounds produce a peak at $m/z = 60$? (2)

c) Both compounds have a strong absorption at 3300 cm^{-1} in their infra-red spectra. Which functional group is present in these molecules? (1)

d) When **A** and **B** are treated separately with concentrated sulphuric acid they both produce compound **C**.
   (i) Give the structure for compound **C**
   (ii) Name the type of reaction involved in the formation of compound **C**. (2)

e) When **A** and **B** are treated separately with warm, acidified potassium dichromate(VI) solution they produce compounds **D** and **E** respectively. **D** and **E** are functional group isomers. The n.m.r. spectrum of **D** has three peaks whereas the n.m.r. spectrum of **E** has only one peak.
   (i) Identify compounds **D** and **E** and explain their n.m.r. spectra.
   (ii) Hence identify the structures of **A** and **B**. (6)

f) Explain why the mass spectrum of **B** contains a peak at $m/z = 45$. Write an equation to show the formation of the species responsible for this peak. (3)

4 The following data are provided for compound **X**. Use these data to identify **X** and explain fully how you arrived at your answer.

- Compound **X** has the following composition by mass: carbon 66.6%; hydrogen 11.1%; oxygen 22.2%.
- The mass spectrum of **X** shows prominent peaks at m/z values equal to 72, 57 and 43.
- The n.m.r. spectrum of **X** contains a singlet, a triplet and a quartet.
- The i.r. spectrum of **X** shows a strong absorption at 1680 cm^{-1}.
- Compound **X** can be reduced to an alcohol but does not undergo mild oxidation. (10)

Organic synthesis and analysis

In organic chemistry the synthesis of a particular compound is often a multi-stage process, involving compounds from several different homologous series. Once the compound has been isolated analysis is necessary to check that the correct compound has in fact been synthesised.

Analysis could involve finding the percentage composition of the elements present in the compound, relative molecular mass determination, functional group tests or analysis of spectra.

This unit brings together all these ideas, showing the links between organic reactions and the various methods of analysis that you have studied in this module and at AS level.

Synthetic routes

In industry new compounds are being synthesised every day. Here we must limit the number of examples we can study. A summary of the synthetic routes from Module 3 is shown in Figure 1.

Notice that crude oil is the raw material for virtually all organic chemicals. To the scheme has been added the reduction of **nitriles**, **esterification** and the formation of **secondary** and **tertiary amines** from Module 4 (shown in [colour]).

The **haloalkanes**, **alkenes** and **alcohols** occupy an important position in organic syntheses and their reactions are summarised individually in Figures 2, 3 and 4.

In Module 4 you have also studied the chemistry of **benzene**. The reactions of benzene are summarised in Figure 5. You will notice that **acyl chorides** are involved in several of these reactions.

By studying these reaction schemes you should become familiar with the interrelationships between different homologous series, the reagents and conditions required to bring about the changes and the mechanisms of the reactions. This knowledge will form the basis of your answers to examination questions.

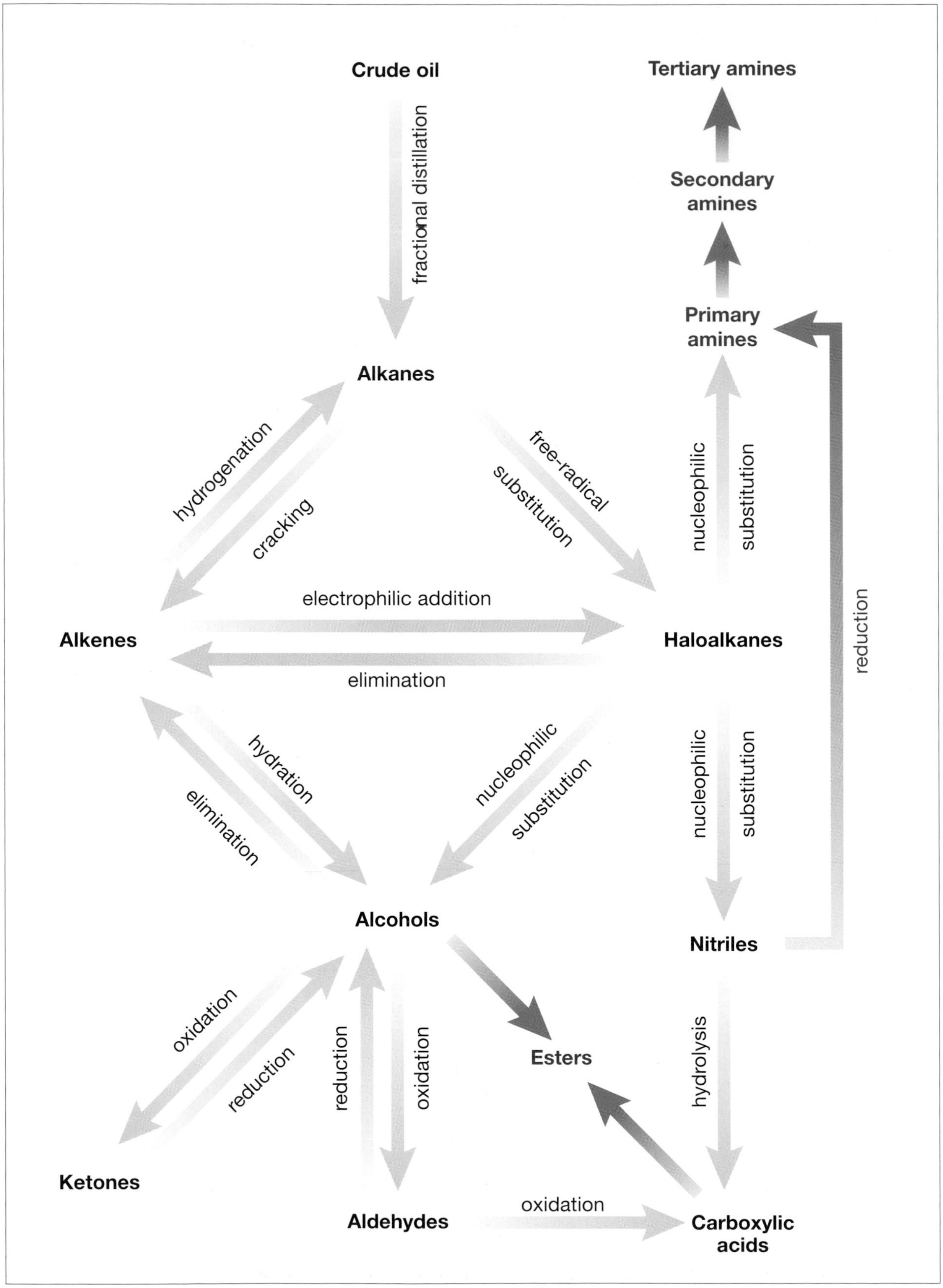

Crude oil
fractional distillation
Alkanes
Tertiary amines
Secondary amines
Primary amines
hydrogenation
cracking
free-radical substitution
nucleophilic substitution
reduction
electrophilic addition
Alkenes
Haloalkanes
elimination
hydration
elimination
nucleophilic substitution
nucleophilic substitution
Alcohols
Nitriles
oxidation
reduction
reduction
oxidation
Esters
hydrolysis
Ketones
Aldehydes
oxidation
Carboxylic acids

Figure 1 *Synthetic routes from Module 3*

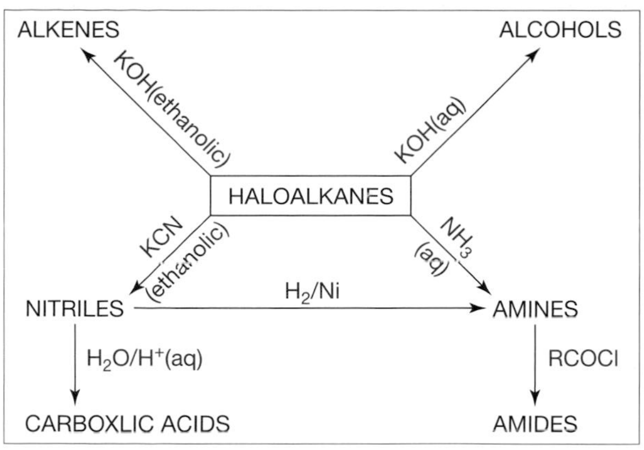

Figure 2 *Reactions of haloalkanes*

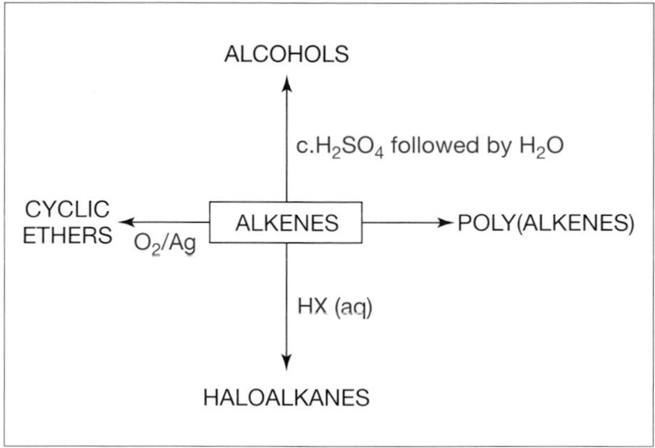

Figure 3 *Reactions of alkenes*

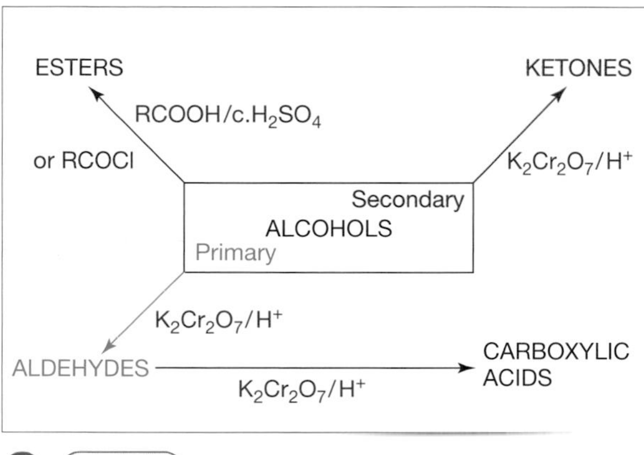

Figure 4 *Reactions of alcohols*

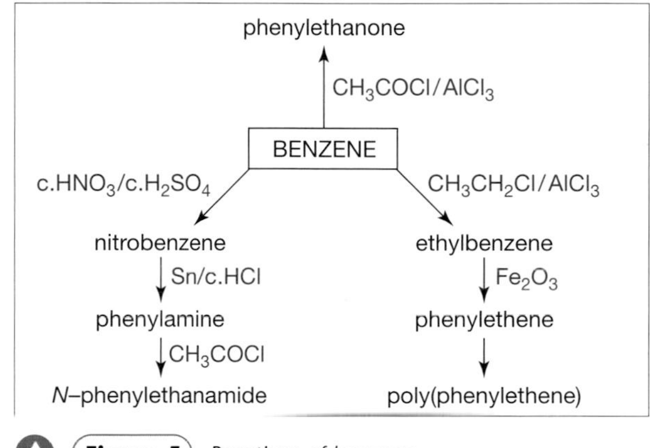

Figure 5 *Reactions of benzene*

Worked examples

1 **Write equations and state essential reaction conditions for the conversion of chloroethane into propylamine.**

Answer

Haloalkanes can be converted directly into amines but in this example the product has one more carbon atom than the reactant so the reaction is a two-stage process via a nitrile:

$$\underset{\text{chloroethane}}{CH_3CH_2Cl} \xrightarrow{\text{step 1}} \underset{\text{propanenitrile}}{CH_3CH_2CN} \xrightarrow{\text{step 2}} \underset{\text{propylamine}}{CH_3CH_2CH_2NH_2}$$

Step 1: Equation: $CH_3CH_2Cl + KCN \rightarrow CH_3CH_2CN + KCl$

Conditions: The haloalkane is refluxed with an ethanolic solution of potassium cyanide.

Step 2: Equation: $CH_3CH_2CN + 2H_2 \rightarrow CH_3CH_2CH_2NH_2$

Conditions: The nitrile is reduced using hydrogen in the presence of a nickel catalyst (or $LiAlH_4$ in anhydrous conditions).

2 **An optically active compound A undergoes the following reactions:**

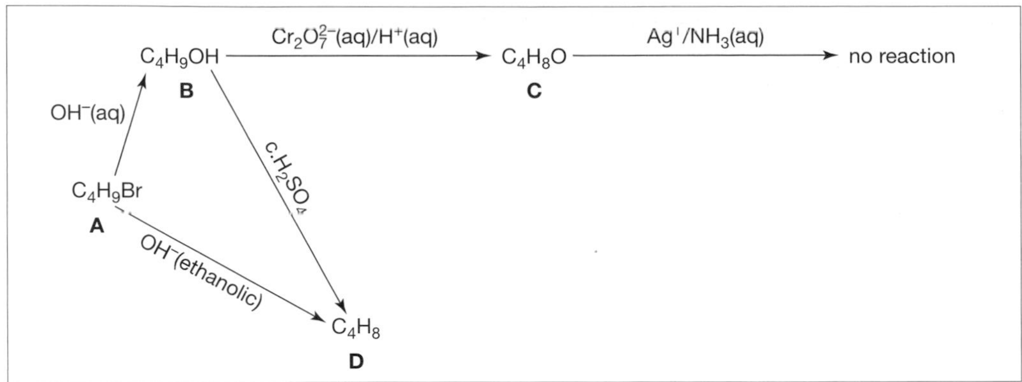

Figure 6

Compound D exhibits geometrical isomerism.

Identify compounds A–D in the following reaction scheme and name the type of reaction occurring at each stage.

Answer

The compounds can be identified by name or formula since the question does not specify which is required.

Compound A is an isomer of bromobutane. The only isomer that contains an asymmetric carbon atom is 2-bromobutane. So A is **2-bromobutane**. It reacts with aqueous hydroxide ions by a **nucleophilic substitution** reaction to form B. Compound B must be **butan-2-ol** since the functional group of the haloalkane is replaced directly by the hydroxyl group.

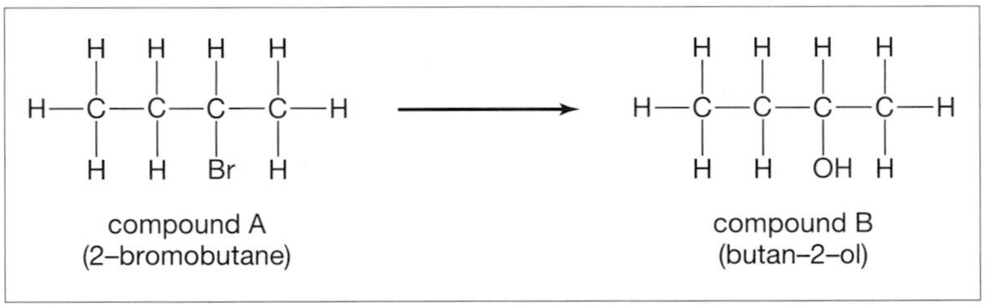

compound A (2–bromobutane) → compound B (butan–2–ol)

Figure 7 *Conversion of A to B by nucleophilic substitution*

Oxidation of a secondary alcohol produces a ketone. So compound C must be **butanone**. This is confirmed by the fact that it gives no reaction with ammoniacal silver ions (Tollen's reagent).

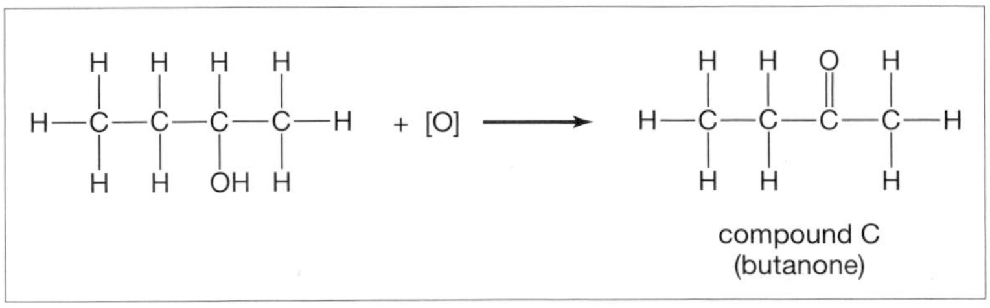

+ [O] → compound C (butanone)

Figure 8 *Conversion of B to C by oxidation*

The conversion of either A or B into compound D is an **elimination** reaction. Compound D is an isomer of butene. Of the two possibilities, but-1-ene and but-2-ene, only the latter exhibits geometrical isomerism so D is **but-2-ene**. Elimination involves the removal of the functional group plus an adjacent hydrogen atom:

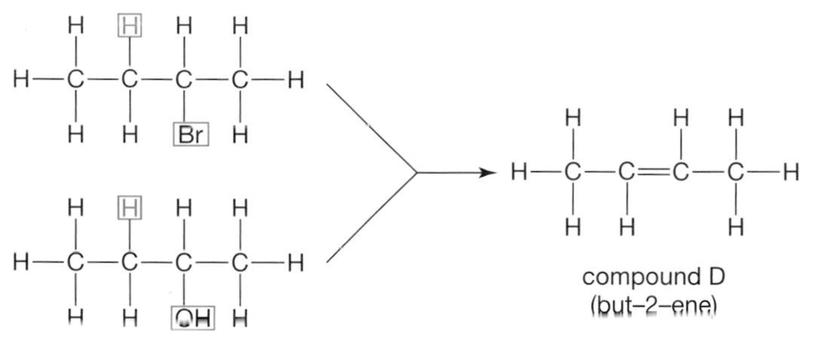

compound D (but-2-ene)

Figure 9 *Elimination reactions*

3 **The synthesis of *N*-phenylethanamide from benzene is outlined below:**

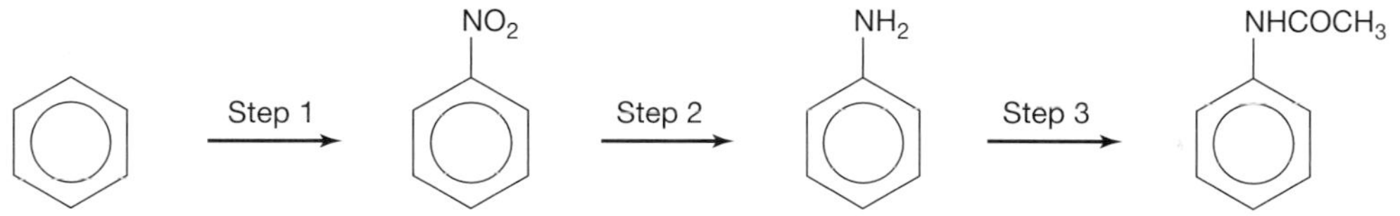

NO_2 NH_2 $NHCOCH_3$ Step 1 Step 2 Step 3

Figure 10

For each step, name the type of reaction taking place and give suitable reagents for the conversions.

Answer

Step 1: Type of reaction – nitration (electrophilic substitution).
Reagents – a mixture of concentrated nitric and sulphuric acids

Step 2: Type of reaction – reduction
Reagents – a mixture of tin and concentrated hydrochloric acid (or hydrogen in the presence of a nickel catalyst)

Step 3: Type of reaction – nucleophilic addition–elimination (acylation)
Reagent – ethanoyl chloride

Key Ideas 138 – 143

- **Organic synthesis often involves a number of steps.**
- **A knowledge of functional group chemistry and the interrelationships between homologous series is essential in this work.**
- **Alkenes, haloalkanes and alcohols are important intermediates in organic syntheses.**

2 Analysis

If the compound is an unknown then several techniques can be employed to find its structure:

- empirical formulae determination from percentage by mass analysis data
- relative molecular mass determination from mass spectra
- functional group tests
- functional group analysis from infra-red spectral data
- structural determination from fragmentation patterns on mass spectra
- structural determination from n.m.r. spectra.

It is common to use two or more of these methods in conjunction with one another to confirm a structural formula. The following examples illustrate common types of examination questions.

Worked examples

1 Analysis of compound A shows that the percentage by mass of the elements present are: carbon 66.7%, hydrogen 11.1%, oxygen 22.2%. When treated with Fehling's solution compound A showed no reaction. The mass spectrum and the infra-red spectrum of compound A are shown in Figures 1 and 2.
Use these data to deduce the structure of compound A.

Answer

First use the % by mass data to calculate the empirical formula of A:

	carbon	hydrogen	oxygen
% by mass	66.7	11.1	22.2
molar ratio	$\frac{66.7}{12} = 5.56$	$\frac{11.1}{1} = 11.1$	$\frac{22.2}{16} = 1.39$
whole no. ratio	$\frac{5.56}{1.39} = 4$	$\frac{11.1}{1.39} = 8$	$\frac{1.39}{1.39} = 1$

C:H:O = 4:8:1 so the empirical formula of A is C_4H_8O

Using the mass spectrum data:

The molecular ion peak ($M^{+\bullet}$) is at 72 so the relative molecular mass of A is 72.
Since the empirical formula mass = (48 + 8 + 16) = 72 then the molecular formula of A is C_4H_8O.

This formula matches the general formula of an aldehyde or ketone. Confirmation of this is provided by studying the infra-red spectrum of A, which shows a prominent sharp absorption at about 1700 cm^{-1}.

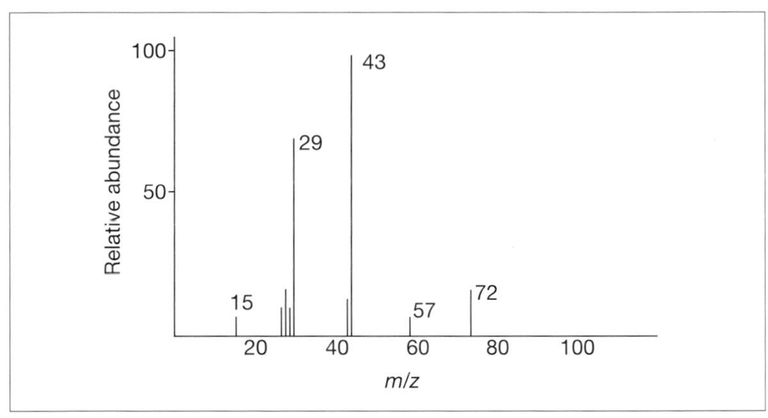

Figure 1 *Mass spectrum of A*

Since compound A gives no reaction with Fehling's solution it must be a ketone. There is only one ketone of molecular formula C_4H_8O so A must be butanone.

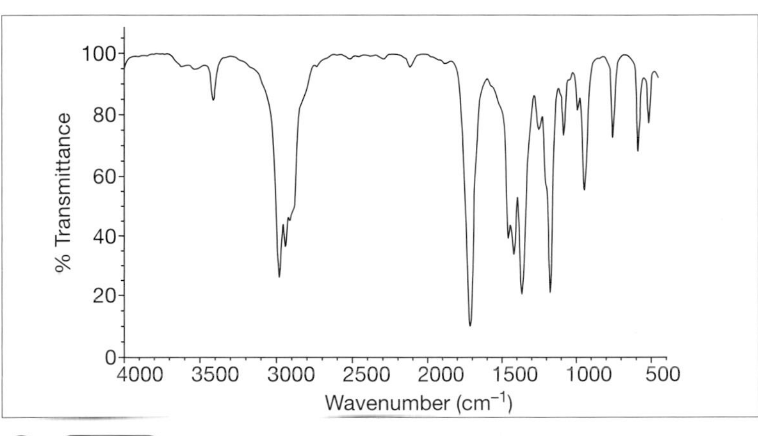

Figure 2 *Infra-red spectrum of A*

This can be confirmed by studying the fragmentation pattern on the mass spectrum:
The peak at m/z = 57 corresponds to $(M-15)^+$, the loss of $CH_3^\bullet$ producing the $C_3H_5O^+$ ion.
The peak at m/z = 43 corresponds to $(M-29)^+$, the loss of $C_2H_5^\bullet$ producing the CH_3CO^+ ion.
Peaks at m/z = 15 and m/z = 29 correspond to CH_3^+ and $C_2H_5^+$ respectively.

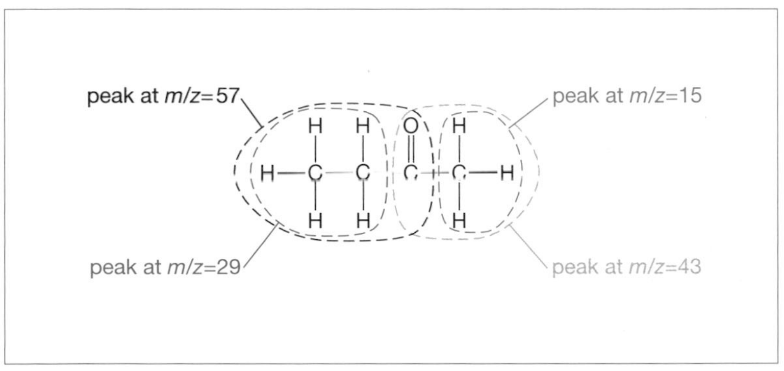

Figure 3 *Summary of the mass spectrum data for compound A*

2 Compound **B** C_3H_6O shows the following reactions.

- It is reduced by $NaBH_4$ to Compound C.
- It reacts with HCN to form compound D. Hydrolysis of D produces an optically active acid, E.
- It reacts with acidified $K_2Cr_2O_7$ to form compound F.

The infra-red spectra for compounds C and D show broad absorptions between 3300–3400 cm^{-1}. The high-resolution proton n.m.r. spectrum of compound B shows three peaks – a triplet, a quartet and a singlet. The integration trace when measured gives the ratio 1.5: 1.0: 0.5.

Use the data above to deduce structures for the compounds B to F

Answer

The formula of B suggests it is an aldehyde or a ketone. If it can be oxidised with acidified $K_2Cr_2O_7$ it must be an aldehyde. The only aldehyde that fits the molecular formula C_3H_6O is propanal so the structure of B is

Figure 4

The structure of compound B can be confirmed using the n.m.r. data:

A molecule of propanal contains three types of non-equivalent hydrogen atoms so its n.m.r. spectrum will show three peaks. The singlet is due to the hydrogen atom on the carbonyl group that does not undergo coupling. The triplet and quartet are due to the presence of an ethyl group, where the CH_2 group is split into a quartet by its three neighbouring hydrogen atoms and the CH_3 group is split into a triplet by its two neighbouring hydrogen atoms.

Figure 5 *Interpretation of the n.m.r. spectrum of propanal*

The integration trace ratio of 1.5:1.0:0.5 gives a whole number ratio of 3:2:1, which matches the formula containing six hydrogen atoms.

When propanal is reduced by $NaBH_4$ it forms compound C. Since aldehydes are reduced to primary alcohols C must be propan-1-ol. The infra-red spectrum of C confirms the presence of the O–H functional group in alcohols by the broad absorption at approximately 3350 cm^{-1}.

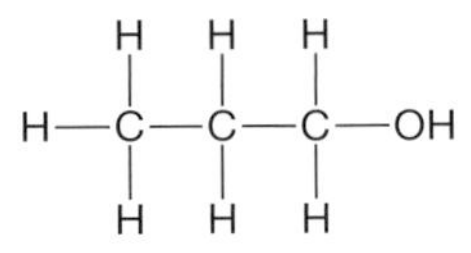

Figure 6 *Compound C is propan-1-ol*

When propanal reacts with HCN it undergoes a nucleophilic addition reaction to form compound D, which is hydrolysed to compound E:

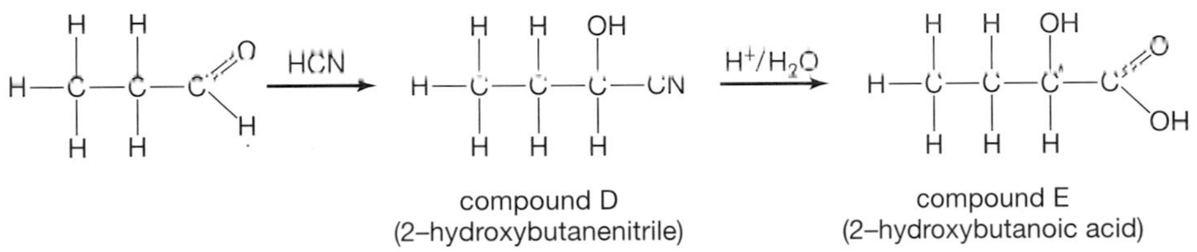

compound D
(2–hydroxybutanenitrile)

compound E
(2–hydroxybutanoic acid)

Figure 7 *Formation of D and E*

The infra-red spectrum of D confirms the presence of the O–H group in alcohols by the broad absorption at approximately 3350 cm^{-1}

Compound E is optically active since it contains a chiral carbon atom (marked * on its structure)

When propanal is oxidised by $K_2Cr_2O_7$ it forms propanoic acid. Compound F is propanoic acid:

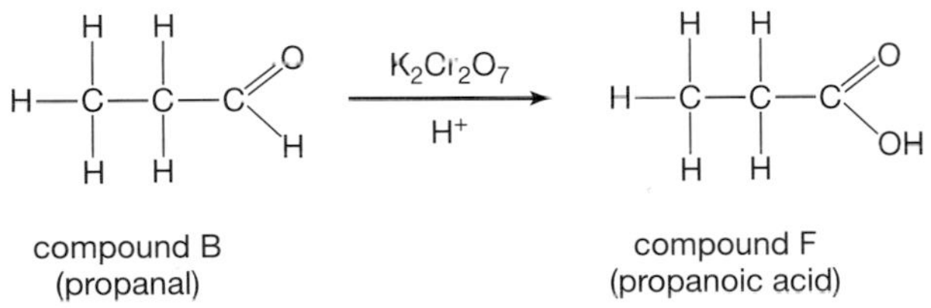

$K_2Cr_2O_7$
H^+

compound B
(propanal)

compound F
(propanoic acid)

Figure 8 *The formation of compound F*

Key Ideas 144 – 147

- **Analysis of a compound may involve a number of different techniques in order to elucidate and confirm its structure.**
- **Infra-red spectra are useful in confirming the results of functional group tests.**
- **Mass spectra can be used in conjunction with empirical formula data to find the molecular formula of a compound.**
- **The n.m.r. spectrum helps to confirm the position of the alkyl groups in a molecule.**

Unit 10 Questions

3

1) A synthesis for phenylethene is shown below:

$$C_6H_6 \xrightarrow{\text{step 1}} C_6H_5COCH_3 \xrightarrow{\text{step 2}} C_6H_5CH(OH)CH_3 \xrightarrow{\text{step 3}} C_6H_5CH{=}CH_2$$

a) For each step, state the type of reaction taking place and give suitable reagents required to bring about these conversions. (7)

b) Outline a mechanism for step 1. (4)

c) Outline a mechanism for step 3. (4)

d) Phenylethene undergoes addition polymerisation. Draw the structure of the repeating unit of the polymer formed. (1)

2) Consider the following reaction scheme:

$$C_6H_5{-}CH_3 \xrightarrow{\text{Step 1}} C_6H_5{-}CH_2Cl \xrightarrow{\text{Step 2}} C_6H_5{-}CH_2CN \xrightarrow{\text{Step 3}} C_6H_5{-}CH_2CH_2NH_2$$

a) For each step, state the type of reaction taking place and give suitable reagents required to bring about these conversions. (6)

b) Give the important reaction conditions required for step 1. (1)

c) Outline the mechanism for step 2. (2)

d) State and explain the difference in basic strength between phenylamine and the product of step 3. (3)

3) 1,4-dibromobutane undergoes the following conversions:
When 1,4-dibromobutane is reacted with ammonia compound **A** is formed. Compound **B** is produced when 1,4-dibromobutane reacts with potassium cyanide. Compound **B** is hydrolysed to compound **C**. Compounds **A** and **C** react together to form a polymer, compound **D**.

Identify compounds **A–D** and outline the mechanism for the formation of compound **A** from 1,4-dibromobutane. (7)

(4) Study the reaction scheme below and answer the questions that follow:

$$\underset{A}{C_4H_9Br} \xrightarrow{1} \underset{B}{C_4H_9OH} \xrightarrow{2} \underset{C}{C_4H_8O} \xrightarrow{3} \text{Ag(s) with Tollen's solution}$$

$$\downarrow 4 \quad (\text{from } A)$$

$$\underset{D}{C_4H_8} \xrightarrow{5} \underset{E}{C_4H_9Br} \xrightarrow{6} \underset{F}{C_4H_9OH} \longrightarrow \text{no reaction with } K_2Cr_2O_7/H^+$$

a) Give the structural formula of each of compounds **A–F**. (6)

b) Name the type of reaction occurring for conversions 1–5. (5)

c) Name

(i) a structural isomer of **C**.

(ii) an isomer of **D** which has *cis* and *trans* forms.

(iii) an isomer of **A** and **E** which exhibits optical isomerism. (3)

(5) A sweet-smelling liquid **X** is hydrolysed in acid conditions into **Y** and **Z**. The mass spectrum for compound **Y** is given below. Its infra-red spectrum shows a strong absorption at 2670 cm^{-1}.

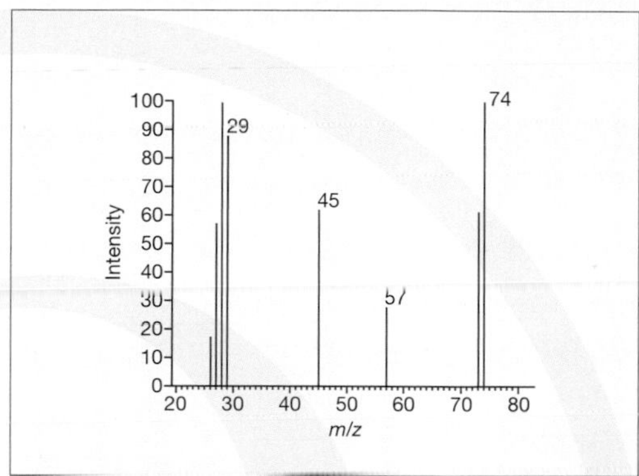

The infra-red absorption data is as follows:

Bond	Range/cm^{-1}	Examples
C–H	2850–3300	most aliphatic organic molecules
O–H	3230–3550	alcohols
O–H	2500–3000	carboxylic acids
C=C	1620–1680	alkenes

a) (i) What is the relative molecular mass of **Y**?

(ii) Suggest fragment ions that could be responsible for the labelled peaks on the mass spectrum. (4)

b) Use the mass spectrum and infra-red data to suggest a structure for compound **Y**. (2)

c) Compound **Z** can be oxidised to a ketone. On analysis it was found to contain 60% by mass of carbon, 13.3% by mass of hydrogen and 26.7% by mass of oxygen. The M_r of **Z** is 60.

Use these data to suggest a structure for compound **Z**. (5)

d) Deduce the structure of compound **X**. (2)

Module 4 Questions

4

(1) The following reaction occurs in a closed vessel at constant temperature:

$$2A(g) + B(g) \rightarrow C(g)$$

The initial rate of reaction was determined for a range of concentrations of A and B. The results are given in the table below:

Run	Initial concentration of A/mol dm^{-3}	Initial concentration of B/mol dm^{-3}	Initial rate /mol $dm^{-3}s^{-1}$
1	0.5	0.5	2.0×10^{-4}
2	1.0	0.5	8.0×10^{-4}
3	1.0	1.0	8.0×10^{-4}
4	1.5	1.5	18.0×10^{-4}

a) Deduce
(i) The rate equation for this reaction
(ii) The value of the rate constant
(iii) The initial rate if the initial concentrations of A and B were 3.0 mol dm^{-3} and 2.5 mol dm^{-3} respectively. (7)

b) If the temperature is altered the value of the rate constant alters. Sketch a graph to show the variation in the rate constant with temperature and explain your answer. (4)

(2) **a)** What is meant by the term *dynamic equilibrium*? (2)

b) Ethanoic acid reacts with ethanol in the presence of concentrated sulphuric acid according to the equation below:

$$CH_3COOH(aq) + CH_3CH_2OH(aq) \rightleftharpoons CH_3COOCH_2CH_3(aq) + H_2O(l)$$

21 g of ethanoic acid, 13.8 g of ethanol and 8.8 g of ethyl ethanoate were mixed in a flask and allowed to reach equilibrium. Once the equilibrium was established it was found that the ethanoic acid in the mixture reacted with 30 cm^3 of 5M NaOH. Calculate the value of the equilibrium constant K_c for the reaction. (5)

(3) **a)** Describe an experiment to determine the acid dissociation constant K_a of a weak monoprotic acid. Give practical details and outline the underlying principles. (10)

b) Discuss how you would expect the value of K_a to vary with
(i) the concentration of the acid
(ii) the temperature. (4)

c) How is pK_a related to K_a? The pK_a of bromoethanoic acid at 298K is 2.88. If the pH of the acid at the same temperature is 1.94 calculate the molarity of the acid. (5)

4 a) Define pH and describe briefly how you would measure the pH of a solution. (3)

b) Sketch pH curves to show the change in pH which results when an excess of 0.1M NaOH(aq) is added by titration to 25 cm^3 of 0.1M solutions of the following acids:
(i) hydrochloric acid
(ii) ethanoic acid (K_a = 1.8 x 10^{-5}mol dm^{-3})
(iii) ethanedioic acid ($H_2C_2O_4$). (8)

c) Explain how acid–base indicators function and how you would select a suitable indicator for a particular titration. (8)

5 a) Outline, by means of equations and by stating essential reaction conditions how 2-bromopropanoic acid can be converted into
(i) 2-hydroxypropanoic acid.
(ii) 2-aminopropanoic acid.
Include the reaction mechanism for one of these reactions. (7)

b) Explain why 2-aminopropanoic acid has a much higher melting point than 2-hydroxypropanoic acid. (3)

c) Outline the mechanism of the reaction of 2-hydroxypropanoic acid with ethanoyl chloride (4)

d) Explain how the addition of acidified potassium dichromate could be used to distinguish between 2-hydroxypropanoic acid and 2-aminopropanoic acid. (3)

6 Four isomeric esters are represented by the molecular formula $C_4H_8O_2$

a) (i) Name and give the structural formulae of these four isomers.
(ii) To what extent would low-resolution proton n.m.r. distinguish between these isomers? Explain your answer. (16)

b) One of these four esters, **X**, was refluxed with aqueous sodium hydroxide and a colourless liquid, **Y**, was distilled from the mixture formed. When warmed with acidified potassium dichromate(VI) solution Y was oxidised to compound **Z**. Compound **Z** reacted with HCN but no colour change was observed when it was boiled with Fehling's solution.
Identify **X**,**Y** and **Z** and explain how you arrived at your answers. (6)

c) The high-resolution proton n.m.r. spectrum of another of these isomeric esters is shown below together with the proton chemical shift data:

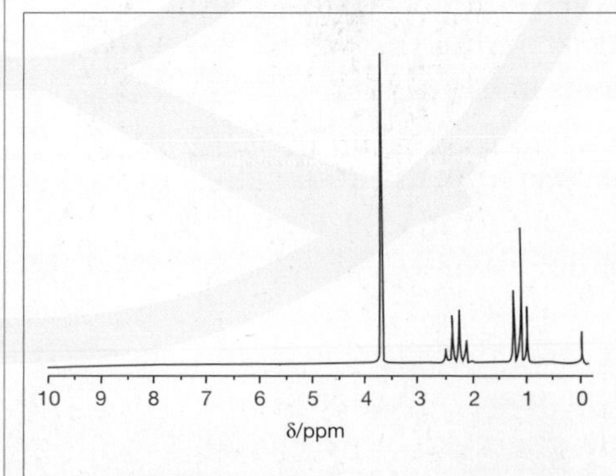

Proton chemical shift data	
Type of proton	δ/ppm
RCH_3	0.7–1.2
R_2CH_2	1.2–1.4
R_3CH	1.4–1.6
$RCOCH_3$	2.1–2.6
$ROCH_3$	3.3–3.9

Deduce the structure of this ester taking into account the number of peaks, their relative positions, the number of protons associated with each peak and the splitting pattern. (9)

7 **a)** Describe the structure and bonding in the benzene molecule. Use the following data to illustrate your answer.

- Benzene is a hydrocarbon containing 92.3% by mass of carbon with a relative molecular mass of 78.
- The enthalpy of hydrogenation of benzene is $-210\,\text{kJ mol}^{-1}$ whereas the enthalpy of hydrogenation of cyclohexene is $-122\,\text{kJ mol}^{-1}$. (10)

b) Explain why benzene undergoes electrophilic attack and why these reactions result in substitution in preference to addition. (5)

c) Outline a laboratory synthesis of phenylethene, the first step of which involves Friedel–Crafts acylation of benzene. Include in your answer the mechanism for the acylation step and reagents for each step. (10)

d) Give one industrial use for phenylethene. (1)

8 Consider the following reaction scheme:

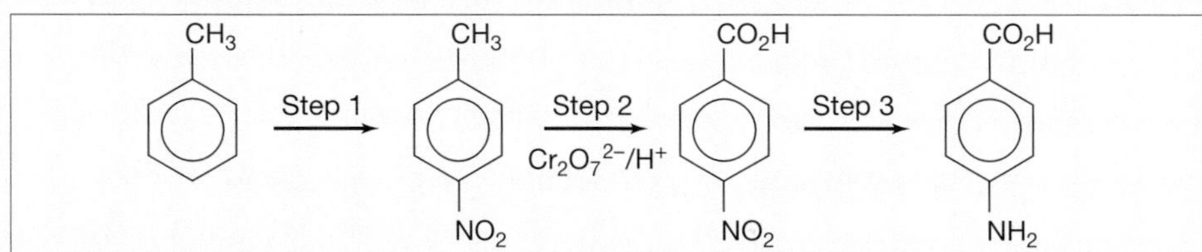

a) State the types of reactions occurring at each of steps 1,2 and 3. (3)

b) Give the reagents required for steps 1 and 3. (4)

c) Outline a mechanism for step 1. (4)

d) Draw the structures of the ions formed when 4-aminobenzene carboxylic acid is reacted with
(i) sodium hydroxide solution
(ii) hydrochloric acid. (2)

e) Deduce the structure of the dimer formed when two molecules of 4-aminobenzene carboxylic acid react together. What does this structure have in common with protein molecules? (3)

9 **a)** Give the structures of the organic products obtained when phenylmethanol ($C_6H_5CH_2OH$) is treated with a mild oxidising agent. State the oxidising agent you would use, the conditions required for the reaction and any observations you would make. (5)

b) (i) State the type of reaction that occurs and give the equation for the reaction when phenylmethanol is heated with propanoic acid in the presence of concentrated sulphuric acid as a catalyst. Show clearly the structure of the organic product.

(ii) Name the mechanism of the reaction that occurs when phenylmethanol is heated with concentrated nitric acid in the presence of concentrated sulphuric acid as a catalyst. Write an equation to show the formation of the intermediate produced when these two acids react together. (5)

10 The structures of the drugs aspirin and benzedrine are shown below:

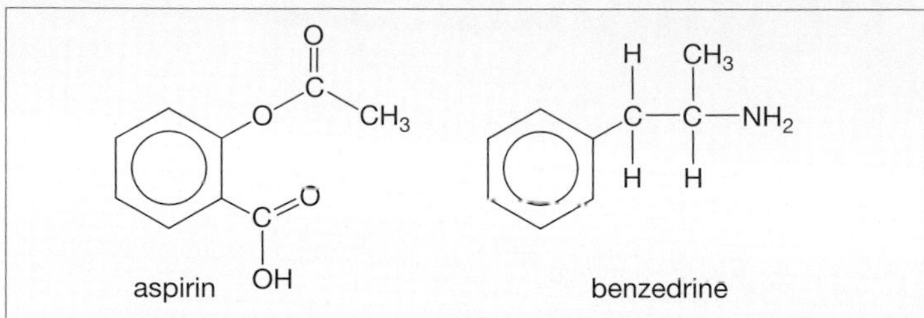

a) Write equations to show how aspirin will react with (i) ethanol and (ii) dilute aqueous sodium hydroxide, showing clearly the structures of the organic products. (4)

b) Write equations to show how benzedrine will react with (i) bromoethane and (ii) ethanoic anhydride, showing clearly the structures of the organic products. (4)

c) The preparation of esters can be achieved by reacting alcohols with a carboxylic acid, an acyl chloride or an acid anhydride. Discuss the advantages and/or disadvantages of each method. Hence write an equation to show how aspirin could best be prepared from 2-hydroxybenzenecarboxylic acid. (8)

11 Identify by name and structural formulae the compounds **A–F** from the information below. Explain how you have used these data to arrive at your answers. (30)

- Two isomers **A** and **B** have the following composition by mass: carbon 54.5%; hydrogen 9.1%; oxygen 36.4%.
- The mass spectrum of **A** has prominent peaks at m/z values of 29, 43, 45 and 88. The mass spectrum of **B** has prominent peaks at m/z values of 29, 57, 59 and 88.
- Both compounds show three peaks on their n.m.r. spectra in a ratio 3:2:3. Each spectrum has a singlet, a triplet and a quartet.
- When compound **A** is heated with NaOH(aq) and the mixture acidified compounds **C** and **D** are formed. Similar treatment of compound **B** produces compounds **E** and **F**.
- Both compounds **C** and **E** show a strong absorption at 3300 cm^{-1} on their infra-red spectra. Both **C** and **E** turn acidified potassium dichromate(VI) solution from orange to green on heating.
- The proton n.m.r. spectrum of **C** has three peaks in a ratio 3:2:1, whereas the proton n.m.r. spectrum of **E** has two peaks in a ratio 3:1
- Compounds **D** and **F** both produce a colourless gas when reacted with aqueous sodium hydrogen carbonate.

12 **a)** Define the term *nucleophile*. Explain why haloalkanes and ketones are susceptible to attack by nucleophiles. (3)

b) With reference to the mechanisms of the reactions of 2-bromopropane and propanone with cyanide ions show the similarities and differences, between these two reactions. (9)

Introduction to Module 5

In this Module the studies of energetics, redox reactions and catalysis introduced at AS are extended, and the chemical properties of the transition metals and Period 3 elements are studied in detail.

In Unit 11 the topic on energetics studied at AS is extended to include chemical thermodynamics which introduces entropy and free energy. These two concepts are used to explain the feasibility of a chemical reaction. The Unit includes Born–Haber cycles, which show the energy changes involved in the formation of ionic solids and in the solvation of ionic compounds.

In Unit 12 the reactions of the elements and some compounds of the Period 3 elements are studied. The reactions of the elements, their oxides and chlorides are used to illustrate the trends across the Periodic Table. The understanding of the properties of the elements and their compounds relies on knowledge of structure and bonding studied at AS level.

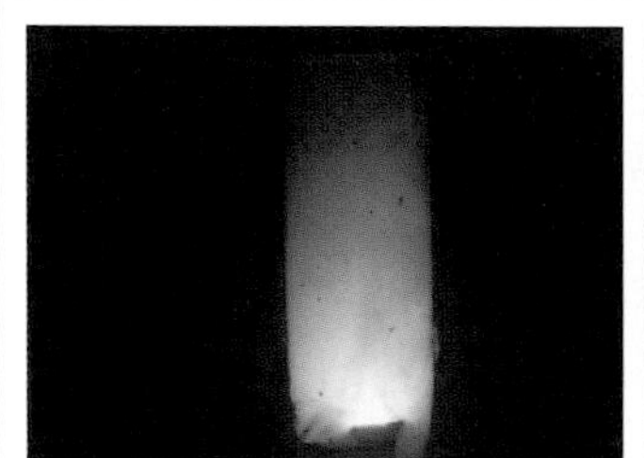

Phosphorus burning in oxygen

Sulphur burning in oxygen

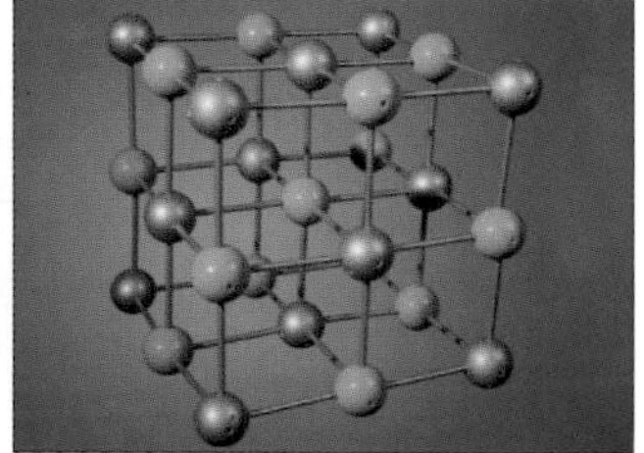

A giant lattice

Figure 1

The ideas of oxidation states and half-equations are extended in Unit 13 to include the transition metals. The unit introduces electrode potentials for oxidation and reduction reactions. Electrode potentials are used to predict the direction of redox reactions.

The general properties of the transition metals are studied in Unit 14. This study includes complex formation, shapes of complexes, formation of coloured ions and ability to act as catalysts. The final part of the Unit looks at some applications of transition metal complexes.

In Unit 15 the reactions of aluminium and transition metal ions in aqueous solution are studied. This includes an explanation of the acid reactions of some metal ions in solution and substitution reactions of complex ions in solution. Many of the reactions studied in this unit reflect the properties of the transition metals studied in Unit 14.

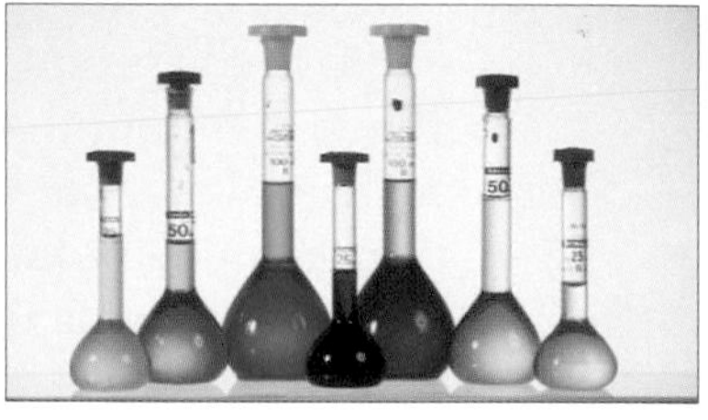

Figure 2 *Transition metal compounds show a variety of colours*

Figure 3 *Finding the % iron in iron tablets by titration*

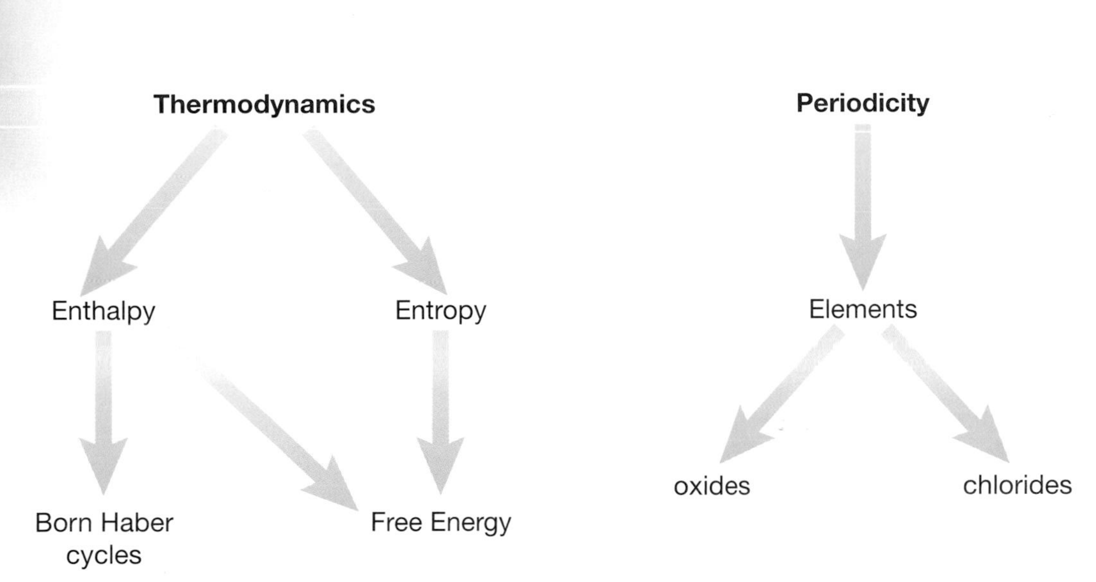

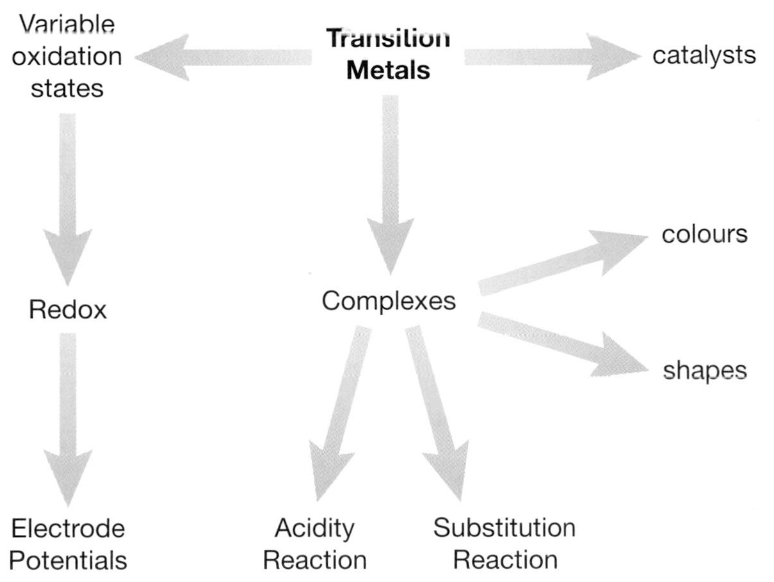

Figure 4 *Module 5 Concept map*

1 Thermodynamics

Thermodynamics is the study of the energy changes in chemical reactions. **Enthalpy changes** for reactions and **Hess's Law** were introduced in AS Chemistry. In A2 Chemistry the study of enthalpy changes is extended to include **Born–Haber cycles** for the formation of simple ionic compounds. This unit also includes a study of **entropy** changes and **Gibbs' free energy**.

The heat energy change in a reaction at constant pressure is known as an **enthalpy** change, ΔH. When the reaction is carried out under standard conditions of a temperature of 298 K and a pressure of 100 kPa (1 bar) it is called a **standard** enthalpy change, $\Delta H^{\ominus}$.

The **standard enthalpy of formation** of a compound is the heat energy change at constant pressure when one mole of a compound is formed from its **elements** in their standard states under standard conditions.

e.g. $C(s) + 2H_2(g) \rightarrow CH_4(g)$

The **standard enthalpy of combustion** of an element or compound is the heat energy released at constant pressure when one mole of the element or compound undergoes complete combustion under standard conditions:

e.g. $CH_4(g) + 2O_2(g) \rightarrow CO_2(g) + 2H_2O(g)$

Hess's Law states that the total energy change in a reaction is independent of the route.

Worked examples using Hess's Law

1 Calculate the standard enthalpy of formation of propan-1-ol using the following standard enthalpies of combustion ($\Delta H_c^{\ominus}$) values:

$CH_3CH_2CH_2OH(l)$ $\Delta H_c^{\ominus} = -2010\ \text{kJ mol}^{-1}$

$C(s)$ $\Delta H_c^{\ominus} = -393.5\ \text{kJ mol}^{-1}$

$H_2(g)$ $\Delta H_c^{\ominus} = -285.8\ \text{kJ mol}^{-1}$

Step 1: Write the equation for the formation of propan-1-ol:

$3C(s) + 4H_2(g) + \frac{1}{2}O_2(g) \rightarrow CH_3CH_2CH_2OH(l)$

Step 2: Construct an energy cycle using the enthalpies of combustion (Figure 1)

Step 3: Apply Hess's Law to the cycle: $\Delta H_f + \Delta H_3 = 3\Delta H_1 + 4\Delta H_2$

Hence:

$\Delta H_f + (-2010) = 3(-393.5) + 4(-285.8)$

$\Delta H_f = -1180.5 + (-1143.2) + 2010$

$\Delta H_f^\ominus = -313.7\,\text{kJ mol}^{-1}$

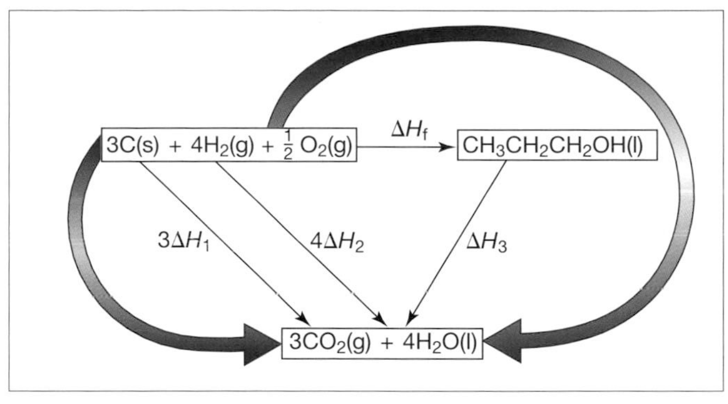

Figure 1 *Hess's cycle for formation of propan-1-ol*

2 Calculate the standard enthalpy change for the following reaction using the standard enthalpies of formation, $\Delta H_f^\ominus$, values given below:

	$2NaHCO_3(s)$	$\rightarrow$ $Na_2CO_3(s)$	+ $CO_2(g)$	+ $H_2O(l)$
$\Delta H_f^\ominus$/kJ mol^{-1}	− 948	−1131	−394	−286

Using: $\Delta H = \Sigma\Delta H_{f\,(products)} - \Sigma\Delta H_{f\,(reactants)}$

$\Delta H = [-1131 + (-394) + (-286)] - [2(-948)]$

$\Delta H = -1811 + 1896$

$\Delta H^\ominus = +85\,\text{kJ mol}^{-1}$

1 Calculate the standard enthalpy of formation of ethyne, C_2H_2, given the following standard enthalpies of combustion:

	C (graphite)	$H_2(g)$	$C_2H_2(g)$
$\Delta H_c^\ominus$ /kJ mol^{-1}	−394	−286	−1300

The energy needed to break a *particular* covalent bond is called the **bond dissociation energy,**

e.g. $H{-}Br(g) \rightarrow H(g) + Br(g) \qquad \Delta H = +366\,\text{kJ mol}^{-1}$

Some bonds, e.g. C—H and O—H, occur in a very large range of compounds, and the individual bond dissociation values will be slightly different in each case. In most calculations it is convenient to use the **mean bond enthalpy** – the average value for a particular type of bond in a range of different compounds.

For example, the value of the C—H bond in methane is 435 kJ mol^{-1} but the average bond enthalpy for the C—H bond across a range of compounds is 412 kJ mol^{-1}. Mean bond enthalpies can be used to calculate the enthalpy change in a reaction, as shown overleaf:

Worked example

3 Use the supplied mean bond enthalpy values in Table 1 to calculate the enthalpy of combustion of ethanol.

$$CH_3CH_2OH(g) + 3O_2(g) \rightarrow 2CO_2(g) + 3H_2O(g)$$

C–C	C–H	O–H	C–O	O=O	C=O	H–H	C=C
348	412	463	360	496	743	436	612

Table 1

Bonds broken	Bonds formed
5 × C–H = 2060	4 × C=O = 2972
1 × C–C = 348	6 × O–H = 2778
1 × C–O = 360	
1 × O–H = 463	
3 × O=O = 1488	
Total = 4719	Total = 5750

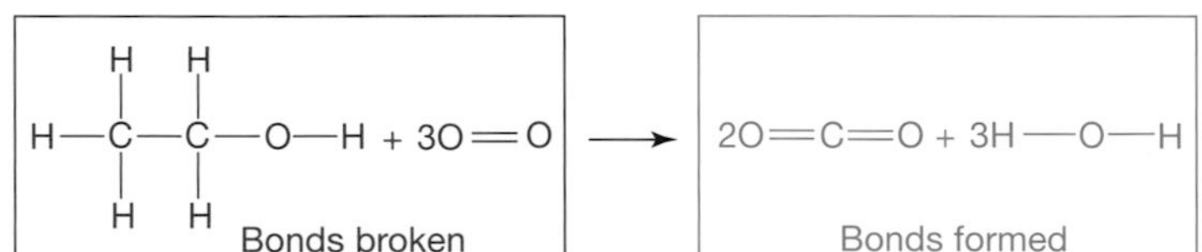

Figure 2 *Calculating the enthalpy of combustion of ethanol from mean bond enthalpies*

Enthalpy change = bonds broken – bonds formed

Hence ΔH = 4719 – 5750 = –1031 kJ mol^{-1}

2 a) Explain the term *mean bond enthalpy*.

b) Use the values in Table 1 to calculate the enthalpy of hydrogenation of ethene.

Note that when mean bond enthalpies are used to calculate the enthalpy change for a reaction then the calculated value will be different from an answer calculated using experimental values of enthalpies of formation and combustion. This difference occurs because the values used are mean values rather than specific bond dissociation energies.

Key Ideas 154 – 158

- **ΔH is the heat change at constant pressure.**
- **Standard enthalpies are measured at 298 K and 100 kPa pressure.**
- **Enthalpies of reaction can be calculated from enthalpies of formation, enthalpies of combustion or mean bond enthalpies.**
- **The mean bond enthalpy is the average value of the bond dissociation energy of a particular type of covalent bond in a range of different compounds.**
- **Enthalpy values calculated from mean bond enthalpies will vary from those calculated using energy cycles.**

2 Born–Haber cycles

Born–Haber cycles give an insight into the theoretical energy changes associated with the formation of ionic solids. They also provide a method of determining the value of the **lattice enthalpy** of an ionic compound since this cannot be determined directly by experiment.

Energy cycles

Born–Haber cycles are energy cycles based on Hess's Law. This type of cycle is best illustrated with a specific example. Note that state symbols are essential throughout this work.

Taking the formation of the ionic solid sodium chloride as the example

$Na(s) + \frac{1}{2}Cl_2(g) \rightarrow Na^+Cl^-(s)$ $\Delta H_f = -411\,kJ\,mol^{-1}$

There are a number of theoretical energy changes involved in the formation of the ions present in sodium chloride. These are:

1 $Na(s) \rightarrow Na(g)$ $\Delta H^\ominus = +109\,kJ\,mol^{-1}$

This equation represents the **enthalpy of atomisation** or the enthalpy of sublimation of sodium.

The enthalpy of atomisation of an element is the enthalpy change when one mole of gaseous atoms is formed from the element in its standard state

2 $Na(g) \rightarrow Na^+(g) + e^-$ $\Delta H^\ominus = +494\,kJ\,mol^{-1}$

This equation represents the **first ionisation enthalpy** of sodium. This process involves the formation of positive ions, usually associated with metal ions.

The first ionisation enthalpy of an element is the energy required to form one mole of gaseous unipositive ions from one mole of gaseous atoms.

3 $\frac{1}{2}Cl_2(g) \rightarrow Cl(g)$ $\Delta H^\ominus = +121\,kJ\,mol^{-1}$

This equation represents the enthalpy of atomisation of chlorine: it also represents *half* of the bond dissociation enthalpy of chlorine, Cl_2.

Bond dissociation enthalpy is the energy required when a particular covalent bond is broken to form gaseous atoms.

e.g. $Cl_2(g) \rightarrow 2Cl(g)$ $\Delta H^\ominus = +242\,kJ\,mol^{-1}$

4 $Cl(g) + e^- \rightarrow Cl^-(g)$ $\Delta H^\ominus = -364\,kJ\,mol^{-1}$

This equation represents the **first electron affinity** of chlorine. This process involves the formation of negatively charged ions, usually associated with non-metal ions.

The first electron affinity of an element is enthalpy change when one mole of gaseous atoms each gain an electron to form a mole of gaseous negative ions.

For the formation of ions of the type X^{2-} the *second* electron affinity values need to be considered. These values are *positive* since an electron is being gained by a species that is already negatively charged.

e.g. $O^-(g) + e^- \rightarrow O^{2-}(g)$ $\Delta H^\ominus = +798\,kJ\,mol^{-1}$

5 $Na^+(g) + Cl^-(g) \rightarrow Na^+Cl^-(s)$ $\Delta H^\ominus = -771\,kJ\,mol^{-1}$

This equation represents the **lattice enthalpy** (lattice formation enthalpy) of sodium chloride. This is an *exothermic* reaction since energy is released as ionic bonds form between the oppositely charged ions.

Lattice enthalpy is the enthalpy change when one mole of an ionic solid is formed from its gaseous ions.

Lattice enthalpy can also be defined as the enthalpy change when one mole of an ionic solid is separated into its gaseous ions (lattice dissociation enthalpy). This is an *endothermic* reaction since energy is required to overcome the attractive forces between the ions and to separate them.

$Na^+Cl^-(s) \rightarrow Na^+(g) + Cl^-(g)$ $\Delta H^\ominus = +771\,kJ\,mol^{-1}$

These energy changes associated with the formation of an ionic solid are usually shown in an *energy cycle* (see Figure 1).

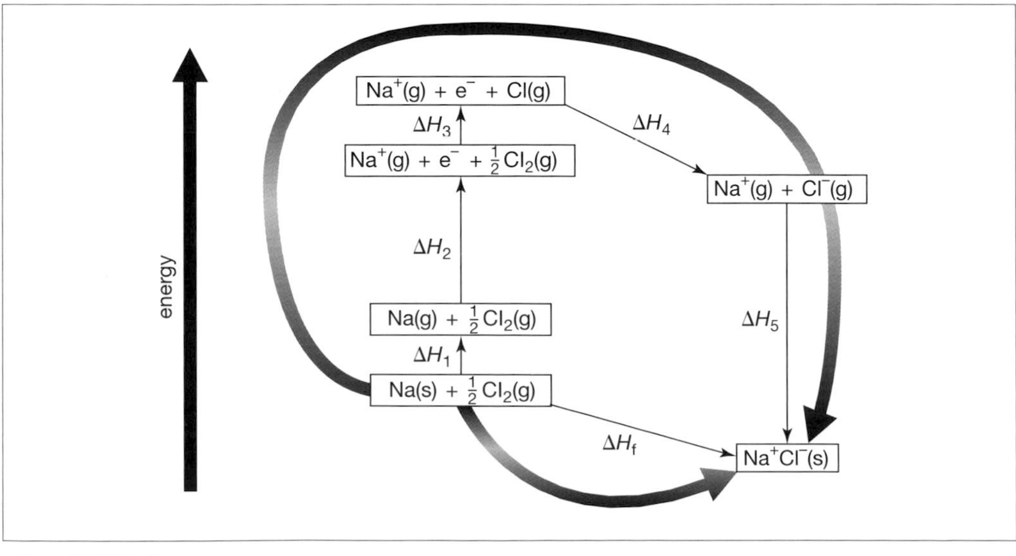

Figure 3 *The Born–Haber cycle for formation of NaCl(s)*

Notice that:

- the endothermic reactions absorb energy (arrows point upwards on the energy axis) and exothermic reactions release energy (arrows point downwards on the energy axis)
- absolute energies cannot be measured, only energy *changes*. As a reference, the enthalpy of any element in its standard state is zero.
- the sum of the enthalpy changes round the cycle must equal zero.

Applying Hess's law, from the cycle:

$\Delta H_f^\ominus = \Delta H_1 + \Delta H_2 + \Delta H_3 + \Delta H_4 + \Delta H_5$

$= +109 + 494 + 121 + (-364) + (-771)$

$= -411 \text{ kJ mol}^{-1}$

3 Use the following data to construct a Born–Haber cycle for the formation of KCl(s) and to calculate $\Delta H_f^\ominus$

Process	$\Delta H^\ominus$/kJ mol^{-1}
$K(s) \rightarrow K(g)$	+90
$K(g) \rightarrow K^+(g)$	+419
$Cl_2(g) \rightarrow 2Cl(g)$	+242
$Cl(g) + e^- \rightarrow Cl^-(g)$	-364
$Cl^-(g) + K^+(g) \rightarrow KCl(s)$	-711

4 Construct Born–Haber cycles for the formation of the following ionic compounds: a) Na_2O b) MgS. (Hint: you will need to know that the second electron affinity values are positive.)

Comparing lattice enthalpies

Theoretical values for lattice enthalpies can be derived by calculating the energy required to separate the charged ions in an ionic solid. In these calculations it is assumed that the solid is 100% ionic.

When lattice enthalpies are calculated from experimental evidence using Born–Haber cycles the values often differ from the theoretical values. The difference between the two values is caused by the bonding in the ionic solid being less than 100% ionic. Some examples are shown in Table 1.

Compound	Theoretical value/kJ mol^{-1}	Experimental value/kJ mol^{-1}
NaCl	765	771
NaBr	735	742
NaI	687	705
AgCl	768	890

Table 1

5 Study the data in Table 1.

a) Why is more energy required to separate sodium and chloride ions than to separate sodium ions and iodide ions?

b) Why are the values for sodium chloride fairly similar when those for silver chloride are significantly different?

The two largest enthalpy changes associated with the formation of an ionic solid are the *ionisation enthalpy* and the *lattice enthalpy*. It is the balance of these two enthalpy changes which effectively determines whether or not an ionic compound can be formed.

The following example will illustrate this principle.

Consider the formation of two different ionic chlorides of magnesium, MgCl and $MgCl_2$. The associated enthalpy changes are given in Table 2.

Process	$\Delta H^{\ominus}$/kJ mol^{-1}	
$Mg(s) \rightarrow Mg(g)$	+150	ΔH_1
$Mg(g) \rightarrow Mg^{+}(g)$	+736	ΔH_2
$Mg^{+}(g) \rightarrow Mg^{2+}(g)$	+1450	ΔH_3
$\frac{1}{2}Cl_2(g) \rightarrow Cl(g)$	+121	ΔH_4
$Cl(g) \rightarrow Cl^{-}(g)$	−364	ΔH_5
$Mg^{+}(g) + Cl^{-}(g) \rightarrow MgCl(s)$	−753	ΔH_6
$Mg^{2+}(g) + 2Cl^{-}(g) \rightarrow MgCl_2(s)$	−2493	ΔH_7

Table 2

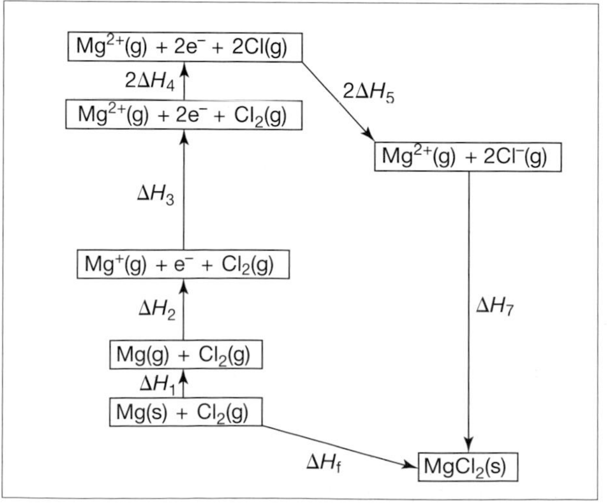

Figure 4 *The Born–Haber cycle for the formation of $MgCl_2(s)$*

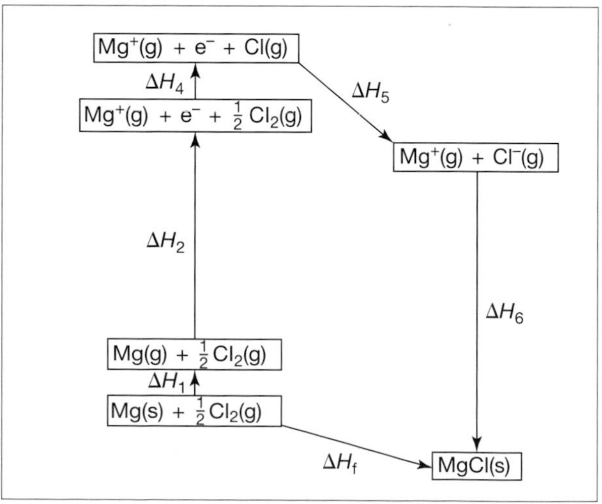

Figure 5 *The Born–Haber cycle for the formation of MgCl(s)*

The cycles are essentially the same except that in the case of $MgCl_2$ there are two ionisation energies involved and the lattice enthalpy for $MgCl_2(s)$ is more negative than the lattice enthalpy of MgCl(s), due to the greater effective nuclear charge of the dipositive ion.

$$\Delta H_f^\ominus \text{ for } MgCl_2(s) = \Delta H_1 + \Delta H_2 + \Delta H_3 + 2\Delta H_4 + 2\Delta H_5 + \Delta H_7$$

$$= 150 + 736 + 1450 + (2 \times 121) + (2 \times -364) + (-2493)$$

$$= -643\,\text{kJ mol}^{-1}$$

$$\Delta H_f^\ominus \text{ for } MgCl\ (s) = \Delta H_1 + \Delta H_2 + \Delta H_4 + \Delta H_5 + \Delta H_6$$

$$= 150 + 736 + 121 + (-364) + (-753)$$

$$= -110\,\text{kJ mol}^{-1}$$

From enthalpy values the formation of both chlorides is feasible but the formation of $MgCl_2$, with the more negative ΔH value, is more favourable. Any MgCl that did form would spontaneously undergo disproportionation to form $MgCl_2$

$$2MgCl(s) \rightarrow MgCl_2(s) + Mg(s)$$

Enthalpies of solution

When an ionic compound dissolves in water the process can either be exothermic or endothermic. Dissolving can be considered to occur in two stages and the resulting enthalpy change, **the enthalpy of solution**, depends upon the balance between the two.

The enthalpy of solution of a compound is the heat energy change at constant pressure when one mole of a compound dissolves completely in water.

For example, when sodium chloride dissolves in water the overall process can be represented as:

$$NaCl(s) + \text{water} \rightarrow Na^+(aq) + Cl^-(aq)$$

The first stage is to separate the ions in the crystal. This requires energy to overcome the attractive forces between oppositely charged ions. This energy is the *lattice energy*:

$$NaCl(s) \rightarrow Na^+(g) + Cl^-(g) \qquad \Delta H^\ominus = +771\,\text{kJ mol}^{-1}$$

The second stage involves the **hydration** of the ions:

$$Na^+(g) \rightarrow Na^+(aq) \qquad \Delta H^\ominus = -406\,\text{kJ mol}^{-1}$$

$$Cl^-(g) \rightarrow Cl^-(aq) \qquad \Delta H^\ominus = -364\,\text{kJ mol}^{-1}$$

Hydration is an exothermic process as the ions form bonds with the water molecules.

The enthalpy of hydration is the enthalpy change when one mole of isolated gaseous ions is dissolved in water forming one mole of aqueous ions under standard conditions.

When ions dissolve in water, **ion–dipole forces** are formed between the ions and the polar water molecules. The positive charges on the sodium ions are attracted to the δ^- charges on the water molecules; the negative charges on the chloride ions are attracted to the δ^+ charges on the water molecules. The formation of ion–dipole bonds results in the reaction being highly exothermic (the enthalpy of hydration is negative).

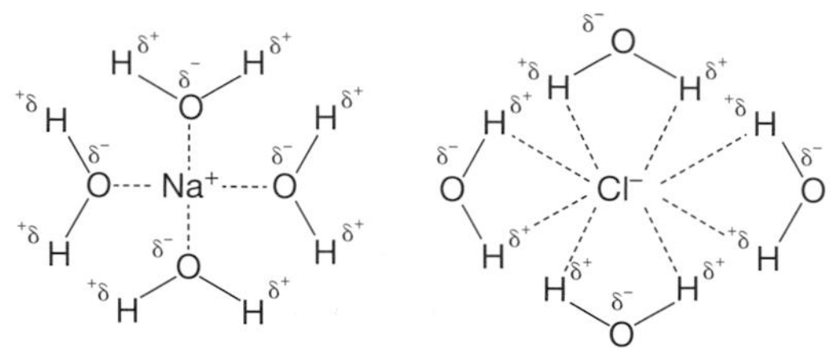

Figure 4 *The formation of ion–dipole bonds*

Calculating the enthalpy of solution

The enthalpy of solution of an ionic compound can be calculated from the lattice enthalpy and the enthalpies of hydration. The energy cycle can be drawn in one of two ways:

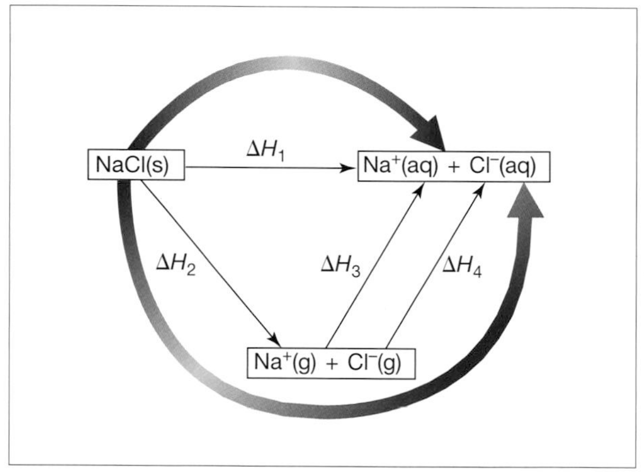

Figure 5 *Energy cycle for the dissolution of NaCl*

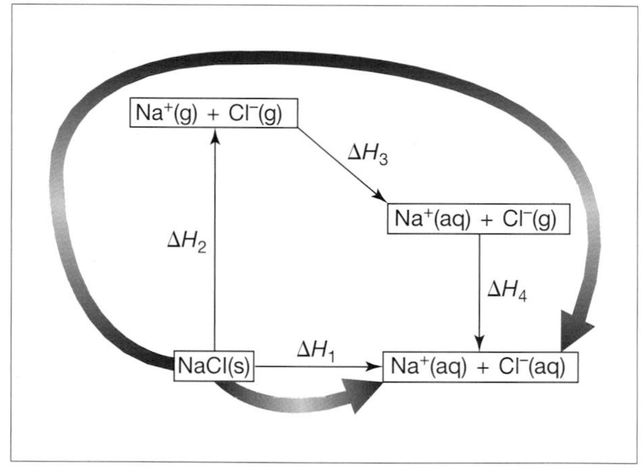

Figure 6 *Energy cycle for the dissolution of NaCl – a Born–Haber type cycle*

By Hess's Law: $\Delta H_1 = \Delta H_2 + \Delta H_3 + \Delta H_4$

Where ΔH_1 = enthalpy of solution

ΔH_2 = lattice enthalpy = +771 kJ mol^{-1}

ΔH_3 = hydration enthalpy for sodium ions = –406 kJ mol^{-1}

ΔH_4 = hydration enthalpy for chloride ions = –364 kJ mol^{-1}

Enthalpy of solution for sodium chloride = 771 – (406 + 364) = +1 kJ mol^{-1}

6 **The enthalpy of solution of $CaF_2(s)$ is +13.4 kJ mol^{-1}.**

a) Draw a cycle to show the enthalpy changes involved in dissolving CaF_2 in water.

b) Describe and explain the change in solubility of CaF_2 as the temperature increases.

7 **The standard enthalpies of hydration for three Group I metal ions are given in the table below. Explain the trend in these values.**

Ion	Li^+	Na^+	K^+
$\Delta H^\ominus$/kJ mol^{-1}	-520	-406	-320

The solubility of an ionic compound will depend upon the relative sizes of the lattice energy and the enthalpies of hydration. A solid with a large positive enthalpy of solution will probably be insoluble in water, e.g. AgCl.

8 **Calculate the enthalpy of solution for AgCl given that the lattice enthalpy is +905 kJ mol^{-1} and the enthalpies of hydration of $Ag^+(g)$ and $Cl^-(g)$ are −446 kJ mol^{-1} and −364 kJ mol^{-1} respectively.**

Key Ideas 159 – 165

- Born–Haber cycles show the theoretical energy changes associated with the formation of an ionic compound.
- Applying Hess's law, Born–Haber cycles can be used to calculate lattice energies.
- The two largest enthalpy changes associated with the formation of an ionic solid are the **ionisation enthalpy** and the **lattice enthalpy**. It is the balance of these two enthalpy changes which effectively determines whether or not an ionic compound can be formed.
- **Lattice enthalpy can be defined in one of two ways:**

  1 Lattice enthalpy is the enthalpy change when one mole of an ionic solid is formed from its gaseous ions. This is an exothermic process.

  e.g. $Na^+(g) + Cl^-(g) \rightarrow NaCl(s)$

  2 Lattice enthalpy is the enthalpy change when one mole of an ionic solid is separated into its gaseous ions. This is an endothermic process.

  e.g. $NaCl(s) \rightarrow Na^+(g) + Cl^-(g)$
- The enthalpy of solution of an ionic compound can be calculated from the lattice enthalpy and the enthalpies of hydration.

3 Entropy and free energy

Enthalpy changes, whilst important, are not sufficient to explain all **spontaneous reactions**. For a more accurate picture we need to study **entropy** changes, ΔS. The balance between ΔH and ΔS determines the feasibility of a reaction. This is given by the relationship $\Delta G = \Delta H - T\Delta S$ where ΔG is **Gibbs' free energy**.

What is a spontaneous reaction?

A football will roll down a hill and lose potential energy; it will only move up the hill if energy is supplied by kicking it.

A beaker of hot water will lose heat energy to the cooler surroundings; the beaker of water will only become hotter than the surroundings when energy is supplied by heating.

The rolling of the ball down the hill and the cooling of the hot water are **spontaneous** events. That is, they occur without having energy supplied to them from the surroundings.

Chemical reactions can be endothermic or exothermic. Most spontaneous reactions are exothermic. Reactions that are endothermic require heat from the surroundings for the reactions to occur; they should not occur spontaneously. However some reactions which are endothermic do occur spontaneously. For example when sodium hydrogen carbonate is added to hydrochloric acid the temperature of the acid drops, indicating an endothermic reaction.

$$NaHCO_3(s) + HCl(aq) \rightarrow NaCl(aq) + H_2O(l) + CO_2(g) \qquad \Delta H \text{ +ve}$$

When ammonium nitrate dissolves in water the reaction is highly endothermic.

$$NH_4^+NO_3^-(s) + \text{water} \rightarrow NH_4^+(aq) + NO_3^-(aq) \qquad \Delta H \text{ +ve}$$

How can endothermic reactions occur spontaneously?

There must be another factor besides the enthalpy change that determines whether or not a reaction can occur spontaneously.

We need to consider not only the energy changes occurring *between* systems and their surroundings but also energy changes *within* a system. This introduces the concept of entropy.

Entropy

The entropy, *S*, of a system is a measure of the **disorder** or randomness of a system. As the disorder *increases* then the entropy *increases*. Solids are usually highly ordered systems and have *low* entropy values.

When a solid melts then the particles are free to move around and therefore liquids are less ordered. Liquids have *higher* entropy values than the corresponding solids.

When a liquid evaporates the particles are in the gas phase and are moving with rapid, random motion. A gaseous substance is very disordered and has a much higher entropy value than the corresponding liquid.

The change in entropy values as ice becomes liquid water and then water vapour are shown in Table 1:

Substance	Entropy, $S^{\ominus}$/J K^{-1} mol^{-1}
$H_2O(s)$	62.1
$H_2O(l)$	70.0
$H_2O(g)$	188.7

Table 1

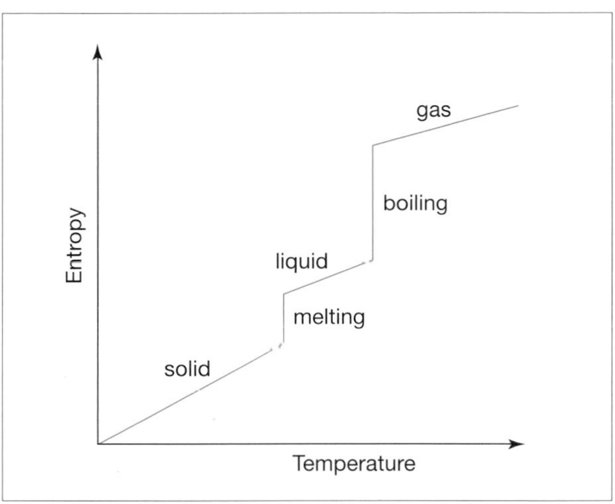

Figure 1 *Variation in entropy for the three states of water*

The entropy values of some simple elements and compounds in the solid state are shown in Table 2.

Substance	Entropy, $S^{\ominus}$/J K^{-1} mol^{-1}	Substance	Entropy, $S^{\ominus}$/J K^{-1} mol^{-1}
$Fe(s)$	27.2	$KNO_3(s)$	133
$Cu(s)$	33.3	$Na_2SO_4(s)$	146
C(graphite)	5.7	$CuSO_4.5H_2O(s)$	305
$NaCl(s)$	72.4	$Na_2SO_4.10H_2O(s)$	593

Table 2

Notice from the tables that:

- Simple substances have low entropy values, whereas larger and more complex substances have much higher entropy values.
- S is the symbol for entropy and the units of entropy are J K^{-1} mol^{-1}.
- The entropy values are in joules (J) and not kilojoules (kJ).
- $S^{\ominus}$ represents standard entropy at 298 K and 100 kPa pressure.

We can now explain why the reaction between sodium hydrogen carbonate and hydrochloric acid is spontaneous. Although the reaction is endothermic a gas is formed:

$$NaHCO_3(s) + HCl(aq) \rightarrow NaCl(aq) + H_2O(l) + CO_2(g)$$

Since the reaction involves the formation of a gas then the reaction results in an increase in entropy.

Any reaction that results in the formation of a gas, or an increase in the number of gaseous moles, will result in an increase in entropy.

When ammonium nitrate is added to water the process is endothermic but the highly ordered ionic crystal structure breaks down to form a solution of hydrated ions:

$NH_4^+NO_3^-(s)$ + water $\rightarrow$ $NH_4^+(aq)$ + $NO_3^-(aq)$

The dissolved ions are highly disordered so the dissolving of ammonium nitrate in water results in a large increase in entropy.

Ions and molecules in solution have higher entropies than the corresponding solids.

9 For each of the following reactions predict whether or not the entropy will increase as the reaction proceeds:

a) $CaCO_3(s) \rightarrow CaO(s) + CO_2(g)$

b) $NaCl(s)$ + water $\rightarrow Na^+(aq) + Cl^-(aq)$

c) $H^+(aq) + OH^-(aq) \rightarrow H_2O(l)$

d) $2Mg(s) + O_2(g) \rightarrow 2MgO(s)$

Calculating ΔS

The change in entropy, ΔS, can be calculated from the entropy values of the reactants and products.

$$\Delta S = \Sigma S_{(products)} - \Sigma S_{(reactants)}$$

Worked example

1 Calculate the standard entropy changes in the following reactions using the supplied entropy data.

	$Li_2CO_3(s)$	$Li_2O(s)$	$H_2S(g)$	$CO_2(g)$	$S(s)$	$SO_2(g)$	$H_2O(g)$
$S^\ominus$/J K^{-1} mol^{-1}	90	39	206	214	32	248	189

Table 3

a) $Li_2CO_3(s) \rightarrow Li_2O(s) + CO_2(g)$

$\Delta S = \Sigma S_{(products)} - \Sigma S_{(reactants)}$

$\Delta S^\ominus = (39 + 214) - (90) = +163$ J K^{-1} mol^{-1}

b) $SO_2(g) + 2H_2S(g) \rightarrow 3S(s) + 2H_2O(g)$

$\Delta S = \Sigma S_{(products)} - \Sigma S_{(reactants)}$

$\Delta S = [3(32) + 2(189)] - [248 + 2(206)] = 474 - 660$

$\Delta S^\ominus = -186$ J K^{-1} mol^{-1}

Note that since entropy values are quoted per mole then we must use the molar quantities given in the equation.

A closer look at entropy

At the start of this section entropy was defined as a measure of the disorder of a system. We need also to consider entropy in terms of heat energy.

When heat energy flows into a system the heat energy increases the entropy of the system by increasing the random motion of the particles in the system.

Entropy change is defined as: $\dfrac{\text{Heat energy transferred}}{\text{Temperature (K)}}$

At constant pressure the heat energy change is the enthalpy change, ΔH.

Therefore $\Delta S = \dfrac{\Delta H}{T}$

The Second Law of Thermodynamics states that all chemical and physical changes result in an increase in entropy. (The total entropy of the Universe can only increase: it cannot decrease). So all spontaneous reactions must result in an increase in entropy. This makes sense since systems will always tend to become more disordered rather than becoming more ordered.

From the Second Law of Thermodynamics we can say that all spontaneous reactions must result in an increase in entropy.

When a reaction is endothermic, the decrease in temperature results in a decrease in entropy *but* the reaction may be spontaneous if the products of the reaction have greater entropy than the reactants.

In the example used before:

$$NaHCO_3(s) + HCl(aq) \rightarrow NaCl(aq) + H_2O(l) + CO_2(g) \quad \Delta H \text{ +ve}$$

The increase in entropy caused by the formation of the products from the reactants is greater than the decrease in entropy caused by the cooling of the reactants in the endothermic reaction, hence there is a net increase in entropy.

Using $\Delta S = \dfrac{\Delta H}{T}$ Then $T\Delta S = \Delta H$

It is the relative magnitudes of $T\Delta S$ and ΔH that control the **feasibility** of a reaction.

Free energy

It is not just the enthalpy change in a reaction that determines whether the reaction can occur at a particular temperature, we have to take the entropy change into account as well. This produces a new quantity called free energy, ΔG.

The relationship between free energy, enthalpy and entropy is:

$$\boldsymbol{\Delta G^{\ominus} = \Delta H^{\ominus} - T\Delta S^{\ominus}}$$

A reaction will be feasible when ΔG is negative, i.e. $\Delta G < 0$

$\Delta G^{\ominus}$ represents the standard free energy change at 298 K and 100 kPa pressure.

We need to distinguish between the terms **spontaneous** and **feasible**. A *spontaneous reaction* is one that occurs without extra energy being supplied to the system at a particular temperature. For example ammonium nitrate dissolves in water at 298 K. A *feasible reaction* is one that is thermodynamically possible but it might not occur spontaneously because there is a very large activation energy to the reaction. For example the formation of magnesium oxide is highly exothermic and ΔG has a high negative value, but magnesium does not burn spontaneously at 298 K because the reaction has a high activation energy. The magnesium must be supplied with energy in the form of heat before it burns.

Calculating free energy

$$\Delta G = \Delta H - T\Delta S$$

The units of ΔG and ΔH are **kJ** mol^{-1} whereas the units for ΔS are **J** K^{-1} mol^{-1} so when using this expression the value of ΔS must be divided by 1000 to convert the joules into kilojoules. Temperature must be in kelvin.

Worked examples

1 Calculate the standard free energy change for the formation of carbon dioxide from graphite given that the standard enthalpy of formation of carbon dioxide is −393.5 kJ mol^{-1} and the standard entropy change for the reaction is +3.3 J K^{-1} mol^{-1}.

The equation for the reaction is: $C(graphite) + O_2(g) \rightarrow CO_2(g)$

The type of carbon must be specified since diamond and graphite have different entropy values. Standard temperature is 298 K.

$$\Delta G^{\ominus} = \Delta H^{\ominus} - T\Delta S^{\ominus}$$

$$= (-393.5) - (298 \times 3.3/1000) = -394.5 \text{ kJ mol}^{-1}$$

2 Is the decomposition of limestone spontaneous at standard temperature?

$CaCO_3(s) \rightarrow CaO(s) + CO_2(g)$ $\quad \Delta H^{\ominus} = +178 \text{ kJ mol}^{-1}$

$\Delta S^{\ominus} = +165 \text{ J K}^{-1} \text{mol}^{-1}$

The ΔH value would suggest that the answer is no but the ΔS value would suggest the answer is yes. To find the correct answer it is necessary to calculate ΔG:

$$\Delta G = \Delta H - T\Delta S$$

$$= +178 - (298 \times 165/1000) = +128.83 \text{ kJ mol}^{-1}$$

This reaction does not occur spontaneously at 298 K since $\Delta G^{\ominus}$ is positive.

10 Sodium hydrogen carbonate decomposes according to the equation:

$$NaHCO_3(s) \rightarrow \tfrac{1}{2}Na_2CO_3(s) + \tfrac{1}{2}H_2O(l) + \tfrac{1}{2}CO_2(g)$$

If $\Delta H = +65 \text{ kJ mol}^{-1}$ and $\Delta S = +167.5 \text{ J K}^{-1} \text{mol}^{-1}$ calculate ΔG at 400 K.

Enthalpy changes and entropy changes can be negative or positive. The controlling factor that decides whether or not a reaction is feasible may be the temperature. We need to consider the feasibility of reactions under the four possible combinations of enthalpy and entropy changes:

1 When ΔH is negative and ΔS is positive then ΔG must be negative at all temperatures and hence the reaction is always feasible.

$$\Delta G = \Delta H - T\Delta S$$

Suppose $\Delta H = -20\,\text{kJ mol}^{-1}$ and $\Delta S = +10\,\text{J K}^{-1}\,\text{mol}^{-1}$

then $\Delta G = -20 - \left[T \times \dfrac{(+10)}{1000}\right]$

At all values of T the term $T\Delta S$ is positive so ΔG must be negative.

2 When ΔH is positive and ΔS is negative then ΔG must be positive at all temperatures and the reaction is never feasible.

Suppose $\Delta H = +20\,\text{kJ mol}^{-1}$ and $\Delta S = -10\,\text{J K}^{-1}\,\text{mol}^{-1}$

then $\Delta G = +20 - \left[T \times \dfrac{(-10)}{1000}\right]$

At all values of T the term $T\Delta S$ is negative so ΔG must be positive.

3 When ΔH is negative and ΔS is negative then ΔG will only be negative when $\Delta H > T\Delta S$. This means that the reaction will be feasible at *lower* temperatures and will not be feasible at *higher* temperatures.

Suppose $\Delta H = -20\,\text{kJ mol}^{-1}$ and $\Delta S = -10\,\text{J K}^{-1}\,\text{mol}^{-1}$

then $\Delta G = 20 - \left[T \times \dfrac{(-10)}{1000}\right]$

In this example, when the temperature reaches 2000 K, then $\Delta G = 0$. At all temperatures *below* 2000 K the reaction is feasible.

The temperatures at which the reaction is feasible are when $T < \Delta H/\Delta S$.

4 When ΔH is positive and ΔS is positive then ΔG will only be negative when $T\Delta S > \Delta H$.

This means that the reaction will be feasible at *higher* temperatures but will not be feasible at *lower* temperatures.

Suppose $\Delta H = +20\,\text{kJ mol}^{-1}$ and $\Delta S = +10\,\text{J K}^{-1}\,\text{mol}^{-1}$

then $\Delta G = +20 - \left[T \times \dfrac{(+10)}{1000}\right]$

In this example, when the temperature reaches 2000 K, $\Delta G = 0$.

At all temperatures *above* 2000 K the reaction is feasible.

The temperatures at which the reaction is feasible are when $T > \Delta H/\Delta S$.

ΔH	ΔS	ΔG	Feasibility
−ve	+ve	always −ve	always feasible
+ve	−ve	always +ve	never feasible
−ve	−ve	-ve when $\Delta H > T\Delta S$	feasible when $\Delta H > T\Delta S$
+ve	+ve	−ve when $T\Delta S > \Delta H$	feasible when $T\Delta S > \Delta H$

Table 4 *Summary*

Most calculations involve calculating the value of ΔG at a particular temperature in order to find out whether the reaction is feasible or not. These calculations assume that ΔH and ΔS do not change with temperature.

Worked examples

3 a) Calculate the change in standard free energy at 298 K for the reaction:

$Fe_2O_3(s) + 3H_2(g) \rightarrow 2Fe(s) + 3H_2O(g)$ **from the data in the table below.**

b) Calculate the temperature at which the reaction becomes feasible.

	$Fe_2O_3(s)$	$H_2(g)$	$Fe(s)$	$H_2O(g)$
$\Delta H^{\ominus}$/kJ mol^{-1}	-822	0	0	-242
$S^{\ominus}$/J K^{-1} mol^{-1}	90	131	27	189

a) **Step 1**: Calculate ΔH for the reaction from the enthalpies of formation using the expression: $\Delta H = \Sigma\Delta H_{f\ (products)} - \Sigma\Delta H_{f\ (reactants)}$

$$\Delta H = [3(-242)] - [-822] = +96\,\text{kJ mol}^{-1}$$

Step 2: Calculate ΔS from the entropy values in the table using the expression:

$$\Delta S = \Sigma S_{(products)} - \Sigma S_{(reactants)}$$

$$\Delta S = [2(27) + 3(189)] - [90 + 3(131)] = 621 - 483 = +138\,\text{J K}^{-1}\,\text{mol}^{-1}$$

Step 3: Calculate ΔG using the expression: $\Delta G = \Delta H - T\Delta S$

$$\Delta G^{\ominus} = +96 - \frac{298(138)}{1000} = +54.88\,\text{kJ mol}^{-1}$$

Hence at 298 K the reaction is not feasible since ΔG is positive.

b) To find the temperature at which the reaction is feasible we need to calculate the temperature at which $\Delta G < 0$. This occurs when $T\Delta S > \Delta H$

$$T > \frac{\Delta H}{\Delta S} \qquad T > \frac{(96 \times 1000)}{138} \qquad T > 695.5\,\text{K}$$

Hence the reaction is feasible at all temperatures equal to or above 695.6 K

A change of state

A change of state at a fixed temperature is an *equilibrium* process and for a change of state the free energy, $\Delta G = 0$. The fixed temperatures at which this is true is the melting point of a solid and the boiling point of a liquid.

Since $\Delta G = \Delta H - T\Delta S$ then for a change of state: $\boldsymbol{\Delta H - T\Delta S = 0}$

Worked example

4 a) Calculate the entropy change when ice melts at 273 K given that the enthalpy of fusion (melting) of ice is + 6.0 kJ mol^{-1}

b) Show that ice does not melt spontaneously at –5 °C

a) At the melting point of ice: $\Delta H - T\Delta S = 0$

Hence $\Delta S = \frac{\Delta H}{T} = \frac{6.0 \times 1000}{273} = +21.9\ J\ K^{-1}\ mol^{-1}$

b) Using: $\Delta G = \Delta H - T\Delta S$

convert T into kelvin: $-5\,^{\circ}C = 268\,K$

$\Delta G = +6.0 - (268 \times 21.9/1000) = +0.13\ kJ\ mol^{-1}$

Since the value of ΔG is positive the reaction is not spontaneous at this temperature (assuming standard pressure is maintained).

11 Calculate the temperature at which the following reaction becomes feasible:

$$2Fe_2O_3(s) \rightarrow 2Fe(s) + 3O_2(g)$$

where $\Delta H = +825\ kJ\ mol^{-1}$ and $\Delta S = +275\ J\ K^{-1}\ mol^{-1}$

Key Ideas 166 – 173

- **Entropy is a measure of the disorder in a system.**
- **A spontaneous reaction occurs without the help of an outside agency (e.g. heat).**
- **The relationship between enthalpy and entropy is given by the expression: $\Delta G = \Delta H - T\Delta S$ where ΔG is the free energy change.**
- **A reaction is feasible when the free energy of the reaction is equal to or less than zero.**
- **Although a reaction may be feasible it may not occur if the reaction has a high activation energy.**

Unit 11 Questions

4

1 a) Give the equation relating entropy change, ΔS, enthalpy change, ΔH, free energy change, ΔG and temperature, T. (1)

b) State the meanings of the following terms:
   (i) entropy
   (ii) a spontaneous reaction
   (iii) a positive enthalpy change. (3)

c) When sodium hydrogen carbonate is added to dilute hydrochloric acid the reaction is endothermic and spontaneous.
   (i) Write an equation for the reaction
   (ii) State the signs on ΔH and ΔS
   (iii) Explain why the reaction is spontaneous. (5)

2 The equation for the combustion of pentane is

$$C_5H_{12}(l) + 8O_2(g) \rightarrow 5CO_2(g) + 6H_2O(g)$$

a) Use the mean bond enthalpy values given below to calculate the ΔH value for the combustion reaction. (4)

$\Delta H^\ominus$/kJ mol^{-1}
C—C: 348; C—H: 412; O—H: 463; O═O: 496; C═O: 743.

b) Use the following enthalpy of formation data to calculate the ΔH value for the combustion reaction. (3)

ΔH_f / kJ mol^{-1}: $C_5H_{12}(l)$: –146; $CO_2(g)$: –394; $H_2O(g)$: –242.

c) Explain why the answers in **a)** and **b)** have different values. (2)

d) Calculate ΔS for the combustion reaction using the entropy values below. (3)

$\Delta S^\ominus$/J K^{-1} mol^{-1}
$C_5H_{12}(l)$: 348; $CO_2(g)$: 214; $H_2O(g)$: 189; $O_2(g)$: 205.

e) Use your answers from parts **b)** and **d)** to calculate the free energy change, ΔG, for the reaction at 310K. (3)

3 **a)** Which of the following reactions will have a positive entropy change? (1)

(i) $CH_4(g) + 2O_2(g) \rightarrow CO_2(g) + 2H_2O(l)$

(ii) $2SO_2(g) + O_2(g) \rightarrow 2SO_3(g)$

(iii) $C(s) + CO_2(g) \rightarrow 2CO(g)$

b) $CH_3OH(l) \rightarrow CH_3OH(g)$ $\Delta S = +113\,J\,K^{-1}\,mol^{-1}$

Explain why this process is accompanied by a positive entropy change. (2)

4 **a)** Construct an energy cycle to show the enthalpy changes involved when the ionic compound CsCl(s) dissolves in water. (2)

b) Explain why the hydration enthalpies involved are highly exothermic. (2)

c) Calculate the enthalpy change for the formation of $Cs^+(aq)$ from Cs(s) using the following data. (2)

Process	ΔH/kJ mol^{-1}
$Cs(s) \rightarrow Cs(g)$	+70
$Cs(g) \rightarrow Cs^+(g)$	+380
$Cs^+(g) \rightarrow Cs^+(aq)$	-270

5 **a)** Write an equation for the standard enthalpy of formation of $Al_2O_3(s)$. (1)

b) Construct a Born–Haber cycle for the formation of this ionic solid showing clearly the enthalpy changes involved. (5)

c) Explain how you would use this cycle to calculate the lattice enthalpy of $Al_2O_3(s)$. (2)

6 Sodium hydrogen carbonate decomposes according to the equation:

$$2NaHCO_3(s) \rightarrow Na_2CO_3(s) + H_2O(g) + CO_2(g)$$

ΔH for this reaction is +130 kJ mol^{-1} and ΔS is +335 J K^{-1} mol^{-1}.

a) Calculate the free energy change for the formation of one mole of carbon dioxide from sodium hydrogen carbonate at 298 K. (3)

b) Why is sodium hydrogen carbonate used in baking? At what temperature does it become effective? (5)

7 **a)** Calculate the entropy change for the melting of ethanol given that its melting point is 156 K and the enthalpy of fusion is 4.6 kJ mol^{-1}. (4)

b) The boiling point of ethanol is 352 K and the enthalpy of vaporisation is 43.5 kJ mol^{-1}. Calculate the change in entropy for the vaporisation of ethanol. (1)

c) Comment on the difference in your answers to **a)** and **b)**. (2)

1 Periodicity

At AS level chemistry the **physical properties** including melting points, boiling points and electrical conductivity of the elements in Period 3 of the Periodic Table were studied. At A2 this study is extended to **chemical properties** including reactions of the elements, their oxides and their chlorides.

The elements of Period 3

Element	Atomic Number	Electronic configuration	Type of element	Bonding in the oxides	Bonding in the chlorides
Na	11	$1s^2 2s^2 2p^6 3s^1$	metal	ionic	ionic
Mg	12	$1s^2 2s^2 2p^6 3s^2$	metal	ionic	ionic
Al	13	$1s^2 2s^2 2p^6 3s^2 3p^1$	metal	ionic	covalent
Si	14	$1s^2 2s^2 2p^6 3s^2 3p^2$	non-metal	covalent	covalent
P	15	$1s^2 2s^2 2p^6 3s^2 3p^3$	non-metal	covalent	covalent
S	16	$1s^2 2s^2 2p^6 3s^2 3p^4$	non-metal	covalent	covalent
Cl	17	$1s^2 2s^2 2p^6 3s^2 3p^5$	non-metal	covalent	covalent
Ar	18	$1s^2 2s^2 2p^6 3s^2 3p^6$	non-metal	–	–

Table 1

Sodium, magnesium and aluminium are all *metals*; they lose the electrons in the third principal energy level when they react to form positively charged ions. Their compounds are therefore predominantly *ionic*. Silicon, phosphorus, sulphur and chlorine are *non-metals*. They form *covalent* compounds with other non-metals. Notice that aluminium, although a metal, does form some covalent compounds, e.g. aluminium chloride. This is because the Al^{3+} ion has a very high charge density. The chloride ion is *polarised* by the Al^{3+} ion resulting in some sharing of the electrons; thus aluminium chloride is predominantly covalent.

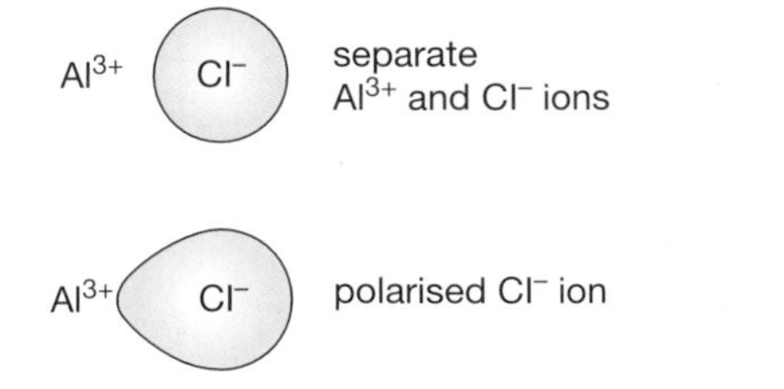

Figure 1 *Polarisation in $AlCl_3$*

1 Give the electronic configuration of the aluminium ion.

The type of bonding in the oxides and chlorides has a great influence on their physical and chemical properties.

Reactions of the elements with water

Sodium and magnesium react with water under different conditions. When these metals react with water they form ions by losing their 3s electrons:

$$\text{Na} - e^- \rightarrow \text{Na}^+$$
$$1s^2 2s^2 2p^6 3s^1 \qquad 1s^2 2s^2 2p^6$$

$$\text{Mg} - 2e^- \rightarrow \text{Mg}^{2+}$$
$$1s^2 2s^2 2p^2 3s^2 \qquad 1s^2 2s^2 2p^2$$

Sodium reacts exothermically with cold water forming sodium hydroxide solution and hydrogen gas:

$$2Na(s) + 2H_2O(l) \rightarrow 2NaOH(aq) + H_2(g)$$

When a freshly cut, small piece of sodium is added to a trough of water, the sodium melts into a sphere and darts about on the surface of the water. The sodium burns with a yellow flame and rapidly dissolves in the water, forming a colourless solution of sodium hydroxide. This solution is strongly alkaline with a pH value of about 13.

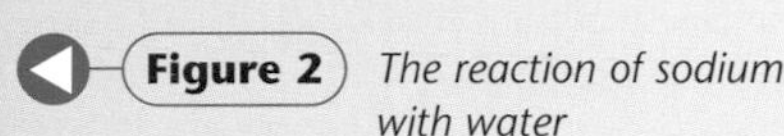

Figure 2 *The reaction of sodium with water*

Sodium metal is dull in appearance because it rapidly tarnishes in air – it reacts with the oxygen present to form a coating of sodium oxide, Na_2O. For this reason sodium is stored under oil, which forms a barrier between the metal and the oxygen and water in air to prevent it from tarnishing. Freshly cut sodium is shiny.

Figure 3 *Sodium is stored under oil*

Figure 4 *Freshly cut sodium*

Magnesium reacts with cold water very slowly, but it does react readily with steam, forming magnesium oxide and hydrogen gas (see Module 1):

$$Mg(s) + H_2O(l) \rightarrow MgO(s) + H_2(g)$$

The other elements of Period 3 do not react with water, although chlorine dissolves to form a solution commonly called chlorine water (see Module 2).

2 **Write an equation to show how lithium, from Period 2, will react with water.**

Reactions of the elements with oxygen

The elements of Period 3 react with oxygen to form oxides. Across the Period the reactivity between the element and oxygen generally *decreases*. Argon does not react with oxygen and chlorine does not combine with oxygen directly.

The metals of Period 3 often appear dull because they react with the oxygen in the air and become coated in a layer of oxide. This oxide layer is generally unreactive and protects the metal from corrosion. This is particularly important for aluminium; its uses depend on this protective oxide layer.

Phosphorus is an unusual element; it is stored under water. When dry it burns spontaneously in oxygen forming the oxide.

Na	Mg	Al	Si	P	S
Very vigorous reaction. Sodium burns with a yellow flame forming sodium oxide	Very vigorous reaction. Magnesium burns with a brilliant white flame forming a white ash of magnesium oxide	Initially a vigorous reaction forming aluminium oxide	Slow reaction forming silicon(IV) oxide (silicon dioxide)	Vigorous reaction forming masses of white fumes of phosphorus(V) oxide	Sulphur melts easily and burns with a blue flame forming sulphur(IV) oxide (sulphur dioxide), a colourless gas with a choking odour
$4Na + O_2 \rightarrow 2Na_2O$	$2Mg + O_2 \rightarrow 2MgO$	$4Al + 3O_2 \rightarrow 2Al_2O_3$	$Si + O_2 \rightarrow SiO_2$	$P_4 + 5O_2 \rightarrow P_4O_{10}$	$S + O_2 \rightarrow SO_2$

Table 2 *Burning the elements in oxygen*

Except for sulphur, the elements burn in oxygen to form the oxide containing the element in its highest oxidation state (see Table 2).

3 **Name the highest oxide of sulphur. How is it made?**

4 **A white solid, X, is formed when element Y burns in oxygen. Identify X and Y and write an equation for the reaction.**

5 **A yellow solid, Z, burns in oxygen to form a colourless gas. Identify solid Z.**

Figure 5 *Sodium burning in pure oxygen*

Figure 6 *Magnesium burning in oxygen*

Reactions of the elements with chlorine

The elements of Period 3 (Na to P) react with chlorine to form *chlorides*. Across the Period the reactivity between the element and chlorine generally *decreases*. All the chlorides formed are solids apart from silicon(IV) chloride.

Na	Mg	Al	Si	P
Very vigorous reaction forming sodium chloride	Vigorous reaction when the elements are heated forming magnesium chloride	Vigorous reaction when the elements are heated under anhydrous conditions forming aluminium chloride	Slow reaction forming silicon(IV) chloride	Slow reaction forming phosphorus(V) chloride
$2Na + Cl_2 \rightarrow 2NaCl(s)$	$Mg + Cl_2 \rightarrow MgCl_2(s)$	$2Al + 3Cl_2 \rightarrow 2AlCl_3(s)$	$Si + 2Cl_2 \rightarrow SiCl_4(l)$	$P_4 + 10Cl_2 \rightarrow 4PCl_5(s)$

Table 3 *Reactions of the elements with chlorine*

Ⓢ **6 Name the shapes of the molecules: a) $AlCl_3$ b) $SiCl_4$ c) PCl_5**

Key Ideas 176 – 179

- **The elements of Period 3 react with oxygen to form oxides.**
- **Sodium, magnesium and aluminium oxides are ionic: the other elements in the Period are covalently bonded to oxygen.**
- **The elements of Period 3 react with chlorine to form chlorides.**
- **Sodium and magnesium chlorides are ionic: the other elements in the Period form covalent chlorides.**
- **Aluminium chloride is predominantly covalent because the aluminium ion is highly polarising.**

179

2 Period 3 oxides and chlorides

In this unit we consider the properties of the oxides and chlorides of the Period 3 elements. Their physical properties are determined by their structure and bonding. We also survey the chemical properties of the compounds by considering their reactions with water.

The properties of the oxides of Period 3 elements

The physical properties of the oxides are determined by their structure and bonding:

Oxide	Na_2O	MgO	Al_2O_3	SiO_2	P_4O_{10}	SO_3
Structure and bonding	giant ionic	giant ionic	giant ionic	giant covalent	simple covalent molecules	simple covalent molecules
m.p./°C	1275	2852	2072	1610	580	17

Table 1

The metal oxides

The three metal oxides exist as *giant ionic lattices*. They have high melting points since a very large number of ionic bonds need to be overcome to break down the ionic lattice. The size and the charge on the ions influence the actual value of the melting points.

The size of the metal ion *decreases* across the Period and the charge on the metal ion *increases* across the Period. This causes stronger electrostatic forces of attraction between the oppositely charged ions and this results in an increase in the melting point of the oxides from sodium to magnesium.

Aluminium oxide does not exactly match the trend because the lattice structure is different from those of sodium and magnesium oxides.

When the metal oxides are melted (fused) the ions are free to move and the compounds will conduct electricity. At AS level you studied the extraction of aluminium by the electrolysis of fused aluminium oxide.

7 Name an ore from which aluminium oxide is obtained.

8 Explain why a magnesium ion is smaller than a sodium ion.

The non-metal oxides

The non-metal oxides are covalent but while the melting point of silicon(IV) oxide is high due to its giant covalent structure, phosphorus(V) oxide and sulphur(VI) oxide have low melting points. This is because they consist of simple molecules with weak *intermolecular forces* which are easily broken.

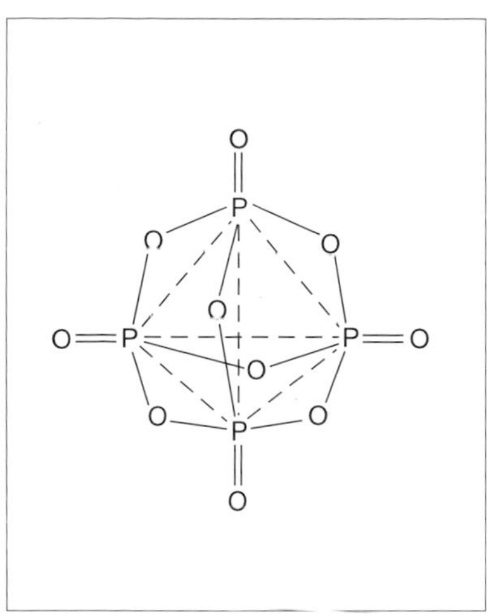

Figure 1 *The structure of phosphorus(V) oxide*

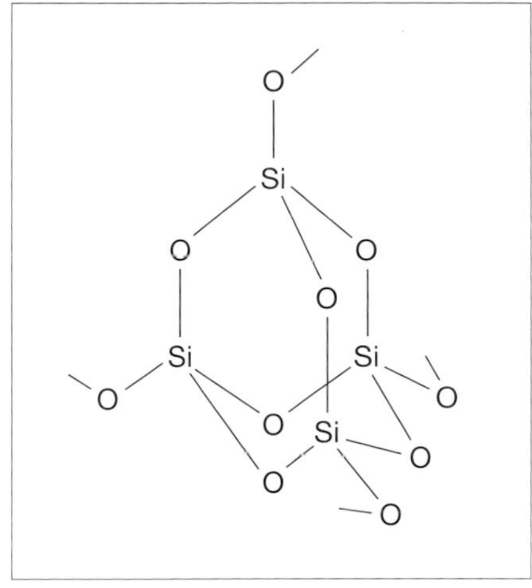

Figure 2 *The structure of silica*

Silicon(IV) oxide (silica) has a giant covalent structure similar to that of diamond (see Figure 2). It is **macromolecular** (a large molecule) and contains a large number of covalent bonds which have to be broken to destroy the giant lattice. This is why it has a high melting point. Silicon(IV) oxide occurs naturally as sand.

9 What types of intermolecular forces will be present between SO_3 molecules?

The acid/base properties of the oxides

The reactions of the oxides depend upon the structure and bonding of these compounds.

The metal oxides

The oxides of sodium, magnesium and aluminium are all ionic. Ionic metal oxides act as *bases*. They will react with acids to form a salt and water. Three examples are shown below:

$$Na_2O + H_2SO_4 \rightarrow Na_2SO_4 + H_2O$$

$$MgO + 2HCl \rightarrow MgCl_2 + H_2O$$

$$Al_2O_3 + 6HNO_3 \rightarrow 2Al(NO_3)_3 + 3H_2O$$

Aluminium oxide is *amphoteric* and can react as an acid and as a base.

As an acid: $Al_2O_3 + 3H_2O + 2OH^- \rightarrow 2[Al(OH)_4]^-$

As a base: $Al_2O_3 + 6HNO_3 \rightarrow 2Al(NO_3)_3 + 3H_2O$

10 Write an equation to show the formation of magnesium nitrate from magnesium oxide.

The oxides show a trend in their reaction with water.

Sodium oxide dissolves exothermically in water. The oxide ion is **hydrolysed** by water:

$$Na_2O + H_2O \rightarrow 2NaOH$$

Ionically: $O^{2-} + H_2O \rightarrow 2OH^-$

The resulting solution will have a high pH. The pH of 0.1 M NaOH is 13.

Magnesium oxide is only sparingly soluble in water:

$$MgO + H_2O \rightarrow Mg(OH)_2$$

The low solubility of MgO results in only a limited amount of *hydrolysis* of the oxide occurring and hence the pH is much lower than when sodium oxide dissolves in water.

11 Explain why sodium hydroxide is a stronger alkali than magnesium hydroxide.

Aluminium oxide is insoluble in water.

The non-metal oxides

The oxides of silicon, phosphorus and sulphur are covalent. Covalent non-metal oxides are **acidic oxides**. These will all react with aqueous alkalis as shown in the examples below:

$$SiO_2 + 2OH^- \rightarrow SiO_3^{2-} + H_2O$$

silicate ion

$$P_4O_{10} + 12OH^- \rightarrow 4PO_4^{3-} + 6H_2O$$

phosphate(V) ion

$$SO_2 + 2OH^- \rightarrow SO_3^{2-} + H_2O$$

sulphite ion

$$SO_3 + 2OH^- \rightarrow SO_4^{2-} + H_2O$$

sulphate ion

The non-metal oxides also show a trend in their reaction with water.

Silicon(IV) oxide (sand) is insoluble in water but the oxides of phosphorus and sulphur dissolve in water forming acidic solutions:

$$P_4O_{10} + 6H_2O \rightarrow 4H_3PO_4$$

phosphoric(V) acid (pH ≈ 0)

$$SO_2 + H_2O \rightarrow H_2SO_3$$

sulphuric(IV) acid (pH ≈ 3)

$$SO_3 + H_2O \rightarrow H_2SO_4$$

sulphuric(VI) acid (pH ≈ 0)

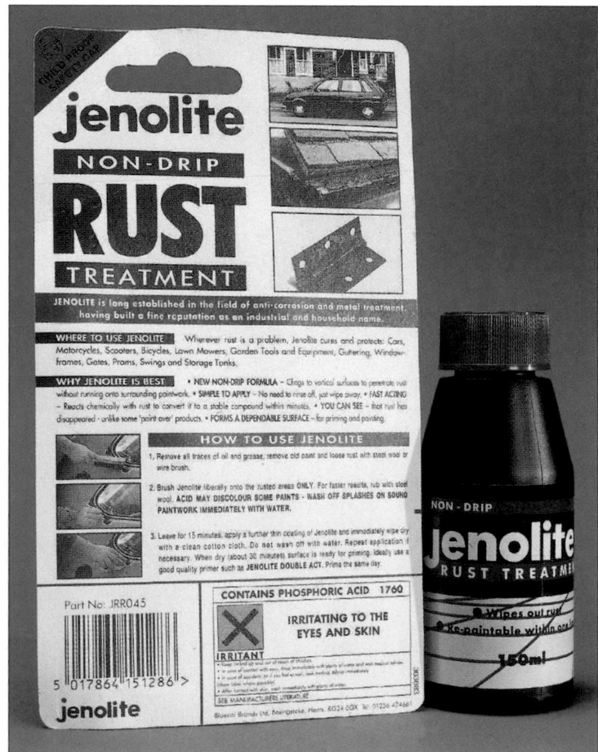

Figure 3 *Phosphoric(V) acid is used in rust removers*

Sulphuric(IV) acid (sulphurous acid) is produced when rainwater reacts with sulphur dioxide in polluted atmospheres (see Module 3). It is easily oxidised in air to sulphuric(VI) acid. Both sulphuric(VI) acid and phosphoric(V) acid are used to make fertilisers. Phosphoric(V) acid is also an excellent rust remover.

12 What is the relationship between the bonding in the oxides and the type of oxide formed?

Oxide	Na_2O	MgO	Al_2O_3	SiO_2	P_4O_{10}	SO_3
Structure and bonding	giant ionic	giant ionic	giant ionic	giant covalent	simple covalent molecules	simple covalent molecules
m.p./°C	1275	2852	2072	1610	580	17
Type of oxide	basic	basic	amphoteric	acidic	acidic	acidic
Approx. pH in water	14	9	insoluble	insoluble	0	0

Table 2 *Summary of the properties of the oxides*

The properties of the chlorides of Period 3 elements

As in the case of the oxides, the physical properties of the chlorides depend upon their structure and bonding.

Chloride	NaCl	$MgCl_2$	$AlCl_3$	$SiCl_4$	PCl_5
Structure and bonding	giant ionic	giant ionic	simple covalent molecules	simple covalent molecules	simple covalent molecules
m.p./°C	801	714	177	−70	162

Table 3

Sodium and magnesium chlorides both have giant ionic structures. These result in high melting points since many strong ionic bonds need to be broken before the chlorides melt.

Aluminium chloride is covalent. It exists as a **dimer**, Al_2Cl_6, in which two aluminium chlorides molecules are joined together by **co-ordinate bonding**.

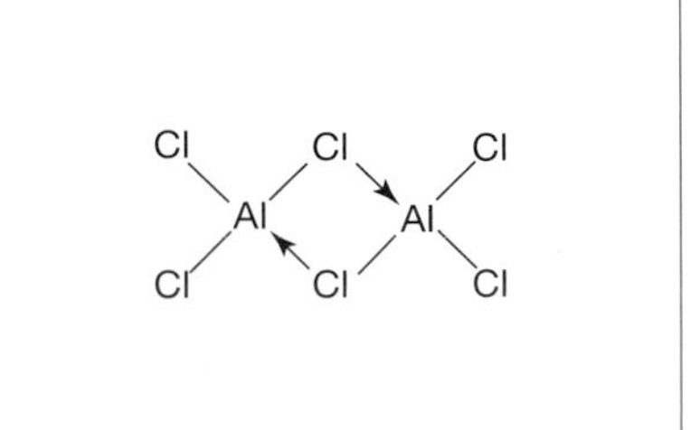

The structure of Al_2Cl_6 **Figure 4**

Reactions of the chlorides of Period 3 elements in water

The **ionic chlorides** dissolve in water forming aqueous ions:

$$NaCl(s) + water \rightarrow Na^+(aq) + Cl^-(aq)$$

$$MgCl_2(s) + water \rightarrow Mg^{2+}(aq) + 2Cl^-(aq)$$

No hydrolysis occurs with sodium chloride and the solution is neutral with a pH of 7. The ions become **hydrated** as polar water molecules surround them.

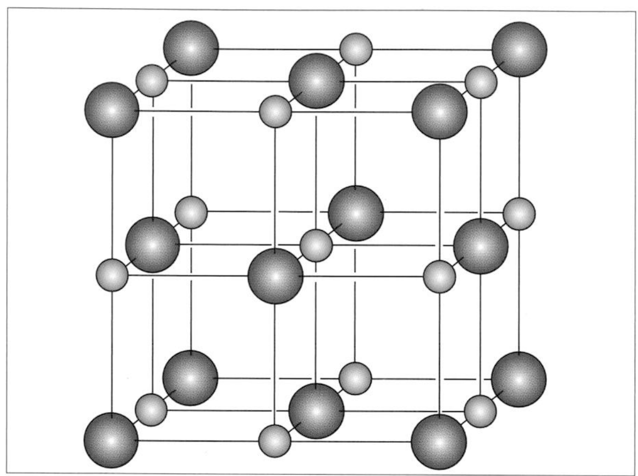

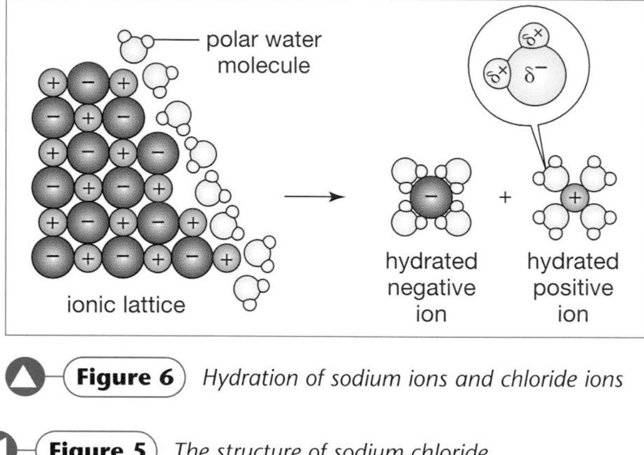

Figure 6 *Hydration of sodium ions and chloride ions*

Figure 5 *The structure of sodium chloride*

Slight hydrolysis occurs with the aqueous magnesium ion, giving a weakly acidic solution with a pH of about 6.

The **covalent chlorides** react exothermically with water. Hydrolysis occurs, producing acidic solutions.

Aluminium chloride reacts violently with water producing steamy fumes:

$$AlCl_3(s) + 6H_2O(l) \rightarrow [Al(H_2O)_6]^{3+}(aq) + 3Cl^-(aq)$$

or

$$Al_2Cl_6(s) + 12H_2O(l) \rightarrow 2[Al(H_2O)_6]^{3+}(aq) + 6Cl^-(aq)$$

Figure 7 *The reaction of $AlCl_3$ with water*

The aluminium ion is highly polarising and a hydrolysis reaction occurs releasing hydrated protons, H_3O^+, which are responsible for the acidity of the resulting solution:

$$[Al(H_2O)_6]^{3+}(aq) + H_2O(l) \rightleftharpoons [Al(H_2O)_5(OH)]^{2+}(aq) + H_3O^+(aq)$$

Silicon tetrachloride is a liquid and reacts very exothermically with water, giving off fumes of HCl and forming a white precipitate of silicon(IV) hydroxide:

$$SiCl_4(l) + 4H_2O(l) \rightarrow Si(OH)_4(s) + 4HCl(aq)$$

The formation of hydrochloric acid makes the resulting solution strongly acidic.

Phosphorus pentachloride reacts with water to form a mixture of phosphoric(V) and hydrochloric acids:

$$PCl_5(s) + 4H_2O(l) \rightarrow H_3PO_4(aq) + 5HCl(aq)$$

13 Distinguish between the terms hydration and hydrolysis.

14 Explain why the metal chloride $AlCl_3$ is covalent.

	Addition to water	Observations	Species present	pH of solution formed
NaCl	dissolves	colourless solution	$Na^+(aq)$	7
$MgCl_2$	dissolves with slight hydrolysis	colourless solution	$Mg^{2+}(aq)$	6
$AlCl_3$	hydrolysed	dissolves exothermically giving off fumes	$[Al(H_2O)_6]^{3+}(aq)$	3
$SiCl_4$	hydrolysed	dissolves very exothermically with fumes of HCl and a white precipitate	$Si(OH)_4(s)$	1 (due to HCl)
PCl_5	hydrolysed	dissolves exothermically with fumes of HCl	$H_3PO_4(aq)$	0

Table 4 *Summary of the chlorides reacting with water*

The reactions of the chlorides with water show a trend across the Period.

The ionic chlorides dissolve in water forming aqueous ions that undergo little or no hydrolysis, forming neutral solutions.

The covalent chlorides undergo hydrolysis reactions with water, forming acidic solutions.

Key Ideas 180 – 185

- **The physical and chemical properties of the oxides and chlorides depend upon the structure and bonding in the compounds.**
- **Sodium, magnesium and aluminium oxides are ionic. The ionic oxides are basic oxides and react with acids to form salts. If they dissolve in water then they form alkaline solutions.**
- **The covalent oxides are acidic and react with bases to form salts. If they dissolve in water they form acidic solutions.**
- **Sodium and magnesium chlorides are ionic. They dissolve in water with no or only slight hydrolysis.**
- **Covalent chlorides are hydrolysed in water forming acidic solutions.**

Unit 12 Questions

3

1. **a)** How could a solid sample of aluminium chloride be prepared in the laboratory? Give the equation and essential conditions for the preparation. (3)
   b) Explain how and why the pH of a 0.5 M solution of aluminium chloride is different from that of a 0.5 M solution of sodium chloride. (5)
   c) Aluminium chloride forms a dimer, Al_2Cl_6. Draw the structure of Al_2Cl_6 and explain how aluminium chloride dimerises. (5)

2. **a)** Write an equation to show the reaction of
   (i) sodium with water
   (ii) sodium oxide with water.
   Why is the resulting solution in both cases strongly alkaline? (4)
   b) How, and under what conditions, does magnesium react with water? Write an equation for the reaction. (2)
   c) Aluminium oxide is amphoteric.
   (i) Explain what is meant by the term *amphoteric*.
   (ii) What would you observe if aqueous sodium hydroxide was added to aluminium oxide until present in excess? Write an equation for the reaction. (3)

S 3. Copy and complete the table below by sketching and naming the shapes of the following Period 3 compounds:

Compound	Sketch of shape	Name of shape
PCl_3		
$SiCl_4$		
$AlCl_3$		
SO_3		

(8)

4. **a)** Explain why $SiCl_4$ is a liquid at room temperature and pressure whereas SiO_2 is a high melting point solid. (3)
   b) (i) Give the electronic configuration of a phosphorus atom.
   (ii) Explain, in terms of the electronic configuration, why phosphorus can form two chlorides, PCl_3 and PCl_5. (3)
   c) Give the equation for the reaction of PCl_5 with an excess of water. (1)

5 a) What would you observe if a sample of anhydrous aluminium chloride was added to water? (2)
b) Write an equation for this reaction. (1)
c) The resulting solution is acidic.
(i) Write an equation to show this.
(ii) What name is given to this type of reaction? (2)

6 a) State the type of bonding in
(i) sodium oxide
(ii) sulphur dioxide. (2)
b) (i) Write equations to show how these oxides react with water.
(ii) Name the product of each of these reactions and give the approximate pH of the solution formed. (6)

7 a) Copy and complete the table below by describing briefly what you would observe if these Period 3 chlorides were added to an excess of water. Give the formulae of the species formed in each case.

Chloride	Observations	Species formed
NaCl		
$AlCl_3$		
$SiCl_4$		
PCl_5		

(8)

b) (i) State the trend in acidity of the chlorides across the Period.
(ii) Explain how this trend is related to the type of bonding in the chloride. (3)

8 a) Why are the elements Na to Ar in Period 3 of the Periodic Table? (1)
b) Why are there eight elements in this Period? (2)
c) Why has argon little or no tendency to form compounds? (2)

1 Redox equilibria

In this unit the ideas of oxidation states and half-equations studied in AS Chemistry are expanded to include the d block elements of the Periodic Table – **the transition metals**. The transition metals have variable oxidation states due to the incomplete 3d sub-level in their atoms and ions. They can therefore undergo **redox reactions**.

Oxidation states

The oxidation state of an element is determined by the number of electrons the element uses in bonding.

For an uncombined element the oxidation state is zero, e.g. Na, O_2, P_4, N_2

When an atom forms an ion, the charge on the ion tells us the oxidation state of that species. Some examples are shown in Table 1 below:

Ion	Oxidation state	Ion	Oxidation state
Cu^{2+}	+2	O^{2-}	−2
Fe^{2+}	+2	S^{2-}	−2
Cr^{3+}	+3	P^{3-}	−3
Co^{3+}	+3	Br^{-}	−1

Table 1

When an element is covalently bonded in a compound, the oxidation state is still equal to the number of electrons used in bonding.

Some elements have fixed oxidation states in ionic and covalent compounds (see Table 2). We can use these to find the oxidation state of a element with variable oxidation state.

Ion	Oxidation state
H^{+}, Li^{+}, Na^{+}, K^{+}	+1
Mg^{2+} ,Ca^{2+}, Ba^{2+}	+2
Al^{3+}	+3
O^{2-}	−2
F^{-}	−1

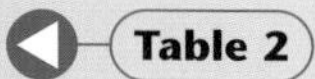
Table 2 *Elements with fixed oxidation states*

Worked examples

1 Cr_2O_3: the three oxygen atoms have a fixed oxidation state of –2 (total –6) and hence the two chromium atoms must each have an oxidation state of +3.

2 $VOCl_2$: the oxygen atom has a fixed oxidation state of –2 and each of the chlorine atoms have a fixed oxidation state of –1 (total –4) and hence the vanadium atom has an oxidation state of +4.

When a species carries an overall charge, do not forget that the charge has to be taken into account when the oxidation states are being worked out.

1 Name $VOCl_2$

3 MnO_4^-: the four oxygen atoms each have a fixed oxidation state of –2 (total –8) and hence the manganese atom must have an oxidation state of +7 if the ion carries a single negative charge. This ion is the manganate(VII) ion.

4 $Cr_2O_7^{2-}$: the seven oxygen atoms have a fixed oxidation state of –2 (total –14) and hence the two chromium atoms will have an oxidation state of +6 (total +12) if the ion carries a double negative charge. The name of this important transition metal ion is dichromate(VI).

5 VO_2^+: the two oxygen atoms have a fixed oxidation state of –2 (total –4) and hence the vanadium atom has an oxidation state of +5 if the ion carries a positive charge.

2 Give the oxidation state of the transition metal and hence the name of the following species: a) MnO_2 b) $TiCl_4$ c) VO^{2+} d) MnO_4^{2-}

3 Give the formulae of the following species:

a) copper(I) chloride b) iron(III) hydroxide c) the chromate(VI) ion

d) the vanadate(V) ion.

Half-equations

Oxidation occurs when a species loses electrons: it also involves an increase in oxidation state.

Reduction occurs when a species gains electrons: it also involves a decrease in oxidation state.

Half-equations show the number of electrons lost when a species is oxidised or the number of electrons gained when a species is reduced.

Two particularly important half-equations in transition metal chemistry are the half-equations for manganate(VII) and dichromate(VI):

$MnO_4^-(aq) + 8H^+(aq) + 5e^- \rightarrow Mn^{2+}(aq) + 4H_2O(l)$

$Cr_2O_7^{2-}(aq) + 14H^+(aq) + 6e^- \rightarrow 2Cr^{3+}(aq) + 7H_2O(l)$

The manganate(VII) ions change colour from an intense purple to a very pale pink as manganese(II) ions are formed. The solution of $Mn^{2+}(aq)$ is so pale it appears colourless. Dichromate(VI) ions are orange in colour. They change to green as chromium(III) ions are formed.

Let us now look at how these equations are constructed:

$$\underset{+7}{MnO_4^-} + 8H^+ + 5e^- \rightarrow \underset{+2}{Mn^{2+}} + 4H_2O$$

Manganese has been reduced from +7 to +2. This involves the addition of five electrons. Four oxygen atoms are lost to form water with eight hydrogen ions. This explains why potassium manganate(VII) has to be acidified when acting as an oxidising agent.

$$\underset{+6}{Cr_2O_7^{2-}} + 14H^+ + 6e^- \rightarrow \underset{+3}{2Cr^{3+}} + 7H_2O$$

Chromium has been reduced from +6 to +3. Since this occurs with two chromium atoms then six electrons are involved. The seven oxygen atoms require fourteen hydrogen ions to form water. Potassium dichromate(VI) can only act as an oxidising agent when it is acidified.

An oxidising agent accepts electrons and is itself reduced.

A reducing agent donates electrons and is itself oxidised.

You should be able to construct a half-equation for oxidation or reduction provided that the reactants and products are given.

Worked examples

1 Write the half-equation for the reduction of VO^{2+} to V^{3+} in acidic solution.

The oxidation state of vanadium in VO^{2+} is +4 and in V^{3+} is +3
Hence one electron is gained by the vanadium.
The oxygen atom will require two hydrogen ions to form water.

$$VO^{2+}(aq) + 2H^+(aq) + e^- \rightarrow V^{3+}(aq) + H_2O(l)$$

As a final check make sure that the overall charge is the same on both sides of the equation. In this case both are 3+.

2 Write the half-equation for the reduction of VO_2^+ to VO^{2+} in acidic solution.

The oxidation state of vanadium in VO_2^+ is +5 and in VO^{2+} is +4
Hence one electron gained.
The oxygen atom requires two hydrogen ions to form water.

$$VO_2^+(aq) + 2H^+(aq) + e^- \rightarrow VO^{2+}(aq) + H_2O(l)$$

4 Balance the following half-equation:

$$MnO_2(s) + H^+(aq) + e^- \rightarrow Mn^{2+}(aq) + H_2O(l)$$

What is the role of MnO_2 as shown by this half-equation?

5 Construct a half-equation for the conversion of MnO_2 into MnO_4^{2-}

What is the role of MnO_2 as shown by this half-equation?

Writing redox equations

This involves the manipulation of two half-equations involving electron transfer. Consider the following examples from transition metal chemistry.

Worked examples

1 The oxidation of iron(II) ions using dichromate(VI) ions.

The two half-equations are:

$Fe^{2+} \rightarrow Fe^{3+} + e^-$	Oxidation
$Cr_2O_7^{2-} + 14H^+ + 6e^- \rightarrow 2Cr^{3+} + 7H_2O$	Reduction

In this case the oxidation half-equation is multiplied by six before adding the two equations together.

$$6Fe^{2+} \rightarrow 6Fe^{3+} + 6e^-$$

$$Cr_2O_7^{2-} + 14H^+ + 6e^- \rightarrow 2Cr^{3+} + 7H_2O$$

$$6Fe^{2+}(aq) + Cr_2O_7^{2-}(aq) + 14H^+(aq) \rightarrow 6Fe^{3+}(aq) + 2Cr^{3+}(aq) + 7H_2O(l)$$

6 Given that the half-equation for the oxidation of hydrogen sulphide is

$$H_2S(g) \rightarrow 2H^+(aq) + S(s) + 2e^-$$

write a balanced ionic equation to show the oxidation of hydrogen sulphide by acidified potassium dichromate(VI).

7 a) Construct a half-equation for the oxidation of the sulphate(IV) ion (sulphite ion) in water to the sulphate(VI) ion.

b) Hence write a balanced ionic equation for the oxidation of sulphate(IV) by potassium manganate(VII).

2 Oxidation of iron(II) ethanedioate, FeC_2O_4 by manganate(VII) ions.

In this reaction both the positive ion (Fe^{2+}) *and* the negative ion ($C_2O_4^{2-}$) are oxidised so three half-equations are involved in the overall redox reaction.

$$C_2O_4^{2-} \rightarrow 2CO_2 + 2e^-$$

$$Fe^{2+} \rightarrow Fe^{3+} + e^-$$

Combining these two half-equations gives the overall oxidation process:

$$FeC_2O_4 \rightarrow Fe^{3+} + 2CO_2 + 3e^- \qquad \text{Oxidation}$$

The half-equation for manganate(VII) is:

$$MnO_4^- + 8H^+ + 5e^- \rightarrow Mn^{2+} + 4H_2O \qquad \text{Reduction}$$

To produce the final equation the oxidation half-equation is multiplied by five and the reduction half-equation is multiplied by three:

$$5FeC_2O_4 \rightarrow 5Fe^{3+} + 10CO_2 + 15e^-$$
$$3MnO_4^- + 24H^+ + 15e^- \rightarrow 3Mn^{2+} + 12H_2O$$

$$3MnO_4^- + 5FeC_2O_4 + 24H^+ \rightarrow 3Mn^{2+} + 5Fe^{3+} + 10CO_2 + 12H_2O$$

or, since in aqueous the ions in iron(II) ethanedioate will be separate, the equation can be written as:

$$3MnO_4^-(aq) + 5Fe^{2+}(aq) + 5C_2O_4^{2-}(aq) + 24H^+(aq) \rightarrow Mn^{2+}(aq) + 5Fe^{3+}(aq) + 10CO_2(g) + 12H_2O(l)$$

You can see from this equation that manganate(VII) ions oxidise the iron(II) ions to iron(III) ions *and* the ethanedioate ions to carbon dioxide.

Key Ideas 188 – 192

- **The oxidation state of an element is equal to the number of electrons used by the element in bonding.**
- **Oxidation involves the loss of electrons; it also involves an increase in oxidation state.**
- **Reduction involves the gain of electrons; it also involves a decrease in oxidation state.**
- **Half-equations show the loss or gain of electrons involved when a species undergoes oxidation or reduction.**
- **Half-equations can be combined to give the equation for the overall redox process.**

2 Standard electrode potentials

If a redox reaction is set up as an electrochemical cell then the voltage of the cell can be measured. This is called the **e.m.f.** (electromotive force) of the cell. The two half-equations involved in the redox reaction are now called **half-cells** or **redox couples**. Each will contribute to the total e.m.f. of the cell. The e.m.f. of a redox couple can be measured against a **standard hydrogen electrode**.

Electrochemical cells

When zinc metal is added to a solution of copper(II) sulphate a redox reaction occurs. The zinc metal slowly dissolves, forming a solution of zinc ions and the blue colour of the copper(II) solution fades as copper metal is precipitated. At GCSE this was treated as a displacement reaction in which the more reactive metal displaces the less reactive metal from its salt; zinc metal displaces copper metal from copper(II) sulphate solution.

$$Zn(s) + CuSO_4(aq) \rightarrow Cu(s) + ZnSO_4(aq)$$

The ionic equation for the reaction is:

$$Zn(s) + Cu^{2+}(aq) \rightarrow Zn^{2+}(aq) + Cu(s)$$

The ionic equation can be broken down to give two half equations (Figure 2).

Figure 1 *Zinc displaces copper ions from solution*

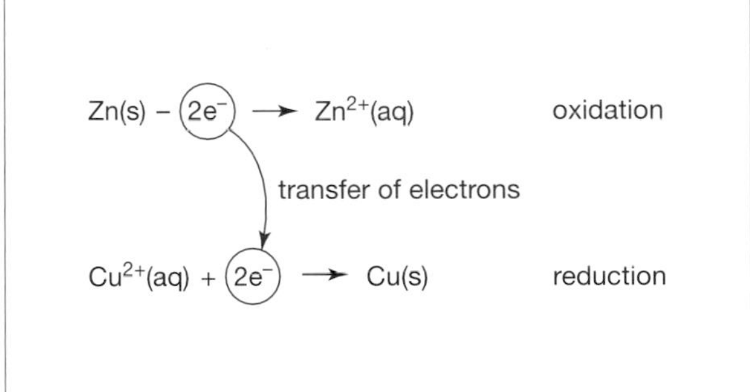

Figure 2

The reaction is a redox reaction in which electrons are transferred from the zinc atoms to the copper(II) ions; zinc atoms have a greater tendency to lose electrons to form ions than do copper atoms.

If the reaction is set up as an electrochemical cell then it is possible to detect this flow of electrons as an electrical current.

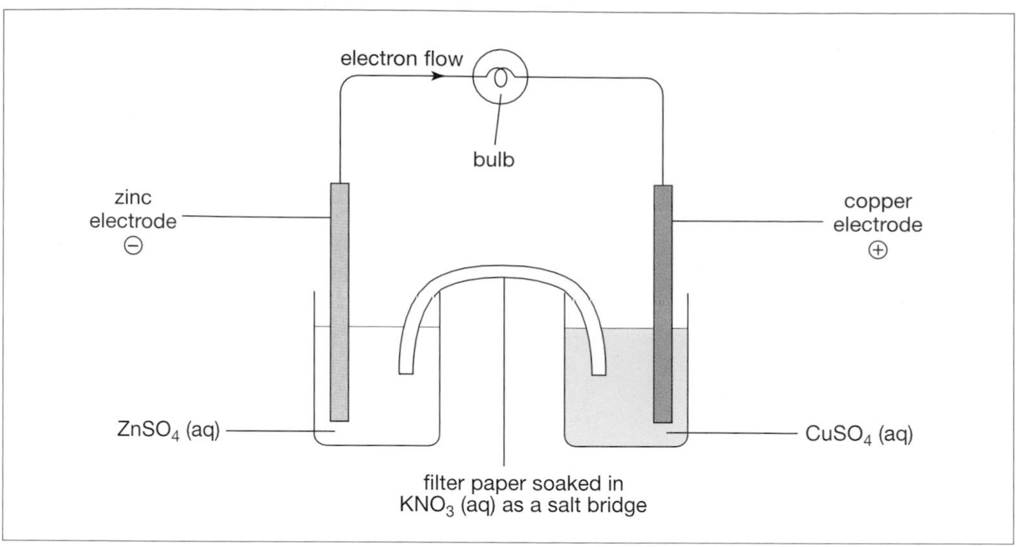

Figure 3 *An electrochemical cell made up of zinc and copper half-cells connected by a salt bridge*

A strip of zinc metal is placed in a solution of Zn^{2+}(aq) (e.g. $ZnSO_4$) in one beaker and a strip of copper metal is placed in a solution of Cu^{2+}(aq) (e.g. $CuSO_4$) in a separate beaker. The two metal strips act as **electrodes** (or terminals).

Each beaker contains a **half-cell** made up of a redox couple. **A redox couple** consists of metal atoms in equilibrium with its aqueous solution of ions. The half-cells can be represented as **Zn^{2+}(aq) | Zn(s)** and **Cu^{2+}(aq) | Cu(s)**.

No reaction can occur until the two half-cells are connected by an **external circuit** and a **salt bridge**. The external circuit is usually a conducting wire through which the electrons can pass from the zinc metal electrode to the copper metal electrode. When the current flows the bulb will glow. The salt bridge allows ions to pass between the solutions and thus completes the electrical circuit. It can be as simple as a piece of filter paper soaked in a solution of a soluble, ionic compound (e.g. potassium nitrate).

When the two half-cells are connected the zinc electrode will start to dissolve, forming zinc ions in solution:

$Zn(s) - 2e^- \rightarrow Zn^{2+}(aq)$ Oxidation

The zinc metal becomes the *negative* electrode. The electrons released will pass through the external circuit to the copper metal (the *positive* electrode) allowing copper ions to gain electrons and form copper metal:

$Cu^{2+}(aq) + 2e^- \rightarrow Cu(s)$ Reduction

The cell can be represented as:

$Zn(s)|Zn^{2+}(aq) \,||\, Cu^{2+}(aq)|Cu(s)$

where the positive electrode is conventionally written or drawn on the right-hand side (see Figure 3). The single vertical line represents the boundary between the two phases and the double vertical lines represent the salt bridge.

Electrons flow from the left-hand half-cell to the right-hand half-cell via the external circuit, so oxidation occurs in the left-hand half-cell and reduction in the right-hand half-cell.

Using this notation the zinc half-cell has been reversed to indicate oxidation.

8 Explain why the colour of Cu^{2+}(aq) fades as the above reaction proceeds.

If the metal ion solutions in the two beakers are both 1 M and a **high resistance voltmeter** is placed in the external circuit then the voltmeter will give an reading of 1.10 volts (V) at 25°C.

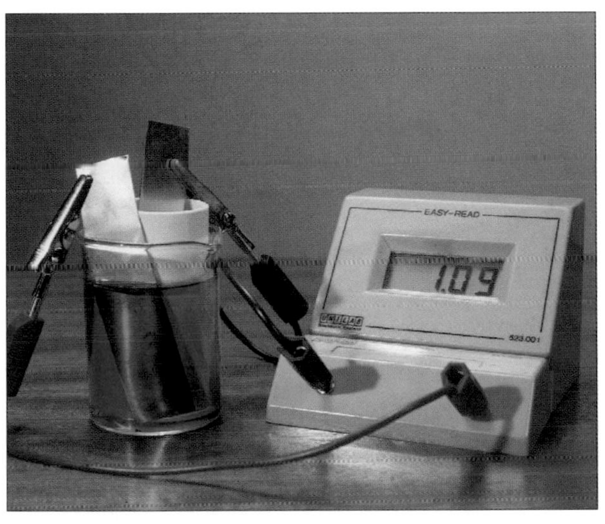

Figure 4 *The Daniell cell. Experimentally, the e.m.f. is found to be 1.09 V*

The two half-cells connected together can be used as a simple battery. Zinc and copper half-cells form the Daniell cell, named after a nineteenth century English chemist.

The reading on the voltmeter shows that the **electromotive force** (e.m.f.) driving the cell reaction has a potential of 1.10 V under standard conditions. A high resistance voltmeter is used since this reduces the current flow to zero and hence there is no work done by the current against internal resistance and the potential difference measured is equal to the e.m.f. of the cell.

How much of this force is caused by the zinc atoms wanting to lose electrons and how much is caused by the copper ions wanting to gain electrons?

It is useful to find the standard **electrode potential** (redox potential), $E^{\ominus}$, of each of the two redox couples separately. The electrode potential is a measure of the e.m.f. of the half-cell. When two half-cells are connected together then their electrode potentials are related to the total e.m.f. of the cell by the expression:

$$\boldsymbol{E^{\ominus}_{cell} = E^{\ominus}_{RHS} - E^{\ominus}_{LHS}} \qquad \text{where } E^{\ominus}_{cell} = \text{e.m.f.}$$

Use is made of this equation in the next section.

Electrode potentials

The electrode potential of a redox couple is measured using a **standard reference electrode**. The hydrogen electrode was selected to be the primary standard reference electrode.

The standard hydrogen electrode

In the hydrogen electrode pure hydrogen gas at 100 kPa pressure is bubbled across a platinum electrode placed in a solution of an acid. Platinum is used since it is an inert metal. The platinum electrode is coated in finely divided platinum to increase its surface area.

The standard conditions employed when using a hydrogen electrode are 298K, 100 kPa pressure and a 1 M solution of $H^+(aq)$, e.g. 1 M HCl.

The notation used to represent this gas electrode is $Pt(s) | H_2(g) | H^+(aq)$

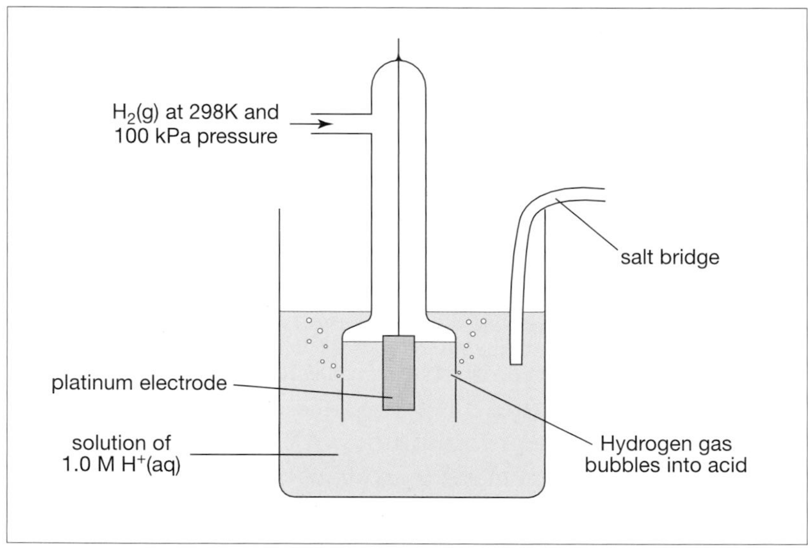

Figure 5 *The standard hydrogen electrode (SHE)*

9 If hydrochloric acid was replaced by sulphuric acid in the standard hydrogen electrode what concentration of sulphuric acid would produce a 1 M solution of $H^+(aq)$?

The electrode potential of the hydrogen electrode is arbitrarily set at 0.00 V

$$H^+(aq) + e^- \rightleftharpoons \frac{1}{2}H_2(g) \qquad E^\ominus = 0.00\,V$$

where $E^\ominus$ is the standard electrode potential

Measuring electrode potentials

The standard electrode potential, $E^{\ominus}$, of any redox couple can be determined by connecting the redox couple to the standard hydrogen electrode. It is important to carry out these determinations under standard conditions so that $E^{\ominus}$ values for different redox couples can be compared.

For example, to determine the standard electrode potential of the $Zn^{2+}(aq)|Zn(s)$ half-cell a strip of zinc metal is placed in a 1 M solution of zinc ions (e.g. 1 M $ZnSO_4$).

The zinc electrode is then connected to a hydrogen electrode. A high resistance voltmeter is placed in the external circuit in order to measure the *potential difference* between the two half-cells. The salt bridge completes the electrical circuit.

The spontaneous cell reaction is:

$$Zn(s) + 2H^+(aq) \rightarrow Zn^{2+}(aq) + H_2(g)$$

The conventional cell notation is:

$$Zn(s)|Zn^{2+}(aq) \,||\, H^+(aq)|H_2(g)|Pt(s)$$

10 Name a substance suitable for use in

a) the salt bridge

b) the external circuit.

Explain your answers.

11 What would you observe during the reaction between zinc and dilute sulphuric acid?

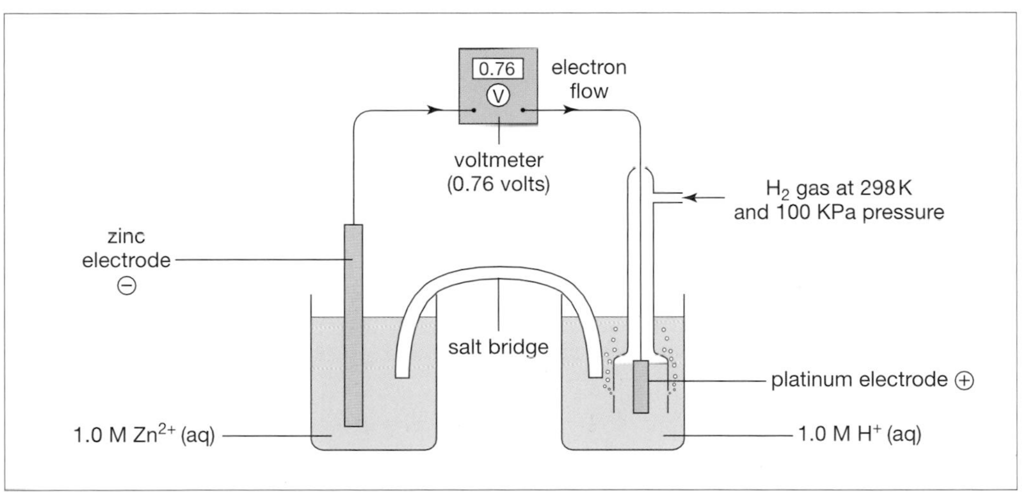

Figure 6 *Measuring the $E^{\ominus}$ value of the $Zn^{2+}(aq)|Zn(s)$ half-cell*

Since the standard reference electrode has an $E^{\ominus}$ value of 0.00 V then the reading on the voltmeter in the external circuit is the $E^{\ominus}$ of the redox couple being measured.

If the electrode in the redox couple has a negative polarity then electrons will flow *from* the redox couple *towards* the hydrogen electrode. Remember that the electrons flow from the left-hand half-cell (negative electrode) to the right-hand half-cell (positive electrode). This means that the $E^{\ominus}$ value of the redox couple is also negative.

In the case of the zinc half-cell connected to a hydrogen electrode the reading on the voltmeter is 0.76 V, so the $E^{\ominus}$ value for the $Zn^{2+}(aq)|Zn(s)$ half-cell is –0.76 V, since the zinc half-cell has a negative polarity.

This can be summarised using the expression:

$$E^{\ominus}_{cell} = E^{\ominus}_{RHS} - E^{\ominus}_{LHS} \quad \text{where } E^{\ominus}_{cell} = \text{e.m.f.}$$

$$0.76 = 0 - E^{\ominus}_{LHS}$$

$$\text{hence } E^{\ominus}_{LHS} = -0.76\,V$$

If the electrode in the redox couple has a positive polarity then the electrons flow *from* the hydrogen electrode *towards* the redox couple. This means that the $E^{\ominus}$ of the redox couple is positive.

In the case of the copper half-cell the $E^{\ominus}$ value is 0.34 V and the copper half-cell has a positive polarity. Hence the $E^{\ominus}$ value for the copper half-cell is +0.34 V.

Using the expression:

$$E^{\ominus}_{cell} = E^{\ominus}_{RHS} - E^{\ominus}_{LHS}$$

$$0.34 = E^{\ominus}_{RHS} - 0$$

$$E^{\ominus}_{RHS} = +0.34\,V$$

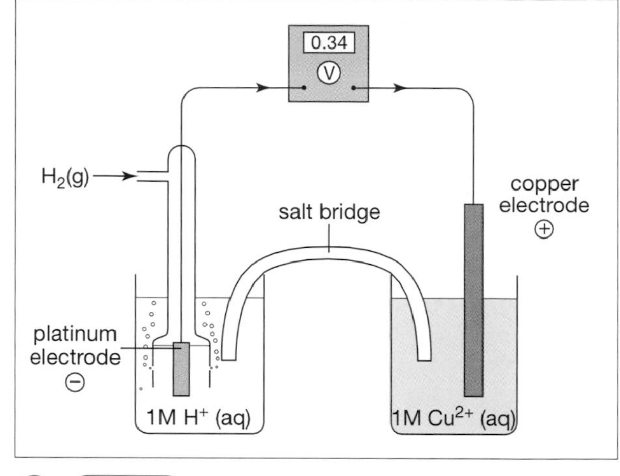

Figure 7 *Measuring the $E^{\ominus}$ value of the $Cu^{2+}(aq)|Cu(s)$ half-cell*

The notation for the cell is: $Pt(s)|H_2(g)|H^+(aq)||Cu^{2+}(aq)|Cu(s)$ and the spontaneous cell reaction can be represented by the following equation:

$$H_2(g) + Cu^{2+}(aq) \rightarrow 2H^+(aq) + Cu(s)$$

12 What would you observe if copper is warmed with dilute sulphuric acid?

13 What are the standard conditions employed when measuring the $E^{\ominus}$ value of a redox couple?

Secondary standards

The hydrogen electrode is difficult to set up and **secondary reference electrodes**, such as the calomel electrode, are normally used to measure standard electrode potentials. These are much more convenient to use once they have been calibrated against a standard hydrogen electrode.

The calomel electrode has a platinum electrode in liquid mercury in contact with a mixture of mercury(I) chloride and potassium chloride.

$$Hg_2Cl_2(aq) + 2e^- \rightarrow 2Hg(l) + 2Cl^-(aq)$$

The $E^{\ominus}$ value for this reduction process is + 0.27 V.

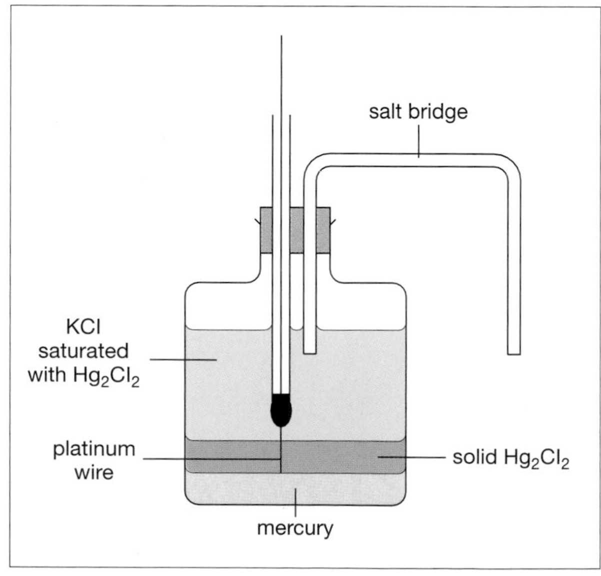

Figure 8 *The calomel electrode*

Using standard electrode potentials

Once the standard electrode potentials of redox couples have been determined experimentally using a primary or secondary standard, then the values can be used to calculate $E^\ominus_{cell}$ values without actually having to determine the values practically.

By convention, standard electrode potentials are always quoted for the reduction process. Some examples are shown in Table 1.

$Zn^{2+}(aq) + 2e^- \rightleftharpoons Zn(s)$	$E^\ominus = -0.76V$
$Cu^{2+}(aq) + 2e^- \rightleftharpoons Cu(s)$	$E^\ominus = +0.34V$
$Hg_2Cl_2(aq) + 2e^- \rightleftharpoons 2Hg(l) + 2Cl^-(aq)$	$E^\ominus = +0.27V$
$Mg^{2+}(aq) + 2e^- \rightleftharpoons Mg(s)$	$E^\ominus = -2.38V$

Table 1

Note that these electrode reactions are reversible equilibrium reactions. The direction that the reaction in a half-cell will assume in the cell depends on which half-cell it is connected to.

The standard convention is to place the half-cell with the more positive $E^\ominus$ on the right-hand side (positive electrode) and the cell with the more negative $E^\ominus$ (negative electrode) on the left-hand side. This results in electrons flowing from the left-hand half-cell to the right-hand side cell.

Using this convention the expression: $E^\ominus_{cell} = E^\ominus_{RHS} - E^\ominus_{LHS}$ can be applied to any pair of redox couples.

Worked examples

1 **Calculate the standard e.m.f. of a cell with zinc and copper electrodes in solutions of 1.0 M zinc sulphate and copper(II) sulphate respectively.**

Step 1: Write the half equations with the $E^\ominus$ values

$$Zn^{2+}(aq) + 2e^- \rightleftharpoons Zn(s) \quad E^\ominus = -0.76V$$

$$Cu^{2+}(aq) + 2e^- \rightleftharpoons Cu(s) \quad E^\ominus = +0.34V$$

Step 2: Use the expression

$$E^\ominus_{cell} = E^\ominus_{RHS} - E^\ominus_{LHS}$$

Remember that the reaction with the more positive $E^\ominus$ value is the RHS half-cell.

$$E^\ominus_{cell} = +0.34 - (-0.76)$$

$$= +1.10V$$

2 a) Calculate the standard e.m.f. of a cell made by connecting

$Zn^{2+}(aq)|\ Zn(s)$ to $Mg^{2+}(aq)|\ Mg(s)$

b) Write the equation for the spontaneous cell reaction

a) $Zn^{2+}(aq) + 2e^- \rightleftharpoons Zn(s)$ $E^\ominus = -0.76\,V$

$Mg^{2+}(aq) + 2e^- \rightleftharpoons Mg(s)$ $E^\ominus = -2.38\,V$

In this combination zinc becomes the *positive* electrode because the $E^\ominus$ value for the $Zn^{2+}(aq)|\ Zn(s)$ redox couple is the more positive.

$$E^\ominus_{cell} = E^\ominus_{RHS} - E^\ominus_{LHS}$$

$$= (-0.76) - (-2.38)$$

$$= 2.38 - 0.76$$

$$= +1.62\,V$$

b) Since the $Zn^{2+}(aq)|\ Zn(s)$ is the right-hand half-cell, the reaction taking place is reduction, i.e.

$Zn^{2+}(aq) + 2e^- \rightarrow Zn(s)$

So the overall cell equation is:

$Mg(s) + Zn^{2+}(aq) \rightarrow Mg^{2+}(aq) + Zn(s)$

14 Use the $E^\ominus$ values given in Table 1 to answer the following questions.

a) Calculate the $E^\ominus_{cell}$ when a strip of copper metal in a 1.0 M solution of copper(II) chloride is connected to a half-cell consisting of a strip of magnesium in a 1.0 M solution of magnesium sulphate.

b) Calculate the e.m.f. of the cell when a $Cu^{2+}(aq)\ |\ Cu(s)$ half-cell is connected to a calomel half-cell under standard conditions.

c) A standard cell has an e.m.f. of +1.03 V. It consists of a calomel half-cell connected to metal X. Metal X is in a 1.0 M solution of its ions. It forms the negative electrode. Calculate the $E^\ominus$ value for X and use this value to identify X.

Altering reaction conditions

Remember that the reaction between the species in a redox couple is a reversible reaction and involves an equilibrium. This means that when the conditions are altered then a change in equilibrium position occurs and the electrode potential value will change.

Consider the standard electrode potential of the $Zn^{2+}(aq)|Zn(s)$ redox couple:

$$Zn^{2+}(aq) + 2e^- \rightleftharpoons Zn(s) \qquad E^\ominus = -0.76\,V$$

This value is only valid at 298 K, 100 kPa pressure using 1.0 M solutions of zinc ions. If the concentration of the zinc ions is increased then the electrode potential will become more positive since the reduction of the zinc ions, by Le Chatelier's Principle, is now more likely to occur. Alternatively, if the concentration of the zinc ions is decreased then the electrode potential becomes more negative since the reduction of the zinc ions is now less likely to occur.

For the cell:

$$Zn(s)|Zn^{2+}(aq) \,||\, Cu^{2+}(aq)|Cu(s)$$

$$E^\ominus_{cell} = E^\ominus_{RHS} - E^\ominus_{LHS}$$

Initially: $E^\ominus = +0.34 - (-0.76) = +1.10\,V$

Once the two half-cells are connected the redox reaction occurs:

$$Zn(s) + Cu^{2+}(aq) \rightarrow Zn^{2+}(aq) + Cu(s)$$

This results in an increase in the concentration of the zinc ions, so the electrode potential of the zinc redox couple becomes more positive. However, the concentration of the copper ions decreases so the electrode potential of the copper redox couple becomes less positive.

As a result the overall e.m.f. of the cell will gradually decrease to zero volts.

Key Ideas 193 –201

- **Redox reactions occur at the electrodes in electrochemical cells.**
- **Oxidation occurs at the negative electrode and reduction occurs at the positive electrode.**
- **Electrons flow via the external circuit from the negative to the positive electrode.**
- **A half-cell consists of a redox couple, i.e. a metal in equilibrium with a solution of its ions.**
- **The hydrogen electrode is used as a primary standard to find the electrode potential of all other half-cells. The standard electrode potential of the hydrogen half-cell is arbitrarily set at 0.00 V.**
- **Standard electrodes potentials are measured under standard conditions: 298 K, 100 kPa pressure, 1.0 M solutions with respect to the ions present.**
- **For a cell the expression: $E^\ominus_{cell} = E^\ominus_{RHS} - E^\ominus_{LHS}$ can be used to calculate electrode potentials providing the cell conventions are adhered to.**

3 The electrochemical series

Standard electrode potentials can be listed in order to produce an **electrochemical series.** From this series the ability of species to act as oxidising agents and reducing agents can be predicted. The values for the standard electrode potentials can also be used to predict whether or not a redox reaction will occur and in which direction.

Listing standard electrode potentials

The electrochemical series is a list of standard electrode potentials placed in order according to the value for the reduction processes.

In the series listed in Table 1 the *most positive* electrode potential is placed at the *top* of the series and the other electrode potentials are placed in *descending* order of electrode potential.

You may meet tables of electrode potentials where the order is reversed and the most negative electrode potential is at the top. Be prepared to understand the data provided in either format; the choice of direction is arbitrary.

From Table 1 you should notice that:

- It is conventional to write all standard electrode potentials for the reduction process i.e. for electron gain. For example:

  $\frac{1}{2}F_2(g) + e^- \rightleftharpoons F^-(aq) \qquad E^\ominus = +2.87\,V$

- State symbols are essential in writing half-equations for standard electrode potentials since a change in conditions will alter the value of the electrode potential.
- These reactions are reversible. An equilibrium is established between the reactants and products. For example:

  $Zn^{2+}(aq) + 2e^- \rightleftharpoons Zn(s) \qquad E^\ominus = -0.76\,V$

  Zinc ions can gain electrons to form zinc atoms and zinc atoms can lose electrons to form zinc ions. When zinc metal is placed in a solution of zinc ions both of these reactions occur until an equilibrium is established.

- The $E^\ominus$ value of a redox couple gives a quantitative measure of the position of the equilibrium.

  The more positive the $E^\ominus$ value the more likely the reaction is to occur.

  $F_2(g)$ is more likely to form $F^-(aq)$ than is $F^-(aq)$ to form $F_2(g)$ since the formation of $F^-(aq)$ has a positive $E^\ominus$ value and the formation of $F_2(g)$ from $F^-(aq)$ has a negative value:

  $F^-(aq) \rightleftharpoons \frac{1}{2}F_2(g) + e^- \qquad E^\ominus = -2.87\,V$

  In all cases the oxidation process has the same numerical value as the reduction process but the sign is changed.

Table 1 *The electrochemical series*

Ability to act as an oxidising agent increases

$\frac{1}{2}F_2(g) + e^-$	$\rightleftharpoons$	$F^-(aq)$	+2.87V
$MnO_4^-(aq) + 8H^+(aq) + 5e^-$	$\rightleftharpoons$	$Mn^{2+}(aq) + 4H_2O(l)$	+1.52V
$\frac{1}{2}Cl_2(g) + e^-$	$\rightleftharpoons$	$Cl^-(aq)$	+1.36V
$Cr_2O_7^{2-}(aq) + 14H^+(aq) + 6e^-$	$\rightleftharpoons$	$2Cr^{3+}(aq) + 7H_2O(l)$	+1.33V
$\frac{1}{2}Br_2(l) + e^-$	$\rightleftharpoons$	$Br^-(aq)$	+1.07V
$Ag^+(aq) + e^-$	$\rightleftharpoons$	$Ag(s)$	+0.80V
$Fe^{3+}(aq) + e^-$	$\rightleftharpoons$	$Fe^{2+}(aq)$	+0.77V
$\frac{1}{2}I_2(s) + e^-$	$\rightleftharpoons$	$I^-(aq)$	+0.54V
$Cu^+(aq) + e^-$	$\rightleftharpoons$	$Cu(s)$	+0.52V
$Cu^{2+}(aq) + 2e^-$	$\rightleftharpoons$	$Cu(s)$	+0.34V
$Sn^{4+}(aq) + 2e^-$	$\rightleftharpoons$	$Sn^{2+}(aq)$	+0.15V
$Cu^{2+}(aq) + e^-$	$\rightleftharpoons$	$Cu^+(aq)$	+0.15V
$H^+(aq) + e^-$	$\rightleftharpoons$	$\frac{1}{2}H_2(g)$	0.00V
$Pb^{2+}(aq) + 2e^-$	$\rightleftharpoons$	$Pb(s)$	−0.13V
$Sn^{2+}(aq) + 2e^-$	$\rightleftharpoons$	$Sn(s)$	−0.14V
$Ni^{2+}(aq) + 2e$	$\rightleftharpoons$	$Ni(s)$	−0.25V
$Fe^{2+}(aq) + 2e^-$	$\rightleftharpoons$	$Fe(s)$	−0.44V
$Zn^{2+}(aq) + 2e^-$	$\rightleftharpoons$	$Zn(s)$	−0.76V
$Al^{3+}(aq) + 3e^-$	$\rightleftharpoons$	$Al(s)$	−1.66V
$Mg^{2+}(aq) + 2e^-$	$\rightleftharpoons$	$Mg(s)$	−2.38V
$Na^+(aq) + e^-$	$\rightleftharpoons$	$Na(s)$	2.71V
$Ca^{2+}(aq) + 2e^-$	$\rightleftharpoons$	$Ca(s)$	−2.87V
$K^+(aq) + e^-$	$\rightleftharpoons$	$K(s)$	−2.92V
$Rb^+(aq) + e^-$	$\rightleftharpoons$	$Rb(s)$	−2.92V
$Li^+(aq) + e^-$	$\rightleftharpoons$	$Li(s)$	−3.02V

Ability to act as a reducing agent increases

15 **Write the half-equation for the reduction of aluminium ions to aluminium metal.**

16 **What is the standard electrode potential for the oxidation of aluminium to aluminium ions?**

Using the electrochemical series

Remember that:

- If a species gains electrons then the species is acting as an oxidising agent.
- If a species loses electrons then the species is acting as a reducing agent.

When redox couples are arranged in numerical order with the most positive $E^{\ominus}$ value at the top then the following generalisations can be made:

1. Ability to act as an oxidising agent

The species at the top left i.e. fluorine (F_2) is the *most powerful oxidising agent* and can oxidise all of the species on the right-hand side.

$$\tfrac{1}{2}F_2(g) + e^- \rightleftharpoons F^-(aq) \qquad E^{\ominus} = +2.87\,V$$

Since the forward reaction has *the* most positive $E^{\ominus}$ value for gaining electrons, F_2 is *the* most powerful oxidising agent.

Any species on the left-hand side can oxidise any species on the right-hand side below it.

For example:

Bromine, Br_2, can oxidise silver metal to silver ions but cannot oxidise chloride ions to chlorine, Cl_2, whereas chlorine can oxidise both bromide ions and silver metal. Chlorine is the most powerful oxidising agent of the three listed in Table 2; its ability to accept electrons is greatest, reflected in the most positive $E^{\ominus}$ value.

$\tfrac{1}{2}Cl_2(g) + e^-$	$\rightleftharpoons$	$Cl^-(aq)$	+1.36V
$\tfrac{1}{2}Br_2(l) + e^-$	$\rightleftharpoons$	$Br^-(aq)$	+1.07V
$Ag^+(aq) + e^-$	$\rightleftharpoons$	$Ag(s)$	+0.80V

Table 2

The following reactions are therefore feasible:

$$\tfrac{1}{2}Cl_2(g) + Br^-(aq) \rightarrow \tfrac{1}{2}Br_2(l) + Cl^-(aq)$$

$$\tfrac{1}{2}Cl_2(g) + Ag(s) \rightarrow Ag^+(aq) + Cl^-(aq)$$

$$\tfrac{1}{2}Br_2(l) + Ag(s) \rightarrow Ag^+(aq) + Br^-(aq)$$

You should recognise the first of these equations as a displacement reaction from Module 2, showing that chlorine is a more powerful oxidising agent than bromine.

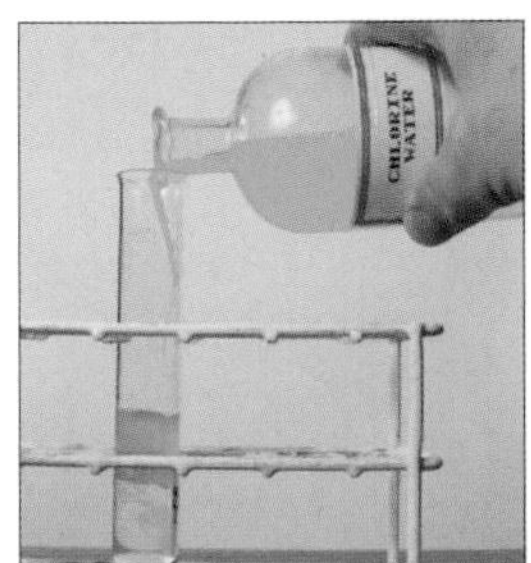

Figure 2 *The displacement of bromine by chlorine*

17 Use the data in Table 1 to predict whether or not the following reactions are feasible:

a) The oxidation of $Sn^{2+}(aq)$ by $Ag^{+}(aq)$

b) The oxidation of $Fe^{2+}(aq)$ by $Cl_2(g)$

c) The oxidation of $Br^{-}(aq)$ by $Cu^{2+}(aq)$

Write equations for the feasible reactions.

2 Ability to act as a reducing agent

The species at the bottom right, i.e. lithium (Li), is the *most powerful reducing agent* and can reduce all of the species on the left-hand side.

$$Li^{+}(aq) + e^{-} \rightleftharpoons Li(s) \qquad E^{\ominus} = -3.02\,V$$

The reverse reaction has a positive $E^{\ominus}$ value for donating an electron:

$$Li(s) \rightleftharpoons Li^{+}(aq) + e^{-} \qquad E^{\ominus} = +3.02\,V$$

Since this reaction has *the* most positive $E^{\ominus}$ value for donating electrons, lithium metal is *the* most powerful reducing agent.

Any species on the right hand side can reduce any species on the left-hand side above it.

For example, nickel metal can reduce tin(II) ions to tin but cannot reduce iron(II) ions to iron whereas iron, being below both nickel and tin, can reduce both their ions to the corresponding metal.

$Sn^{2+}(aq) + 2e^{-}$	$\rightleftharpoons$	Sn(s)	−0.14V
$Ni^{2+}(aq) + 2e^{-}$	$\rightleftharpoons$	Ni(s)	−0.25V
$Fe^{2+}(aq) + 2e^{-}$	$\rightleftharpoons$	Fe(s)	−0.44V

For iron to behave as a reducing agent it must donate electrons so the equation above needs to be reversed:

$$Fe(s) \rightarrow Fe^{2+}(aq) + 2e^{-} \qquad E^{\ominus} = +0.44\,V$$

18 Write equations for the reduction of tin(II) ions using

a) Ni(s) b) Fe(s).

Predicting redox reactions

Standard electrode potentials can be used to predict whether or not a redox reaction is feasible.

In order to determine the possible redox reaction between given reactants several stages need to be followed.

1 Identifying the appropriate half-equations

Redox involves both oxidation and reduction, and hence one of the half-equations involved must show electron gain (reduction) and the other half-equation must show electron loss (oxidation).

Since half-equations are always quoted for the reduction process, one of the half-equations has to be reversed.

2 Using the $E^\ominus$ values

The $E^\ominus$ values for the two half-equations identified are then *added* together. Note that the values are *not* adjusted in terms of the different number of electrons involved.

If the overall $E^\ominus$ ($E^\ominus_{total}$) is positive then the reaction is *feasible*.

In most cases, when the $E^\ominus_{total}$ is positive, the reaction will occur *spontaneously*. In some cases, however, the reaction does *not* occur because a high activation energy makes the rate of reaction too slow to observe.

Such a reaction is *thermodynamically favourable* under standard conditions but is *kinetically unfavourable*.

If the $E^\ominus_{total}$ is negative then the reaction cannot occur. The reaction is thermodynamically impossible under standard conditions.

Note that the half-equations are equivalent to the half-cells in the previous section, and $E^\ominus_{total}$ is the same as $E^\ominus_{cell}$.

Worked examples

1 **Determine the feasible reaction when a solution containing Fe^{2+}(aq) and Fe^{3+}(aq) is mixed with I^-(aq).**

The relevant half-equations and standard electrode potentials are:

$Fe^{3+}(aq) + e^- \rightleftharpoons Fe^{2+}(aq) \quad E^\ominus = +0.77V$

$\frac{1}{2}I_2(s) + e^- \rightleftharpoons I^-(aq) \quad E^\ominus = +0.54V$

$Fe^{2+}(aq) + 2e^- \rightleftharpoons Fe(s) \quad E^\ominus = -0.44V$

The solution contains Fe^{2+}(aq), Fe^{3+}(aq) and I^-(aq). The half-equations used must have these **reactants** on the left-hand side.

Reverse the iodine half-equation to show the oxidation of iodide ions and change the sign of the $E^\ominus$ value:

$I^-(aq) \rightleftharpoons \frac{1}{2}I_2(s) + e^- \quad E^\ominus = -0.54V$

Now combine pairs of half-equations (one involving reduction and one involving oxidation):

$Fe^{3+}(aq) + e^- \rightleftharpoons Fe^{2+}(aq)$ $E^\ominus = +0.77V$

$I^-(aq) \rightleftharpoons \frac{1}{2}I_2(s) + e^-$ $E^\ominus = -0.54V$

$E^\ominus_{total} = +0.77 + (-0.54) = +0.23\ V$

The $E^\ominus_{total}$ is positive and therefore this reaction is feasible. The overall equation for the reaction is:

$Fe^{3+}(aq) + I^-(aq) \rightarrow Fe^{2+}(aq) + \frac{1}{2}I_2(s)$

Now consider the reaction between iodide ions and iron(II) ions:

$Fe^{2+}(aq) + 2e^- \rightleftharpoons Fe(s)$ $E^\ominus = -0.44V$

$I^-(aq) \rightleftharpoons \frac{1}{2}I_2(s) + e^-$ $E^\ominus = -0.54V$

$E^\ominus_{total} = -0.44 + (-0.54) = -0.98V$

Since the $E^\ominus$total is negative, this reaction cannot occur.
Conclusion: When iodide ions are added to an aqueous mixture of Fe^{2+} and Fe^{3+} ions the iodide ions will reduce Fe^{3+} to Fe^{2+} but cannot reduce Fe^{2+} to Fe.

19 Predict what you would observe when a solution of iron(III) chloride is mixed with a solution of potassium iodide.

2 Use the standard electrode potentials below to explain why manganate(VI) ions MnO_4^{2-} are unstable in acid solution.

$MnO_4^{2-}(aq) + 4H^+(aq) + 2e^- \rightleftharpoons MnO_2(s) + 2H_2O(l)$ $E^\ominus = +2.26V$

$MnO_4^-(aq) + e^- \rightleftharpoons MnO_4^{2-}(aq)$ $E^\ominus = +0.56V$

Reversing the second half equation so manganate(VI) ions appear as reactants in both equations:

$MnO_4^{2-}(aq) \rightleftharpoons MnO_4^-(aq) + e^-$ $E^\ominus = -0.56V$

$MnO_4^{2-}(aq) + 4H^+(aq) + 2e^- \rightleftharpoons MnO_2(s) + 2H_2O(l)$ $E^\ominus = +2.26V$

$E^\ominus_{total} = +2.26 + (-0.56) = +1.70V$

The reaction is feasible and the equation for the reaction is:

$$\underset{+6}{3MnO_4^{2-}}(aq) + 4H^+(aq) \rightleftharpoons \underset{+7}{2MnO_4^-}(aq) + \underset{+2}{MnO_2}(s) + 2H_2O(l)$$

This shows that manganate(VI) ions are unstable in acid solution, since they undergo a redox reaction. This reaction is an example of **disproportionation**, in which the same species is simultaneously oxidised and reduced.

3 Use standard electrode potentials to explain why hydrochloric acid can be used in potassium dichromate(VI) titrations but not for potassium manganate(VII) titrations. Write balanced equations for any reactions that occur.

When an acid is added to potassium dichromate(VI) or potassium manganate(VII) the acid provides the H^+ ions needed for the dichromate(VI) ions and manganate(VII) ions to act as oxidising agents. It is important that the acid used to acidify the oxidising agent is not itself oxidised. If, for example the oxidising agent is being used to determine the concentration of $Fe^{2+}(aq)$ then any other oxidation occurring will ruin the titration procedure. When hydrochloric acid is used the solution contains chloride ions.

The appropriate half equations are:

$MnO_4^-(aq) + 8H^+(aq) + 5e^- \rightleftharpoons Mn^{2+}(aq) + 4H_2O(l)$ $\quad E^\ominus = +1.52V$

$\frac{1}{2}Cl_2(g) + e^- \rightleftharpoons Cl^-(aq)$ $\quad E^\ominus = +1.36V$

$Cr_2O_7^{2-}(aq) + 14H^+(aq) + 6e^- \rightleftharpoons 2Cr^{3+}(aq) + 7H_2O(l)$ $\quad E^\ominus = +1.33V$

Reversing the chlorine half-equation to show the oxidation of the chloride ions:

$Cl^-(aq) \rightleftharpoons \frac{1}{2}Cl_2(g) + e^-$ $\quad E^\ominus = -1.36V$

First consider the dichromate(VI) titration:

$Cr_2O_7^{2-}(aq) + 14H^+(aq) + 6e^- \rightleftharpoons 2Cr^{3+}(aq) + 7H_2O(l)$ $\quad E^\ominus = +1.33V$

$Cl^-(aq) \rightleftharpoons \frac{1}{2}Cl_2(g) + e^-$ $\quad E^\ominus = -1.36V$

$$E^\ominus_{total} = +1.33 + (-1.36V) = -0.03V$$

Since the $E^\ominus_{total}$ is negative the reaction cannot occur.
Conclusion: Dichromate(VI) ions will not oxidise chloride ions to chlorine and therefore hydrochloric acid can be used to provide the H^+ ions in dichromate(VI) titrations.

Now consider the manganate(VII) titration:

$MnO_4^-(aq) + 8H^+(aq) + 5e^- \rightleftharpoons Mn^{2+}(aq) + 4H_2O(l)$ $\quad E^\ominus = +1.52V$

$Cl^-(aq) \rightleftharpoons \frac{1}{2}Cl_2(g) + e^-$ $\quad E^\ominus = -1.36V$

$$E^\ominus_{total} = +1.52 + (-1.36) = +0.16V$$

The reaction is feasible and the equation for the reaction is:
$MnO_4^-(aq) + 8H^+(aq) + 5Cl^-(aq) \rightleftharpoons Mn^{2+}(aq) + 4H_2O(l) + 2\frac{1}{2}Cl_2(g)$
Conclusion: Manganate(VII) will oxidise the chloride ions in hydrochloric acid to chlorine and therefore hydrochloric acid cannot be used in manganate(VII) titrations.

20 Predict what you would observe when sodium chloride is added, in the presence of an acid, to a) potassium manganate(VII) b) potassium dichromate(VI).

21 Use the following data to discuss possible methods of preparation of chlorine from 1.0 M HCl(aq).

$\frac{1}{2}Cl_2(g) + e^- \rightleftharpoons Cl^-(aq)$ $E^\ominus = +1.36V$

$MnO_4^-(aq) + 8H^+(aq) + 5e^- \rightleftharpoons Mn^{2+}(aq) + 4H_2O(l)$ $E^\ominus = +1.52V$

$MnO_2(s) + 4H^+(aq) + 2e^- \rightleftharpoons Mn^{2+}(aq) + 2H_2O(l)$ $E^\ominus = +1.23V$

$Cr_2O_7^{2-} + 14H^+ + 6e^- \rightleftharpoons 2Cr^{3+}(aq) + 7H_2O$ $E^\ominus = +1.33V$

Altering the reaction conditions

From question 21 you should have concluded that the standard electrode potentials indicate that the reaction between manganese(IV) oxide and 1.0 M hydrochloric acid is not feasible.

$MnO_2(s) + 4H^+(aq) + 2e^- \rightleftharpoons Mn^{2+}(aq) + 2H_2O(l)$ $E^\ominus = +1.23V$

$\frac{1}{2}Cl_2(g) + e^- \rightleftharpoons Cl^-(aq)$ $E^\ominus = +1.36V$

Reversing the chlorine half-equation:

$Cl^-(aq) \rightleftharpoons \frac{1}{2}Cl_2(g) + e^-$ $E^\ominus = -1.36V$

$MnO_2(s) + 4H^+(aq) + 2e^- \rightleftharpoons Mn^{2+}(aq) + 2H_2O(l)$ $E^\ominus = +1.23V$

$E^\ominus_{total} = -0.13V$ and hence the reaction is not feasible

If however concentrated hydrochloric acid is used and the reaction mixture is warmed then the reaction occurs:

$MnO_2(s) + 4HCl(aq) \rightarrow MnCl_2(aq) + Cl_2(g) + 2H_2O(l)$

This is the common method used to prepare chlorine in the laboratory.

Increasing the concentration of the chloride ions from the hydrochloric acid makes the electrode potential of the chlorine redox couple less positive, since the equilibrium shifts to the left, and hence $Cl^-(aq) \rightleftharpoons \frac{1}{2}Cl_2(g) + e^-$ has a less negative electrode potential, since the forward reaction is more likely to occur.

Key Ideas 202 – 209

- **When standard electrode potentials are placed in rank order an electrochemical series is formed.**
- **Standard electrode potentials are quoted for the reduction process.**
- **Species with positive standard electrode potentials tend to be oxidising agents whilst those with negative potentials tend to be reducing agents.**
- **Standard electrode potentials can be used to predict whether a redox reaction is possible.**
- **If the overall $E^\ominus$ value is positive then the reaction is feasible.**
- **If the overall $E^\ominus$ value is negative then the reaction cannot occur unless the reaction conditions are altered.**

4

Unit 13 Questions

Ⓢ (1) The redox reaction between hydrogen iodide and concentrated sulphuric acid is shown below:

$$8HI(aq) + H_2SO_4(aq) \rightarrow H_2S(g) + 4H_2O(l) + 4I_2(s)$$

a) What is the role of HI in this reaction? (1)
b) Deduce the half-equation for the conversion of H_2SO_4 to H_2S. (2)

(2) **a)** What are the oxidation states for the manganese species MnO_4^-, MnO_4^{2-} and MnO_2? (3)
b) Given the standard redox potentials below calculate the $E°_{total}$ for the spontaneous reaction and hence deduce the overall equation for the reaction. (3)

$MnO_4^-(aq) + e^- \rightarrow MnO_4^{2-}(aq)$ $E^\ominus = +0.564\,V$
$MnO_4^{2-}(aq) + 4H^+(aq) + 2e^- \rightarrow MnO_2(s) + 2H_2O(l)$ $E^\ominus = +2.260\,V$

c) What special type of redox reaction is this an example of? (1)

(3) **a)** (i) Why is it necessary to designate a standard electrode to which the potentials of all other electrodes are related?
(ii) What are the standard conditions employed when determining electrode potentials? (5)
b) (i) Which electrode is selected as the primary standard?
(ii) What is the potential assigned to this electrode?
(iii) Give a brief description of this electrode. (6)
c) (i) Give an example of a secondary electrode, including the half-cell reaction.
(ii) Why is this used in preference to a primary electrode when measuring redox potentials? (3)

(4) A circuit is set up using two half-cells:

$Ag^+(aq)|Ag(s)$; $E^\ominus = +0.80\,V$ and $Zn^{2+}(aq)|Zn(s)$; $E^\ominus = -0.76\,V$

a) (i) Write an equation for the spontaneous cell reaction.
(ii) Explain, using the $E^\ominus$ values quoted, how you have chosen the direction for the reaction. (5)
b) How and why would the voltage of the cell change as the cell was in use? (3)

5 Use the redox potentials below to decide what products, if any, would be obtained when acidified potassium dichromate(VI) is reacted with

a) iron(II) chloride solution
b) zinc
c) cerium(III) chloride solution. (4)

Redox couple	Zn^{2+}| Zn	Fe^{2+}| Fe	Fe^{3+}| Fe^{2+}	Ce^{4+}| Ce^{3+}	$Cr_2O_7^{2-}$| Cr^{3+}
$E^{\ominus}$/V	–0.76	–0.44	+0.77	+1.45	+1.33

Table 1

6 Standard electrode potentials are shown in Table 2, for redox couples in acid solution measured at 298K.

Redox couple	$E^{\ominus}$/V
$Ag^{2+} + e^- \rightleftharpoons Ag^+$	+1.98
$Br_2 + 2e^- \rightleftharpoons 2Br^-$	+1.07
$Ag^+ + e^- \rightleftharpoons Ag$	+0.80
$I_2 + 2e^- \rightleftharpoons 2I^-$	+0.54
$Cu^{2+} + 2e^- \rightleftharpoons Cu$	+0.34
$Cd^{2+} + 2e^- \rightleftharpoons Cd$	–0.40

Table 2

a) Define a reducing agent. (1)
b) Which is the strongest reducing agent listed? (1)
c) Which is the strongest oxidising agent listed? (1)
d) What is the initial voltage of the following cell under standard conditions?

$Cd(s)\,|\,Cd^{2+}(aq)\,||\,Ag^+(aq)\,|\,Ag(s)$ (2)

e) Explain, using the data in the table, why
(i) bromine liberates iodine from an aqueous solution of potassium iodide
(ii) silver(I) does not disproportionate in acid solution. (6)

7 **a)** (i) Write a half-equation for the oxidation of ethanedioate ions to carbon dioxide.
(ii) Write a half-equation for the reduction of manganate(VII) ions to manganese(II) ions in acid conditions.
(iii) Hence write an overall equation for this redox reaction. (3)

b) 1.713 g of sodium ethanedioate were dissolved in water and made up to 250 cm^3. When 25 cm^3 aliquots of this solution were acidified and titrated against potassium manganate(VII) solution, 23.9 cm^3 of this solution was required to complete the reaction. Calculate the molarity of potassium manganate(VII) solution. (5)

Transition metals

You will have met the transition metals in AS Chemistry as the d block elements of the Periodic Table. The electronic structures of the first row transition metals, which are studied at 'A' level, include the filling of the 3d sub-level in the atoms. From GCSE you will know that the transition metals have high melting points, they form coloured compounds and can act as catalysts.

General properties

Transition metals have some general characteristics.

They: form complexes
form coloured ions
have variable oxidation state
have catalytic activity.

All of the characteristic properties of the transition metals are a result of their electronic structure. **The transition metals have a partially filled 3d energy sub-level in their atoms or ions**.

The electronic structures for the first row transition metal atoms are shown in Table 1.

Scandium	$1s^2 2s^2 2p^6 3s^2 3p^6 3d^1 4s^2$
Titanium	$1s^2 2s^2 2p^6 3s^2 3p^6 3d^2 4s^2$
Vanadium	$1s^2 2s^2 2p^6 3s^2 3p^6 3d^3 4s^2$
Chromium	$1s^2 2s^2 2p^6 3s^2 3p^6 3d^5 4s^1$
Manganese	$1s^2 2s^2 2p^6 3s^2 3p^6 3d^5 4s^2$
Iron	$1s^2 2s^2 2p^6 3s^2 3p^6 3d^6 4s^2$
Cobalt	$1s^2 2s^2 2p^6 3s^2 3p^6 3d^7 4s^2$
Nickel	$1s^2 2s^2 2p^6 3s^2 3p^6 3d^8 4s^2$
Copper	$1s^2 2s^2 2p^6 3s^2 3p^6 3d^{10} 4s^1$

Table 1

Remember from studying electronic structures at AS that the 4s sub-level fills *before* the 3d sub-level.

Note also that the electronic structures of **chromium** and **copper** are anomalous: chromium has a **half-filled** and copper a **full** 3d sub-level. This results in a more stable arrangement of the electrons in the atoms of these two metals.

When the transition metal atoms form ions it is the 4s electrons that are lost *before* the 3d electrons. Electronic structures of some ions are shown in Table 2.

Sc^{3+}	$1s^2 2s^2 2p^6 3s^2 3p^6$
Fe^{2+}	$1s^2 2s^2 2p^6 3s^2 3p^6 3d^6$
Co^{3+}	$1s^2 2s^2 2p^6 3s^2 3p^6 3d^6$
Cu^+	$1s^2 2s^2 2p^6 3s^2 3p^6 3d^{10}$

Table 2

Notice that Sc^{3+} and Cu^+ are *not* transitional since they do not have a partially filled 3d energy level.

1 Give the full electronic structures for:
a) Ti^{3+} b) Fe^{3+} c) Cr^{3+}.

2 Explain, in terms of the electronic structures of their ions, why a solution of iron(II) is rapidly oxidised to iron(III).

Complexes

Complexes are formed when transition metals or their ions form co-ordinate bonds with **ligands**.

Ligands are species that can donate one or more lone pairs of electrons.

The ligands form co-ordinate bonds by the overlap of an orbital containing a lone pair of electrons with a vacant orbital on the transition metal atom or ion. The transition metal ion acts as a **Lewis acid** (accepts a pair of electrons) and the ligand acts as a **Lewis base** (donates a pair of electrons).

All of the complexes studied in this unit are formed from the first-row transition metal ions, with the exception of silver.

A complex ion consists of a central metal ion surrounded by ligands. A typical example is shown in Figure 1.

This complex is usually written as $[Cu(H_2O)_6]^{2+}$. The Cu^{2+} ion is co-ordinately bonded to six water ligands, each of which has donated one lone pair of electrons to the copper ion from the oxygen atom. The number of co-ordinate bonds formed in this complex is six. The complex is said to have a **co-ordination number** of six.

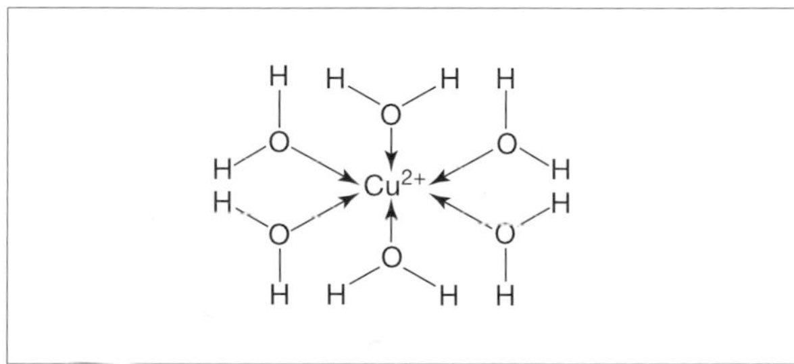

Figure 1 *The structure of a typical complex*

The co-ordination number of a complex is defined as the number of co-ordinate bonds formed in the complex.

Co-ordination numbers are usually two, four or six, involving the formation of two, four or six co-ordinate bonds respectively. This number will also dictate the shape of the complex ion (see page 217).

3 Define the following terms:
a) ligand b) Lewis acid c) complex.

Different types of ligands

Ligands are classified by the number of co-ordinate bonds that they are able to form in complexes (the number of **donor atoms**).

Unidentate ligands form *one* co ordinate bond since they donate one lone pair of electrons each to the central metal ion. (Unidentate means 'single-toothed'.) In this case the co-ordination number is equal to the number of ligands attached to the central metal ion.

Water molecules are examples of unidentate ligands. Other common examples include chloride ions (Cl^-), ammonia molecules (NH_3) and cyanide ions (CN^-). Ligands can be negatively charged ions or neutral molecules.

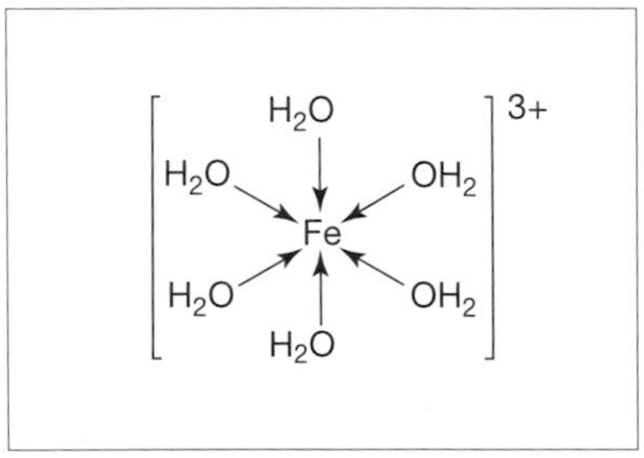

Figure 2 The hexaqua-iron(III) ion, $[Fe(H_2O)_6]^{3+}$

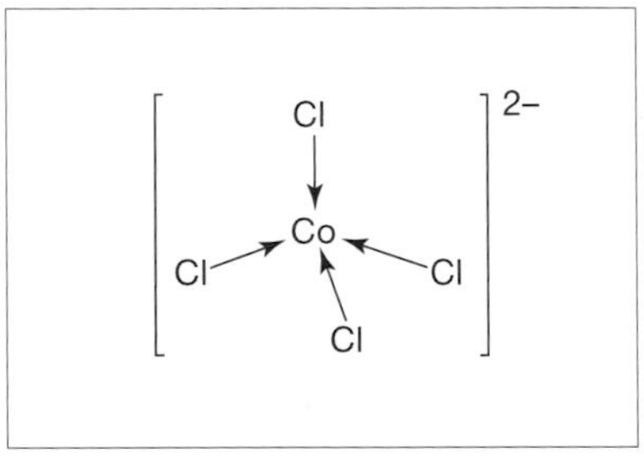

Figure 3 The tetrachlorocobaltate(II) ion, $[CoCl_4]^{2-}$

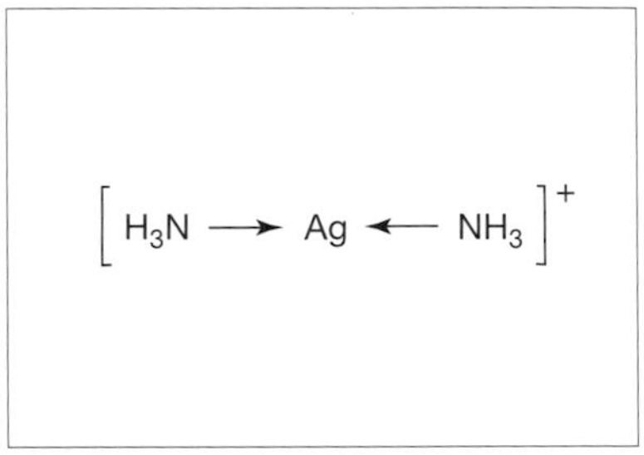

Figure 4 The diammine silver(I) ion, $[Ag(NH_3)_2]^+$

Notice from the examples above that the charge on the ligand and the oxidation state of the metal ion determines the overall charge of the complex. Neutral ligands result in positively charged complexes where the overall charge of the complex equals the oxidation state of the central metal ion. Negatively charged ligands result in a negatively charged complex. Silver is included in this study since it forms complexes with a co-ordination number of two.

4 Give the oxidation state of the transition metal, and the co-ordination number in each of the following complex ions:

a) $[Co(H_2O)_6]^{2+}$

b) $[AgCl_2]^-$

c) $[Cu(NH_3)_4(H_2O)_2]^{2+}$

5 The *transition metal* cobalt forms an anionic complex with chloride ions. The bonds in this complex are *co-ordinate bonds*. The complex has a *co-ordination number* of 4.

a) Define the terms in italics.

b) Give the formula for the complex ion described.

Bidentate ligands can form two co-ordinate bonds, since they donate two lone pairs of electrons (two donor atoms).

1,2-diaminoethane, $H_2NCH_2CH_2NH_2$ (often shortened to 'en'), and the ethanedioate ion, $C_2O_4^{2-}$, are examples of bidentate ligands.

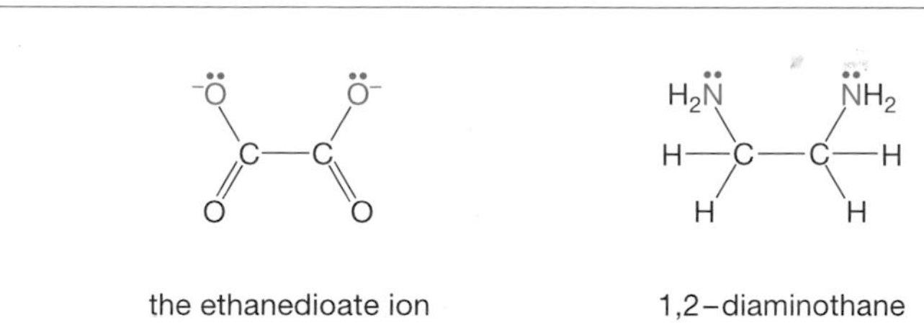

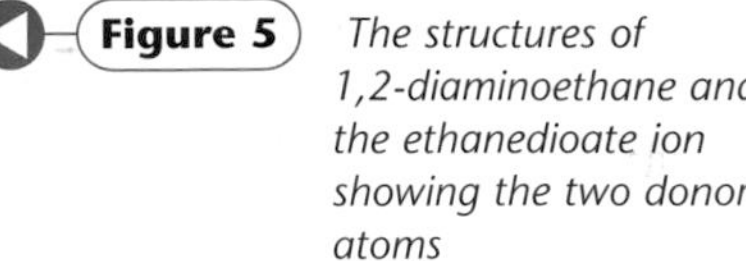
Figure 5 *The structures of 1,2-diaminoethane and the ethanedioate ion showing the two donor atoms*

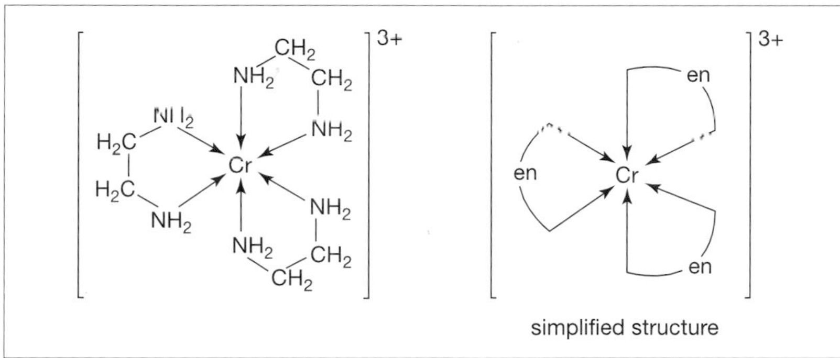

Figure 6 *A complex containing bidentate ligands*

The complexes formed are called **chelates** (meaning 'crab-like') and the ligands chelating agents. The complexes containing chelating ligands are more stable complexes than unidentate ligand complexes since their formation results in a more positive entropy change (see page 166).

6 **Explain why ammonia is a unidentate ligand whereas 1,2-diaminoethane is bidentate.**

7 **Could ethylamine behave as a ligand? Explain your answer.**

8 **Explain why the complex $[Cr(H_2NCH_2CH_2NH_2)_3]^{3+}$ does *not* have a co-ordination number of three.**

Multidentate ligands can form three or more co-ordinate bonds since they donate at least three lone pairs of electrons. Bis[di(carboxymethyl)amino]ethane, commonly called EDTA, exists as the $EDTA^{4-}$ ion. This ligand can form six bonds with a metal ion. The lone pairs, which are donated to form co-ordinate bonds, are shown on its structure in Figure 7.

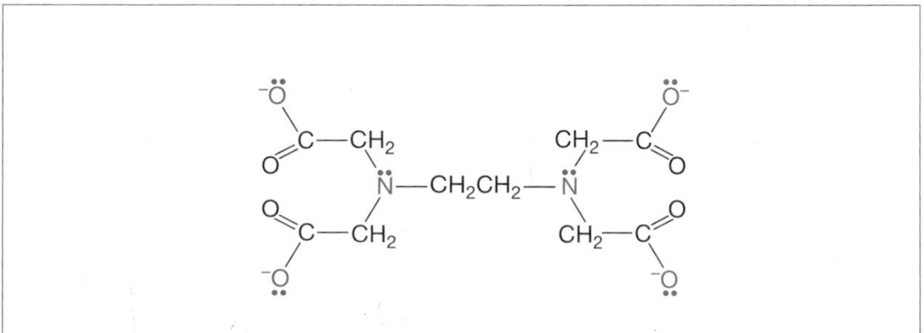

Figure 7 *The structure of $EDTA^{4-}$ showing the six lone pairs*

Figure 8 *The structure of an EDTA complex*

You can see from Figure 8 that when EDTA forms a complex it completely surrounds the metal ion (M). EDTA is a commonly used chelating agent and its complexes are extremely stable. The reason for this greater stability is because the reaction results in an increase in entropy.

e.g. $[Cu(H_2O)_6]^{2+} + EDTA^{4-} \rightleftharpoons [Cu(EDTA)]^{2-} + 6H_2O$

The six water ligands are replaced by one EDTA ligand and this results in an increase in the number of particles in solution and hence an increase in entropy.

EDTA has many useful applications due to its ability to 'trap' metal ions.

- It is used as an antidote to metal poisoning, as it removes dangerous metal ions, e.g. lead and mercury, from the blood which are then excreted as the stable EDTA complex.
- It is used in blood transfusions and surgical operations to remove calcium ions, which cause blood clotting.
- It is used to remove the calcium ions from hard water which if present cause the blockage of water pipes and form a nasty scum on bathwater. For this reason, many cleaning products, e.g. shampoo, contain EDTA.

Blood naturally contains a multidentate ligand in a complex called **haem**. The haem molecule contains four nitrogen atoms that are co-ordinately bonded to iron(II) (see Figure 9).

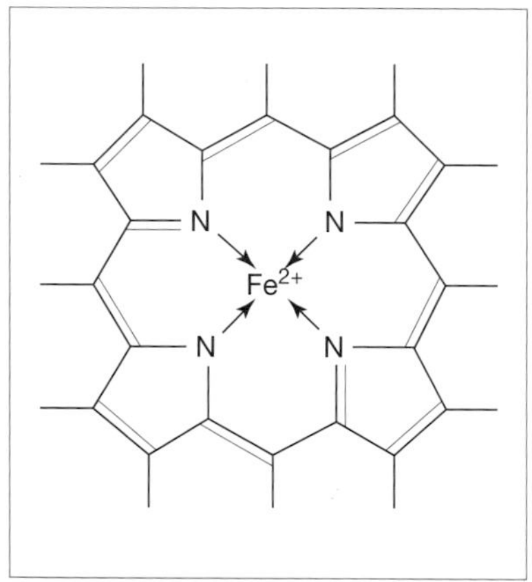

Figure 9 *Haem structure*

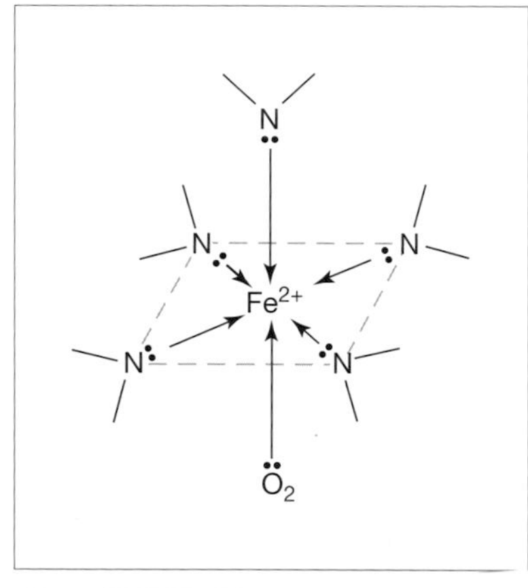

Figure 10 *Haemoglobin*

Two more co-ordinate bonds are formed with the iron(II) giving overall a co-ordination number of six. The fifth bond is between iron and a nitrogen atom in the protein globin. This produces **haemoglobin**. The sixth bond is formed between iron and either a water molecule (deoxyhaemoglobin), or an oxygen molecule (oxyhaemoglobin) (see Figure 10).

This complex plays an important role in the transport of oxygen in the blood. Oxygen molecules form weak co-ordinate bonds with the iron(II) ions in the complex and oxygen is transported in the bloodstream in this way.

Carbon monoxide can also form co-ordinate bonds with the complex but the bond thus formed is more stable than the one formed with oxygen molecules. When carbon monoxide is present in blood the oxygen-carrying capacity is greatly reduced. If the carbon monoxide concentration is high enough then life can be threatened (due to the formation of carboxyhaemoglobin).

9 Why is it essential that the bond formed between oxygen and iron(II) in haemoglobin is weak?

Shapes of complex ions

The commonest shapes are *octahedral* when there are six ligands attached and *tetrahedral* when four ligands are attached. You met these shapes when studying simple molecules in Module 1.

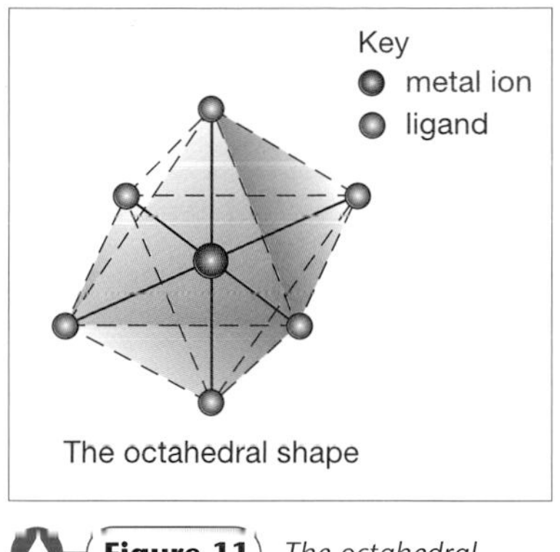

Figure 11 *The octahedral shape*

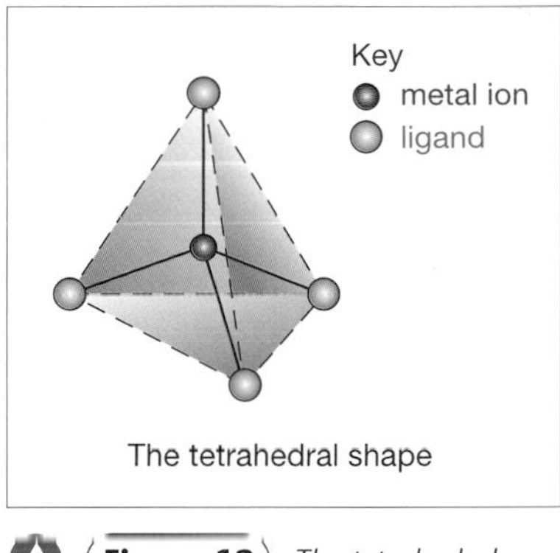

Figure 12 *The tetrahedral shape*

Complexes containing water and/or ammonia ligands usually have a co-ordination number of six, so they have an octahedral shape. Complexes containing chloride ligands normally have a co-ordination number of four, so they are tetrahedral in shape. The difference is due to the *size* of the ligands. Six water or ammonia molecules can fit around the transition metal ion but because the chloride ion is larger than a water or ammonia molecule there is only space for four chloride ligands.

$[Cu(H_2O)_2(NH_3)_4]^{2+}$ (Cu bonded to H_2O, H_2O, H_3N, H_3N, NH_3, NH_3) $[CuCl_4]^{2-}$ (Cu bonded to Cl, Cl, Cl, Cl)

Figure 13 *Examples of octahedral and tetrahedral complexes*

The complexes of copper(I) and silver(I), with a co-ordination number of two, have a *linear* shape.

$[H_3N \rightarrow Cu \leftarrow NH_3]^+$ $[NC \rightarrow Ag \leftarrow CN]^-$ $[Cl \rightarrow Ag \leftarrow Cl]^-$

Figure 14 *Examples of linear complexes*

When complexes have bidentate and multidentate ligands then the shape depends upon the number of co-ordinate bonds formed. EDTA and 1,2-diaminoethane form octahedral complexes (p. 215).

10 For each of the following complexes, give the shape, co-ordination number and oxidation state of the central metal ion:

a) $[Co(H_2O)_6]^{2+}$ **b)** $[Cu(EDTA)]^{2-}$
c) $[Cr(NH_3)_6]^{3+}$ **d)** $[CuCl_2]^-$

Naming complexes

The examples in Table 3 illustrate the systematic naming of complexes.

Formula	Name	Ligand	Number of ligands	Oxidation state of metal
$[Cu(H_2O)_6]^{2+}$	hexaquacopper(II)	H_2O	6	+2
$[CoCl_4]^{2-}$	tetrachlorocobaltate(II)	Cl^-	4	+2
$[Cr(NH_3)_6]^{2+}$	hexamminechromium(III)	NH_3	6	+3
$[Ag(NH_3)_2]^+$	diamminesilver(I)	NH_3	2	+1

Table 3

The name contains information about the complex. It gives:

1 the name of the ligand
2 the number of ligands
3 the oxidation state of the transition metal ion

The name of a ligand is changed when the ligand complexes with a transition metal ion:

Ligand	Name in complex
water	aqua
chloride	chloro
ammonia	ammine

Table 4

The prefixes are used to indicate the number of ligands:

Prefix	Number of ligands
hexa	6
tetra	4
di	2

Table 5

Notice that when the complex is negatively charged (anionic complex) then the name of the metal changes:

Positively charged complex	Negatively charged complex
silver	argentate
copper	cuprate
iron	ferrate
manganese	manganate
chromium	chromate
cobalt	cobaltate
vanadium	vanadate

Table 6

11 Name the following complexes

a) $[Co(H_2O)_6]^{2+}$ b) $[CuCl_4]^{2-}$
c) $[Co(NH_3)_6]^{3+}$ d) $[AgCl_2]^-$

12 Give the formula of each of the following complexes

a) hexaquascandium(III)
b) tetrachloromanganate(II)
c) hexamminecobalt(II)
d) diaquasilver(I)

The colour of transition metal ion complexes

One of the interesting features of transition metal chemistry is the variety of colours shown by the different complexes. Transition metal complex ions are coloured because they can absorb visible light. But the complex ions only absorb some of the visible light; the transmitted (or reflected) light therefore contains the frequencies that are not absorbed. This results in the complex ion having a characteristic colour.

The colour of a transition metal ion depends upon several factors including

1 the type of ligand attached
2 the co-ordination number
3 the oxidation state of the transition metal.

When any of these factors change then the colour of the transition metal ion changes, as illustrated by the examples below.

If an aqueous solution of a chromium(III) salt, containing the hexaqua ion, is treated with an excess of concentrated ammonia solution then the colour changes from blue/green to purple. This colour change is due to a *change of ligand*. The water ligands are replaced by ammonia ligands.

If an aqueous solution of a copper(II) salt, containing the hexaqua ion, is treated with an excess of concentrated hydrochloric acid the solution changes colour from blue to yellow/green. This is due to a *change in co-ordination number* as the water ligands are exchanged for chloride ligands.

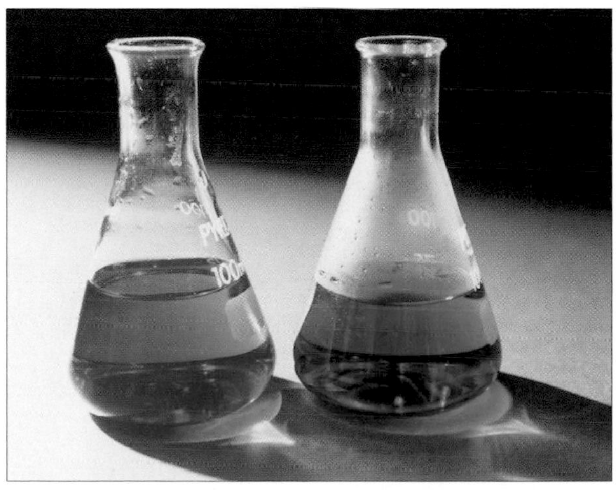

Figure 15 *$[Cu(H_2O)_6]^{2+}$ is blue, $[CuCl_4]^{2-}$ is yellow/green*

If an aqueous solution of a cobalt(II) salt, containing the hexaqua ion, is treated with an excess of ammonia solution then the colour changes from pink to pale yellow ('straw-coloured'). This colour rapidly darkens on exposure to air. The first colour change is due to a change of ligand. The second colour change is due to a *change in oxidation state* as cobalt(II) becomes cobalt(III) in the presence of oxygen.

These reactions are dealt with in more detail in Unit 15 (see pages 241–242) but a summary of the ions and their colours is given in Table 7.

$[Cr(H_2O)_6]^{3+}$	blue/green
$[Cr(NH_3)_6]^{3+}$	purple
$[Cu(H_2O)_6]^{2+}$	blue
$[CuCl_4]^{2-}$	yellow
$[Co(H_2O)_6]^{2+}$	pink
$[Co(NH_3)_6]^{2+}$	pale yellow
$[Co(NH_3)_6]^{3+}$	dark brown

Table 7

13 Give the formula of the cobalt(II) complex responsible for the pink colour when cobalt(II) chloride is dissolved in water.

14 Given that the electronic configuration of silver is [Kr] $4d^{10}5s^1$ deduce the colour of $[AgCl_2]^-$. Explain your answer.

The origin of colour

Coloured complexes are formed from transition metal ions having incomplete 3d sub-levels. When ligands are attached to a transition metal ion the 3d sub-level, consisting of five orbitals, splits to form two slightly different energy levels (see Figure 16). Electrons in the lower 3d sub-level absorb energy from visible and ultraviolet radiation which promotes (excites) them to the higher 3d sub-level. These are known as d–d transitions.

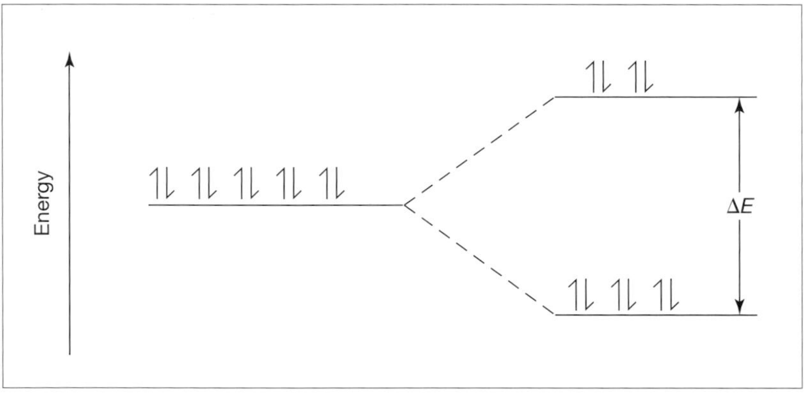

Figure 16 *The splitting of the 3d sub-level*

The difference in energy between the two sets of 3d sub-levels dictates the frequency of visible light absorbed and hence the colour of the complex.

This energy difference, ΔE, is related to the frequency of absorbed radiation, ν, by the expression:

$$\Delta E = h\nu$$

where h is Planck's constant.

Species with a $3d^0$ configuration do not normally show colour because there are no d electrons to excite. Species with a $3d^{10}$ configuration do not show colour because there is no vacant orbital for the electrons to be promoted to.

The colour we observe is due to the frequencies that are *not* absorbed, i.e. those that are reflected. When light of a particular colour is absorbed, its **complementary** colour is reflected. The regions of the visible spectrum are shown as a colour wheel in Figure 17 with the appropriate wavelength ranges.

For example, hexaquacopper(II) ions appear blue/green in colour because red light in the wavelength range 605–750 nm is absorbed (white light–red light = blue/green light). Blue/green is said to be complementary to red. The colour wheel shows the complementary colours.

15 A complex ion absorbs yellow light. What is the observed colour of this complex?

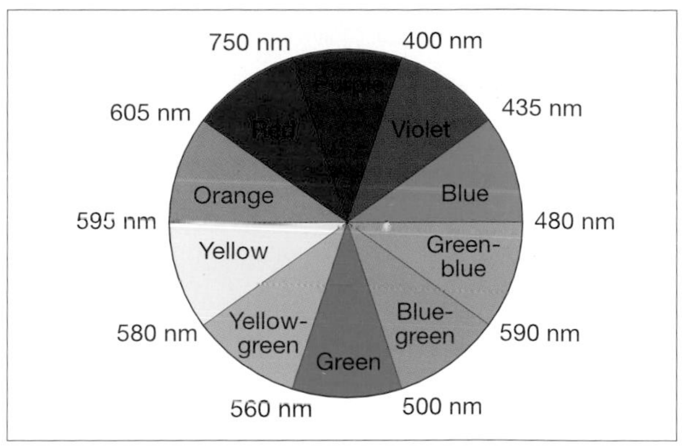

Ultraviolet and visible spectrophotometry can be used to measure the absorption frequency of a coloured compound. The visible absorption spectrum for hexaquacopper(II) ions is shown below (Figure 18).

Figure 17 *The colour wheel shows the range of absorbed light and the complementary colour which is reflected.*

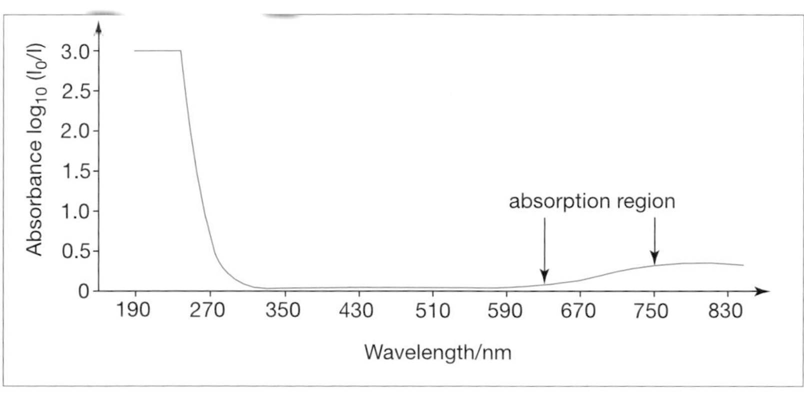

Figure 18 *The visible absorption spectrum for hexaquacopper(II) ions*

Using colour to determine concentration

A **colorimeter** can be used to measure the absorption of visible radiation. A colorimeter is a simple type of visible spectrophotometer. It consists of a visible light source, the radiation from which passes through an appropriate coloured filter, chosen so that the light it transmits will be absorbed by the sample. The radiation is then split into two beams. One of the beams is passed through a solution of the sample being analysed, the other is passed through pure solvent in the reference cell. The two beams are then compared by a light detector which determines the percentage of radiation absorbed (or transmitted) by the solution.

In a colorimeter the dilute solution to be tested is placed in a cuvette which is then placed in the colorimeter.

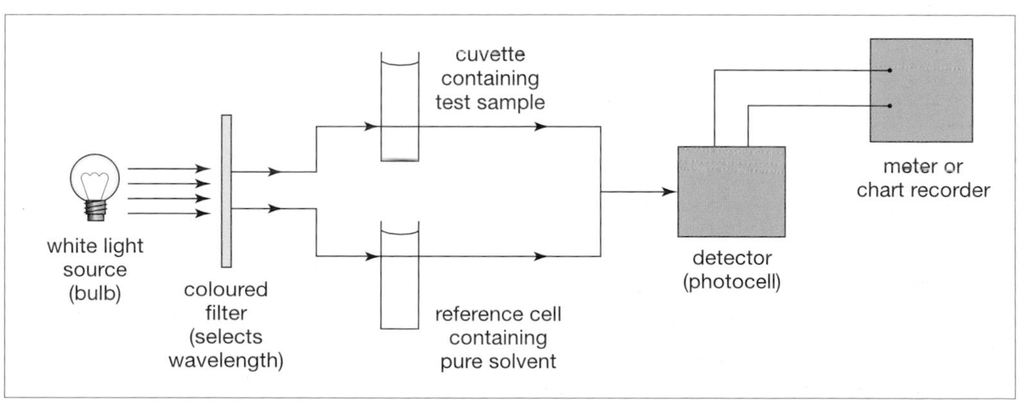

Figure 19 *Simplified diagram of a colorimeter*

Colorimeters can be used to determine the concentration of a coloured transition metal ion solution. The more concentrated the solution the more light it will absorb. The presence of a complexing ligand (e.g. EDTA) will intensify the colour. Solutions of known concentrations are placed in the colorimeter and their absorption values recorded by a meter. From these values a graph of concentration against absorption is plotted (calibration graph).

A solution of unknown concentration is then placed in the colorimeter and its absorption recorded. The concentration of this solution is then found from the calibration graph.

16 What is the term used to describe the relationship between the colours green and purple?

17 A solution of a complex ion has a peak equivalent to a wavelength of 600 nm on its visible spectrum. Use the colour wheel to deduce its observed colour.

18 The ion, $[CuCl_4]^{2-}$ is yellow/green in colour.

a) Explain briefly why it is coloured.

b) What colour of light will this complex absorb?

Applications of transition metal complexes

The uses of EDTA as a complexing agent have already been discussed (see page 215). Another complex used medicinally is **cisplatin**.

This is a platinum complex, $[Pt(NH_3)_2Cl_2]$, used to treat some types of cancer. The complex has a square planar shape with the chloride ions next to each other. (Trans-platin has the chloride ions opposite to each other.)

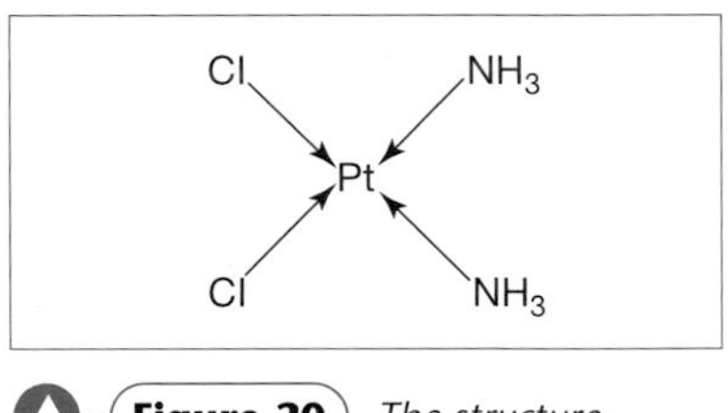

Figure 20 *The structure of cisplatin*

The complexes of silver

1 The diammine silver(I) complex, $[Ag(NH_3)_2]^+$ is formed by dissolving silver nitrate solution in aqueous ammonia. It is used to differentiate between aldehydes and ketones and is commonly called Tollen's reagent.

For example, with ethanal a characteristic 'silver mirror' is formed:

$$CH_3CHO(aq) + 2Ag^+(aq) + H_2O(l) \rightarrow 2Ag(s) + CH_3COOH(aq) + 2H^+(aq)$$

Ⓢ **19 What happens when a ketone is treated with Tollen's reagent? Explain your answer.**

2 The cyanide complex $[Ag(CN)_2]^-$ is used in electroplating. A solution containing this complex is formed when a silver salt is dissolved in aqueous potassium or sodium cyanide. The resulting solution is used as the electrolyte in silver plating. The positive electrode is pure silver and the object to be plated is the negative electrode.

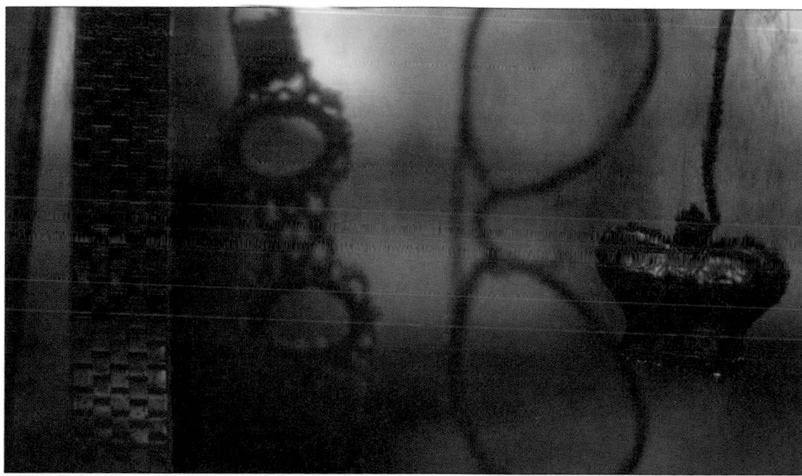

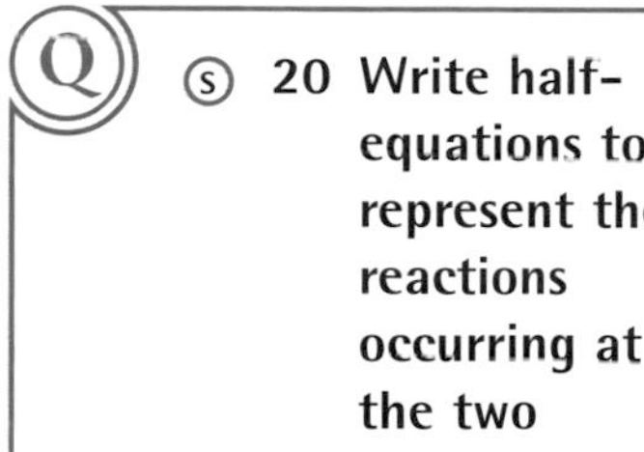

Ⓢ **20 Write half-equations to represent the reactions occurring at the two electrodes.**

Figure 21 *Silver electroplating*

3 The thiosulphate ion can act as a ligand. One of its complexes is $[Ag(S_2O_3)_2]^{3-}$ which is formed when sodium thiosulphate ('hypo') is used in the development of photographic negatives. When a photographic film is exposed to light the silver bromide on the surface of the film is reduced to silver metal. During developing, the unexposed silver bromide on the photographic film is dissolved by the sodium thiosulphate and is removed from the surface of the film so that not all the negative turns black (see Module 2).

$$AgBr(s) + 2S_2O_3^{2-}(aq) \longrightarrow [Ag(S_2O_3)_2]^{3-}(aq) + Br^-(aq)$$

Ⓢ **21 Write an equation to show the effect of light on silver bromide.**

Key Ideas 212 – 223

- **The characteristics of transition metals arise from an incomplete 3d sub-level in the atoms or ions.**
- **These characteristics include complex formation and the formation of coloured ions.**
- **Complexes contain lone pair donors called ligands.**
- **Ligands can be unidentate, bidentate or multidentate depending on how many lone pairs of electrons they donate to the transition metal ion.**
- **Ligands form co-ordinate bonds with the transition metal ions. The number of bonds formed, the co-ordination number, dictates the shape of the ion.**
- **The colour of a complex ion depends on the oxidation state of the metal ion, the type of ligand present and the co-ordination number of the complex.**

2 Variable oxidation states

Oxidation states were first introduced at AS Chemistry. They are particularly important when discussing the properties of transition metals. The 4s and the 3d electrons in the transition metals are available for bonding and this results in the transition metal having a variable oxidation state. Oxidation states of the transition metal compounds help dictate their colour and their chemical properties.

The common oxidation states

The common oxidation states of the transition metals are shown in Table 1.

Sc	Ti	V	Cr	Mn	Fe	Co	Ni	Cu
								+1
	+2	+2	+2	+2	+2	+2	+2	+2
+3	+3	+3	+3	+3	+3	+3		
	+4	+4		+4				
		+5						
			+6	+6				
				+7				

Table 1

Apart from scandium, which only has an oxidation state of +3, all the first row transition metals have an oxidation state of +2 when the 4s electrons are used in bonding. The stability of this oxidation state increases across the series as the nuclear charge increases and the remaining electrons are held more tightly.

For oxidation states greater than +2 the 3d electrons, as well as the 4s electrons, are used in bonding. From scandium the oxidation states increase up to manganese, which has a maximum oxidation state of +7. After this the +3 and +2 oxidation states predominate.

22 a) Give the electronic structures for the following transition metals in the oxidation states shown: (i) Ti(III) (ii) Ti(IV) (iii) V(IV) (iv) Ni(II)

b) Which of these species are non-transitional? Explain your answer.

The lower oxidation states are found as simple ions, M^{2+} or M^{3+}. The higher oxidation states *only* exist when the metals are covalently bonded to very electronegative elements such as oxygen.

e.g. VO_2^+, VO_3^-, MnO_4^-, CrO_4^{2-} and $Cr_2O_7^{2-}$

23 Give the oxidation states of the metal in the oxyions on the left.

The *higher* oxidation states are *oxidising*. The MnO_4^- ions and the $Cr_2O_7^{2-}$ ions are powerful oxidising agents (see page 228).

The *lower* oxidation states are *reducing*, e.g. Cr^{2+} and Fe^{2+}

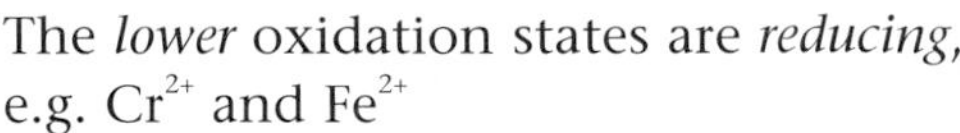

24 Write an equation to show the oxidation of Fe^{2+}(aq) by $Cr_2O_7^{2-}$(aq).

The oxidation states of vanadium

Vanadium has four common oxidation states, vanadium(IV) being the most stable. The different oxidation states can be observed when a solution of ammonium vanadate(V) is reduced using zinc and concentrated hydrochloric acid. Ammonium vanadate(V) is a white powder that dissolves slowly in hydrochloric acid forming an orange solution. The addition of zinc to this acidic solution reduces the vanadium from +5 to +2. This is observed as a series of colour changes from orange through blue and green to violet.

25 Why is ammonium vanadate(V) white?

	Vanadium species present	Colour
Vanadium(V)	VO_3^-	colourless
Vanadium(V)	VO_2^+	orange
Vanadium(IV)	$[VO(H_2O)_5]^{2+}$	blue
Vanadium(III)	$[V(H_2O)_6]^{3+}$	green
Vanadium(II)	$[V(H_2O)_6]^{2+}$	violet

Table 2 Note that the simple ions V^{5+}(aq) and V^{4+}(aq) do *not* exist

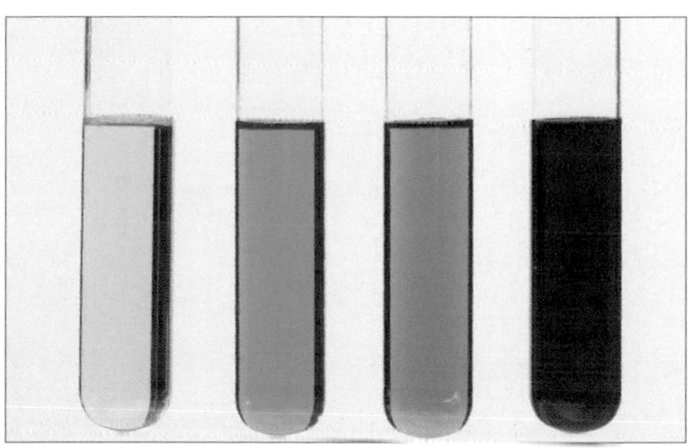

Figure 1 *The colours of vanadium species*

The vanadium(II) ion is unstable and the solution is rapidly oxidised in air if the zinc is removed.

26 What colour changes will be observed as the vanadium(II) is oxidised?

27 Which one of the following species is most likely to act as a reducing agent: VO_2^+, VO_3^-, V^{2+}, V^{3+}. Explain your answer.

The oxidation states of chromium

Chromium has three common oxidation states, +2, +3 and +6.

	Chromium species	Colour
Chromium(VI)	$Cr_2O_7^{2-}$	orange
Chromium(VI)	CrO_4^{2-}	yellow
Chromium(III)	$[Cr(H_2O)_6]^{3+}$	green
Chromium(II)	$[Cr(H_2O)_6]^{2+}$	blue

Note that the simple ion $Cr^{6+}(aq)$ does *not* exist

28 Name the ions $Cr_2O_7^{2-}$ and CrO_4^{2-}

When potassium chromate(VI) is reacted with zinc and concentrated hydrochloric acid the chromium is reduced from +6 to +2.
The colour changes observed are yellow to orange to green to blue. Vigorous effervescence is observed as hydrogen, the reducing agent, is produced.

29 Write an equation to show the formation of hydrogen from the reactants stated above.

30 Why does the solution turn orange?

The Cr^{2+} ion is very highly reducing and only exists in the absence of air. If the zinc metal is filtered off and the solution allowed to stand in air, then the chromium(II) is rapidly oxidised to chromium(III) and the colour of the solution will change from blue to green.

Solutions of chromium(III) can be readily oxidised to chromium(VI) by heating with hydrogen peroxide in excess alkaline solution (or using sodium peroxide).

$$2Cr^{3+}(aq) + 3O_2^{2-}(aq) + \underset{\text{excess}}{4OH^-(aq)} \rightleftharpoons \underset{\text{chromate(VI)}}{2CrO_4^{2-}(aq)} + 2H_2O(l)$$

If this solution is acidified then the chromate(VI) changes to dichromate(VI):

$$2CrO_4^{2-}(aq) + 2H^+(aq) \rightleftharpoons Cr_2O_7^{2-}(aq) + H_2O(l)$$

Note that in this equilibrium reaction there is *no* change in oxidation state. The equilibrium is pH dependent. Adding an acid shifts the equilibrium to the right and adding a base shifts the equilibrium to the left, as the H^+ ions are removed as water:

$$H^+(aq) + \underset{\text{base}}{OH^-(aq)} \rightarrow H_2O(l)$$

31 a) Explain the following observations by identifying the species A–C. Green solution A turns yellow on the addition of an oxidising agent in the presence of sodium hydroxide. Yellow solution B forms an orange solution, C, on addition of dilute sulphuric acid but the yellow colour returns when alkali is added.

b) Name a suitable oxidising agent for the conversion of A into B.

Dichromate(VI) can be reduced, in acid solution, to chromium(III) using a variety of reducing agents, e.g. Fe^{2+}.

$$6Fe^{2+} + Cr_2O_7^{2-} + 14H^+ \rightarrow 6Fe^{3+} + 2Cr^{3+} + 7H_2O$$

This redox reaction was discussed in Unit 13 and is revisited in the following section on redox titrations below.

Cobalt(II) solutions are readily oxidised to cobalt(III) in alkaline solution. The oxidation is slow in air but is rapid when an oxidising agent such as hydrogen peroxide is used (see page 246).

Key Ideas 224 – 227

- **Transition metals show variable oxidation states in their compounds.**
- **The higher oxidation states are oxidising and the lower oxidation states are reducing.**
- **Vanadium(V) can be reduced to oxidation states +4. +3 and +2 using zinc and concentrated hydrochloric acid.**
- **Chromium(VI) can be reduced to oxidation states +3 and +2.**
- **A pH-dependent equilibrium exists between dichromate(VI) and chromate(VI).**

3 Redox titrations

Potassium manganate(VII) and potassium dichromate(VI) are widely used as quantitative oxidising agents in redox titrations.

$MnO_4^- + 8H^+ + 5e^- \rightarrow Mn^{2+} + 4H_2O \quad E^\ominus = +1.52V$

$Cr_2O_7^{2-} + 14H^+ + 6e^- \rightarrow 2Cr^{3+} + 7H_2O \quad E^\ominus = +1.33V$

In acid solution they are both capable of oxidising any redox couple with an $E^\ominus$ value of less than +1.33V.

Analysis of iron tablets

This is a typical experiment that you may carry out in the laboratory.

Introduction

Iron tablets from the pharmacist contain anhydrous iron(II) sulphate, a cheap and soluble form of iron, plus unreactive binders. Iron tablets are taken to boost the Fe^{2+} concentration of the blood in people who suffer from anaemia.

Each tablet can be dissolved in dilute sulphuric acid. Assuming that all the iron in the tablets is in the form of Fe^{2+} and that it all dissolves, it is possible to estimate the percentage iron II sulphate content of each tablet by titration against standardised potassium manganate VII.

Method

1. Weigh out 8 iron tablets.
2. Dissolve the tablets in about 100 cm^3 of 2 M sulphuric acid in a beaker.
3. The outer coat of the tablet will probably not dissolve so the solution will need filtering.
4. Pour the filtrate into a 250 cm^3 volumetric flask. Ensure that all the washings from the conical flask and filter paper are included. Make up to the mark with distilled water.
5. Pipette 25 cm^3 of this solution into a conical flask. Add about 25 cm^3 of dilute sulphuric acid.
6. Titrate against 0.020 M potassium manganate VII solution until you reach the end-point, which is a change from colourless to permanent pale pink.
7. Repeat until concordant results are obtained. In this experiment, since it is difficult to read the meniscus, concordance of ± 0.10 cm^3 is acceptable.

This type of titration is carried out with the potassium manganate(VII) solution, or potassium dichromate(VI) solution, in the burette and the acidified iron(II) solution in the conical flask. Both oxidising agents only work in strongly acidic conditions, since H^+ ions are required for the reactions:

$$MnO_4^-(aq) + 8H^+(aq) + 5e^- \rightarrow Mn^{2+}(aq) + 4H_2O(l)$$

$$Cr_2O_7^{2-}(aq) + 14H^+(aq) + 6e^- \rightarrow 2Cr^{3+}(aq) + 7H_2O(l)$$

The choice of acid is important. Notice that dilute sulphuric acid is used in the titration described above. Hydrochloric acid *cannot* be used in manganate(VII) titrations since the manganate will oxidise the chloride ions to chlorine. However hydrochloric acid can be used in dichromate(VI) titrations since the dichromate(VI) ions are not powerful enough to oxidise chloride ions (see page 207). Weak acids such as ethanoic acid cannot be used since they do not provide a high enough concentration of H^+ ions.

Notice that no indicator is used in the titration described. The potassium manganate(VII) acts as its own indicator. As the reaction proceeds the purple manganate(VII) is reduced to manganese(II), which is effectively colourless. At the end point one drop of excess manganate(VII) will produce a permanent pale pink coloration in the solution.

Potassium dichromate(VI) titrations need an indicator. The indicator used is barium *N*-phenylphenylamine-4-sulphonate, and the titration has an end point of blue-green to violet. When potassium dichromate(VI) is used to oxidise iron(II) to iron(III) then some concentrated phosphoric(V) acid, H_3PO_4, is added to enhance the end point.

Dealing with the results

Both oxidising agents can be used to quantitatively oxidise iron(II) to iron(III):

$$Fe^{2+}(aq) \rightarrow Fe^{3+}(aq) + e^-$$

The balanced equations for the redox reactions are:

$$5Fe^{2+}(aq) + MnO_4^-(aq) + 8H^+(aq) \rightarrow 5Fe^{3+}(aq) + Mn^{2+}(aq) + 4H_2O(l)$$

$$6Fe^{2+}(aq) + Cr_2O_7^{2-}(aq) + 14H^+(aq) \rightarrow 6Fe^{3+}(aq) + 2Cr^{3+}(aq) + 7H_2O(l)$$

In the experiment described the mass of the iron tablets was 6.82 g. The mean titre value, found by averaging the concordant titrations results, was 24.55 cm^3 of 0.020 M $KMnO_4$.

Number of moles of $MnO_4^-(aq)$ $= MV/1000$

$= 0.020 \times 24.55/1000$

$= 4.91 \times 10^{-4}$

From the equation, the molar ratio of $MnO_4^-(aq)$: $Fe^{2+}(aq)$ = 1 : 5, hence

Number of moles of $Fe^{2+}(aq)$ in 25 cm^3 $= 4.91 \times 10^{-4} \times 5 = 2.45 \times 10^{-3}$

Number of moles of $Fe^{2+}(aq)$ in 250 cm^3 $= 2.45 \times 10^{-3} \times 10 = 2.45 \times 10^{-2}$

The M_r of $FeSO_4$ = 152

So the mass of $FeSO_4$ in the tablets $= 2.45 \times 10^{-2} \times 152 = 3.73$ g

The percentage by mass of $FeSO_4$ in the tablets $= 3.73/6.82 \times 100 = 54.7\%$

32 How is the end-point detected in a potassium manganate(VII) titration?

The examples shown below illustrate different types of redox titrations and how the calculations should be attempted.

Worked examples

1 A sample of steel with a mass of 0.25 g was dissolved in dilute sulphuric acid. The resulting solution required 42.05 cm^3 of 0.0166 M potassium dichromate for complete oxidation. Calculate the percentage, by mass, of the iron in the steel.

The sulphuric acid reacts with the iron in the steel, forming iron(II):

$$Fe(s) + 2H^+(aq) \rightarrow Fe^{2+}(aq) + H_2(g)$$

The potassium dichromate(VI) then oxidises Fe^{2+} to Fe^{3+}:

$$6Fe^{2+}(aq) + Cr_2O_7^{2-}(aq) + 14H^+(aq) \rightarrow 6Fe^{3+}(aq) + 2Cr^{3+}(aq) + 7H_2O(l)$$

From the equation the reacting molar ratio is 6 : 1.

Moles of dichromate(VI) $= MV/1000$

$= (0.0166 \times 42.05)/1000 = 6.98 \times 10^{-3}$

Moles of iron(II) $= 6.98 \times 10^{-3} \times 6 = 4.188 \times 10^{-3}$ mol

Mass of iron $= 4.188 \times 10^{-3} \times 56 = 0.235$ g

Percentage of iron in the steel $= (0.235/0.25) \times 100 = 93.8\%$

2 Ammonium iron(II) sulphate crystals $(NH_4)_2SO_4.FeSO_4.xH_2O$ contain water of crystallisation. Find the value of x using the experimental data below.

In an experiment 9.750 g of the crystals were dissolved in water and the solution made up to 250 cm^3. A 25 cm^3 portion of the solution was acidified with dilute sulphuric acid and titrated with 0.0200 M potassium manganate(VII) solution: 24.85 cm^3 of the potassium manganate solution were required.

In the ammonium iron(II) sulphate crystals the only ion which undergoes redox is $Fe^{2+}(aq)$:

$$5Fe^{2+}(aq) + MnO_4^-(aq) + 8H^+(aq) \rightarrow 5Fe^{3+}(aq) + Mn^{2+}(aq) + 4H_2O(l)$$

Moles of MnO_4^- $= MV/1000 = (0.02 \times 24.85)/1000 = 4.97 \times 10^{-4}$

Moles of Fe^{2+} in 25 cm^3 $= 4.97 \times 10^{-4} \times 5 = 2.485 \times 10^{-3}$

Moles of Fe^{2+} in 250 cm^3 $= 2.485 \times 10^{-3} \times 10 = 0.02485$

Since one iron(II) is present in $(NH_4)_2SO_4.FeSO_4.xH_2O$ then the number of moles of $(NH_4)_2SO_4.FeSO_4.xH_2O = 0.02485$

M_r = mass/moles = 9.750/0.02485 = 392.3

So the M_r of the hydrated crystals is 392.3

But $(NH_4)_2SO_4.FeSO_4$ = 284

Hence xH_2O = (392.3 − 284) = 108.3

1 mol of H_2O = 18 g; x mol of H_2O = 108.3 g

therefore x = 108.3/18 = 6.02

In the formula x must be a whole number

Hence the full formula is $(NH_4)_2SO_4.FeSO_4.6H_2O$

33 Calculate the concentration of a solution of iron(II) if 25.0 cm^3 of the solution requires 26.50 cm^3 of 0.0200 M potassium dichromate(VI) for complete oxidation.

34 7.490 g of $FeSO_4.xH_2O$ were dissolved in water, acidified and the solution made up to 250 cm^3. A 25 cm^3 portion of this solution needed 26.50 cm^3 of 0.017 M potassium dichromate(VI) for complete oxidation. Calculate the value of x.

Mixtures of iron(II) and iron(III) salts can be analysed by titrations with potassium manganate(VII) or potassium dichromate(VI).

3 A solution contained $Fe^{2+}(aq)$ and $Fe^{3+}(aq)$.

A 25 cm^3 portion of the solution was acidified with dilute sulphuric acid and required 17.8 cm^3 of 0.0166 M potassium dichromate for complete oxidation.

A further 25 cm^3 sample was reacted with zinc and dilute sulphuric acid to reduce the Fe^{3+} to Fe^{2+}: the unreacted zinc was removed by filtration. The resulting solution required 21.5 cm^3 of 0.0166 M potassium dichromate(VI) for complete oxidation.

Calculate the concentration of the $Fe^{2+}(aq)$ and $Fe^{3+}(aq)$ in the solution and hence the percentage Fe^{2+} in the mixture.

$$6Fe^{2+}(aq) + Cr_2O_7^{2-}(aq) + 14H^+(aq) \rightarrow 6Fe^{3+}(aq) + 2Cr^{3+}(aq) + 7H_2O(l)$$

In the first titration only the Fe^{2+} reacts:

Moles of $Cr_2O_7^{2-}$ = $MV/1000$ = $(0.0166 \times 17.80)/1000 = 2.955 \times 10^{-4}$

Moles Fe^{2+} = $2.955 \times 10^{-4} \times 6 = 1.773 \times 10^{-3}$

Molarity of Fe^{2+} = (moles × 1000)/V = $(1.773 \times 10^{-3} \times 1000)/25 = 0.0709$ M

In the second titration the *total* iron concentration (i.e. Fe^{2+} and Fe^{3+}) is found, since the iron(III) content of the mixture has been reduced to iron(II) using zinc.

Moles of $Cr_2O_7^{2-}$ = $MV/1000$ = $(0.0166 \times 21.90)/1000 = 3.635 \times 10^{-4}$

Moles Fe^{2+} = $3.635 \times 10^{-4} \times 6 = 2.181 \times 10^{-3}$

Molarity of Fe^{2+} = (moles × 1000)/*V* = $(2.181 \times 10^{-3} \times 1000)/25 = 0.0872$ M

Hence molarity of Fe^{3+}(aq) in the mixture was 0.0872 − 0.0709 = 0.0163 M

The percentage of Fe^{2+}(aq) in the solution $= \dfrac{0.0709}{0.0872} \times 100 = 81.3\%$

Note that the **percentage** of Fe^{2+}(aq) could have been calculated directly from the titre values.

Percentage Fe^{2+}(aq) $= \dfrac{\text{first titre}}{\text{second titre}} \times 100 = \dfrac{17.80}{21.90} \times 100 = 81.3\%$

35 A 25 cm³ sample of a solution containing iron(II) and iron(III) sulphates together with dilute sulphuric acid required 21.90 cm³ of 0.02 M potassium manganate(VII) for complete oxidation. A further sample of the same solution was treated with tin(II) chloride solution to reduce the iron(III) to iron(II): this solution then needed 36.60 cm³ of 0.02 M potassium manganate(VII) for complete oxidation.

Calculate the concentrations of the iron(II) and iron(III) in grams per dm³.

36 25.0 cm³ of a solution containing a mixture of sulphuric and ethanedioic acids required 37.5 cm³ of 0.100 M NaOH for complete neutralisation. Excess dilute sulphuric acid was then added to the resulting solution; 12.5 cm³ of 0.020 M $KMnO_4$ were required for oxidation. Determine the molarities of the two acids in the original mixture.

Key Ideas 228 – 232

- **Potassium manganate(VII) and potassium dichromate(VI) are widely used as quantitative oxidising agents in redox titrations.**
- **These titrations must be carried out in acid solution.**
- **Typical titrations involve the oxidation of iron(II) and ethanedioate ions.**
- **Potassium manganate(VII) is self-indicating.**
- **Dilute sulphuric acid can be used to acidify both of the oxidising agents, but dilute hydrochloric acid can only be used with potassium dichromate(VI).**
- **Calculations can be performed using the reacting molar ratio.**

4 Catalysis

At GCSE you will have studied catalysts as substances that increase the rate of a chemical reaction. In AS Chemistry, the introduction of activation energy and Maxwell–Boltzmann distribution curves extended this study. In this unit we will consider the action of transition metals and their compounds behaving as **homogeneous** and **heterogeneous** catalysts.

Increasing the rate of a chemical reaction

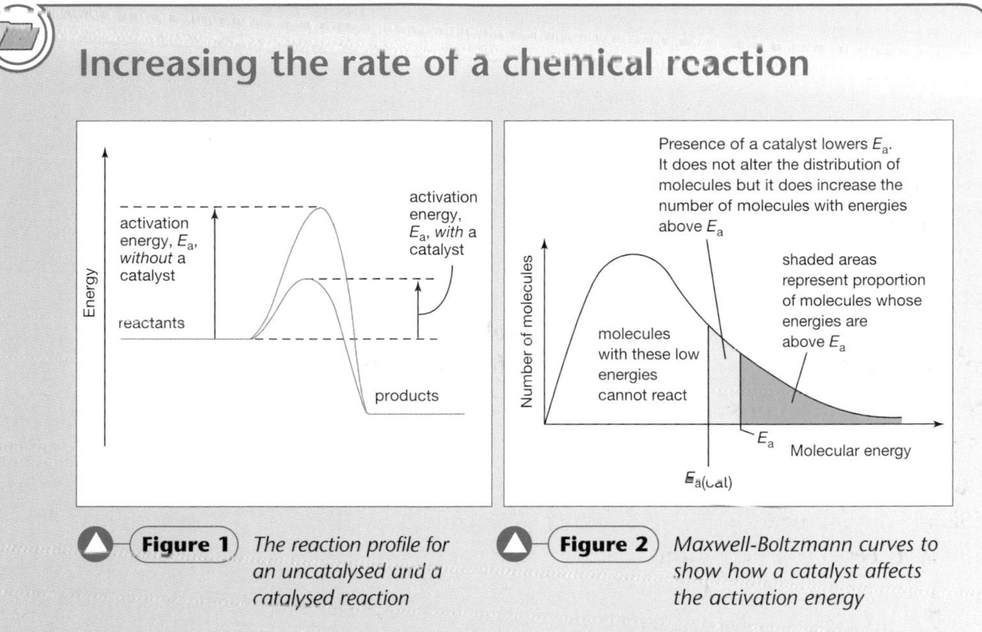

Figure 1 *The reaction profile for an uncatalysed and a catalysed reaction*

Figure 2 *Maxwell-Boltzmann curves to show how a catalyst affects the activation energy*

Essentially a catalyst provides an alternate reaction pathway that has a *lower* **activation energy**, E_a. In the presence of a catalyst *more* of the reactant particles will have energy in excess of the lowered activation energy. Therefore, there is an increase in the percentage of successful collisions, resulting in an increase in the rate of reaction.

In reversible reactions a catalyst increases the rate of *both* the forward and reverse reaction *equally*. The equilibrium position of the reaction is reached more quickly but there is no change in the position of the equilibrium.

Transition metals and transition metal compounds have **variable oxidation states** and this allows many of them to act as catalysts in a wide range of reactions and industrial processes.

Transition metals can act as heterogeneous and as homogeneous catalysts. A catalyst will be specific to a particular reaction or type of reaction.

37 Explain the following observations. A solution of hydrogen peroxide shows no observable reaction until a small amount of solid manganese(IV)oxide is added. Then vigorous effervescence occurs.

Heterogeneous catalysts

These are catalysts that are in a different state to the reactants.

Solid transition metals and their compounds catalyse many reactions involving gases. Examples include **iron** in the Haber Process, **vanadium(V) oxide** in the Contact Process and **nickel** in hydrogenation reactions involving organic compounds (see in Module 3 the manufacture of margarine from vegetable oils). The equations for these reactions are given below:

The Haber Process: $N_2(g) + 3H_2(g) \overset{Fe}{\rightleftharpoons} 2NH_3(g)$

The Contact Process: $SO_2(g) + \frac{1}{2}O_2(g) \overset{V_2O_5}{\rightleftharpoons} SO_3(g)$

Hydrogenation reactions, e.g. $CH_2{=}CH_2(g) + H_2(g) \overset{Ni}{\rightarrow} CH_3CH_3(g)$

The Contact Process can be used to illustrate the action of a heterogeneous catalyst. The mechanism can be divided into two steps:

Step 1: Sulphur dioxide diffuses onto the surface of the catalyst and a redox reaction occurs. The vanadium(V) oxide oxidises the sulphur dioxide forming sulphur trioxide.

$$\underset{+5}{V_2O_5(s)} + SO_2(g) \rightarrow \underset{+4}{V_2O_4(s)} + SO_3(g)$$

Step 2: The vanadium(IV) oxide formed then reacts with oxygen to regenerate vanadium(V) oxide.

$$\underset{+4}{V_2O_4} + \frac{1}{2}O_2(g) \rightarrow \underset{+5}{V_2O_5(s)}$$

Overall: $SO_2(g) + \frac{1}{2}O_2(g) \rightleftharpoons SO_3(g)$

Ⓢ **38 a) Explain why, in the Contact Process, sulphur dioxide does not react readily with oxygen at 298K even though the K_p for the reaction is 4×10^{22} kPa^{-1}.**

b) How does the presence of V_2O_5 increase the reaction rate?

c) What effect does V_2O_5 have on the position of the equilibrium?

Surface adsorption theory

Heterogeneous catalysis occurs on the *surface* of the solid catalyst. There are **active sites** on the catalyst's surface where the catalysed reactions occur. Surface catalysis occurs in three separate steps:

1 **adsorption** of a reactant
2 reaction
3 **desorption** of a product.

The reactants diffuse onto the surface of the catalyst. In the first step of a catalytic process the reactant molecules *adsorb* onto the surface of the catalyst. This often involves the formation of weak bonds between the reactant and the catalyst surface.

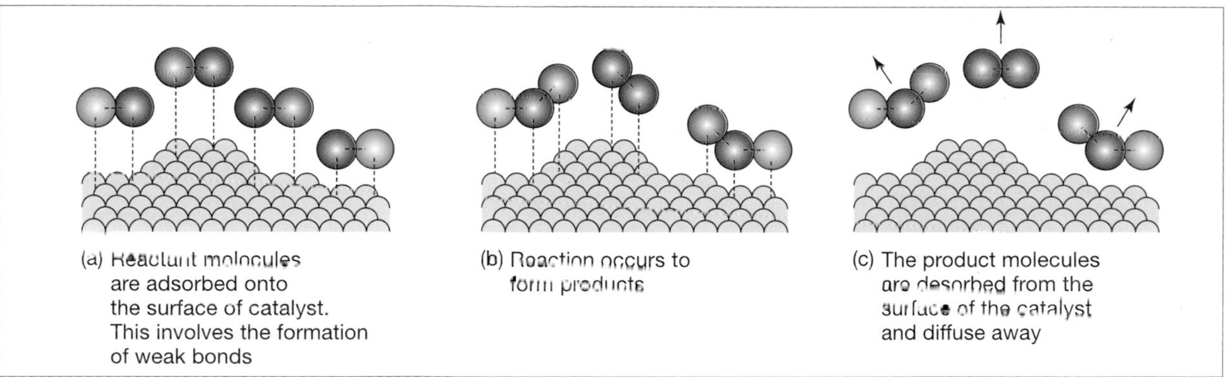

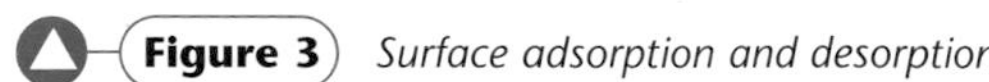
Figure 3 *Surface adsorption and desorption*

Once the reactant has been adsorbed onto the surface then an increased rate of reaction in step 2 can occur in one of several different ways:

- Some of the bonds in the molecule may be weakened or broken, forming a more reactive species.
- The orientation of the adsorbed reactant may be such that collisions with other reactant particles are more favourable.
- When the molecules are adsorbed onto the surface they can migrate across the surface of the catalyst.
- The adsorption of reactant molecules on a catalyst surface effectively increases the concentration of the molecules.

In the third step the products are *desorbed* from the surface of the solid catalyst and diffuse away (see Figure 3).

We can compare surface catalysis to the catalytic action of **enzymes**. The enzymes have active sites that act as a 'lock'. The reactant molecules (substrate) must have the correct configuration ('key') to fit into the 'lock'. Once the substrate is attached bonds are broken and formed producing the product, which then leaves the active sites, allowing other substrate molecules to react.

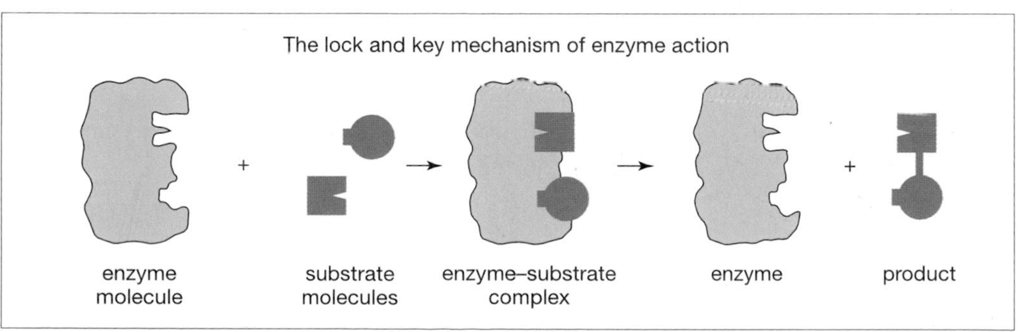

Figure 4 *The lock and key mechanism of enzymes*

The efficiency of a catalyst

The strength of adsorption on, and desorption from, the catalyst's surface plays an important role in the efficiency of a catalyst.

If the adsorption is too weak then the reactant does not stay on the surface of the catalyst long enough for a reaction to occur. For example, the adsorption on the surface of silver is very weak and as a result silver has poor catalytic activity. This is sometimes useful since it may help to produce a slow enough reaction when required. This is the case in the formation of epoxyethane, which is catalysed by silver.

$$CH_2 = CH_2\,(g) + \tfrac{1}{2}O_2 \longrightarrow \underset{\text{(ring with O)}}{CH_2{-}CH_2}\,(g)$$

The reaction of ethene and oxygen is an exothermic reaction and the heat produced can cause the ethoxyethane to react explosively. When silver is used as a catalyst, the poor catalytic activity results in a slow release of heat energy and this reduces the chance of the epoxyethane reacting (see Module 3).

Ⓢ **39 Explain, in terms of its structure, why epoxyethane is so reactive.**

40 Why is the production of epoxyethane carried out at low temperatures?

Once the reaction has occurred the active sites are only regenerated if the product desorbs from the surface. If the adsorption is too strong then desorption does not occur quickly enough and thus the rate of migration of more reactant molecules over the surface of the catalyst is reduced. Tungsten is an example of a strong adsorber, and thus a poor catalyst. It does not release the reaction products quickly enough to increase the overall reaction rate.

41 What is the chemical symbol for tungsten?

Efficient catalysts achieve a good balance between adsorption of reactants and desorption of products. This is illustrated by the 'volcano' curves shown in Figure 5.

42 Give two reasons why iron, as opposed to silver, is used as a catalyst in the Haber Process.

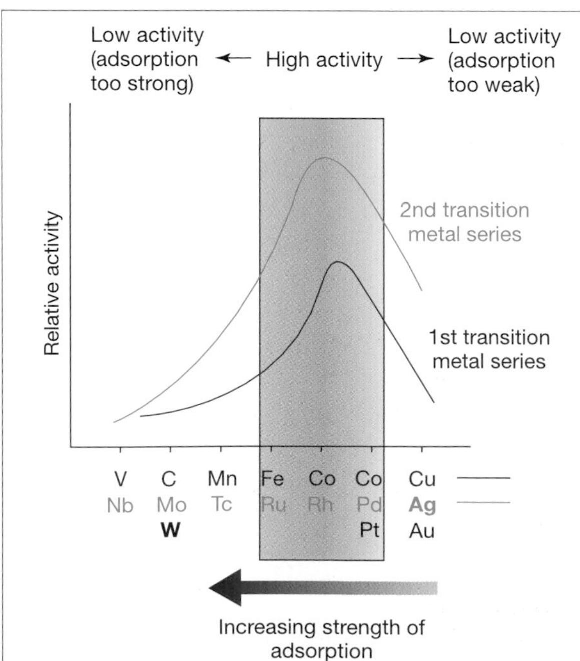

Figure 5 *Volcano curves*

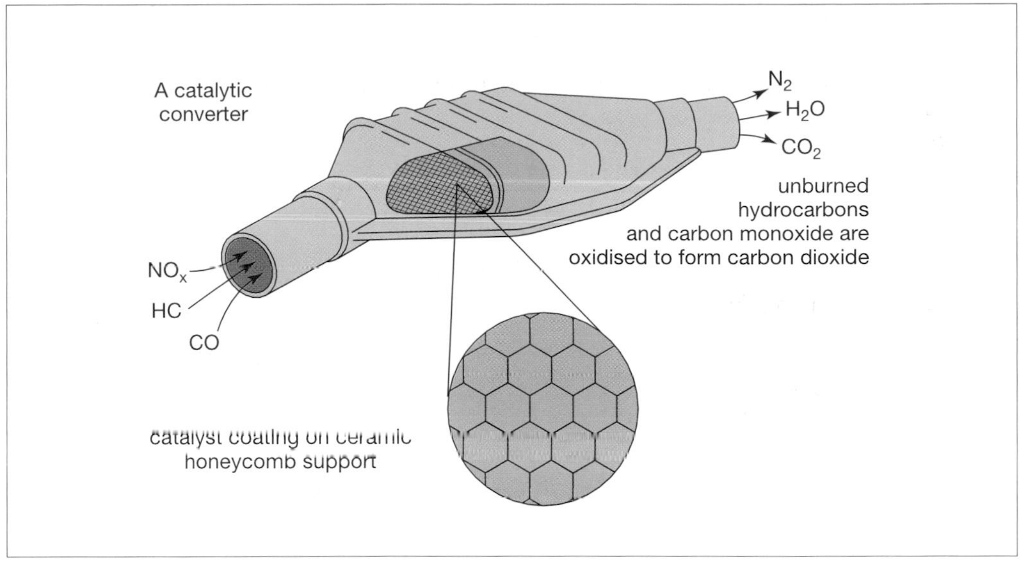

Figure 6 *A large surface area increases the efficiency of a catalyst*

To increase the efficiency of a solid catalyst the surface area should be as large as possible in order to increase the number of active sites available. A good example of this is in **catalytic converters**, used to clean the emissions from car engines (see Module 3). The catalyst in the converter is a mixture of platinum and rhodium metals, both of which are very expensive. The metals are sprayed onto a ceramic honeycomb support to provide maximum surface area for minimum cost.

43 Why are platinum and rhodium metals used as catalysts in catalytic converters, despite their expense?

Catalytic 'poisoning'

The active sites play a key role in heterogeneous catalysis and impurities present in the reaction can 'poison' the catalyst by blocking the active sites. This reduces the efficiency of the catalyst and increases the cost of the process. The platinum and rhodium catalysts used in catalytic converters are 'poisoned' by lead compounds and cars fitted with these converters must not use leaded petrol.

The catalyst used in the Haber Process is iron, which is 'poisoned' by sulphur. The hydrogen used in the process is obtained by the reaction of steam with natural gas. Natural gas contains some sulphur compounds, and the gases used in the Haber Process are cleaned (scrubbed) to remove any sulphur compounds before they are passed over the catalyst.

44 a) Give two examples of the use of transition metals as heterogeneous catalysts in industrial processes.

b) Explain briefly how a heterogeneous catalyst functions.

Homogeneous catalysts

These are catalysts that are in the same state (phase) as the reactants.

Many transition metal compounds can act as homogeneous catalysts for reactions in solution (usually aqueous). The catalysed reaction proceeds through an **intermediate species**.

An example is the redox reaction between peroxodisulphate ions and iodide ions, where peroxodisulphate ions oxidise iodide ions to iodine:

$$S_2O_8^{2-}(aq) + 2I^-(aq) \rightarrow 2SO_4^{2-}(aq) + I_2(aq)$$

The reaction is very slow in the absence of a catalyst, since the reactants are both negatively charged ions and will repel each other. This means that very few collisions occur between the reactants and this results in a very slow rate of reaction.

A small quantity of an iron(II) or iron(III) solution acts as an excellent catalyst for the reaction. The positively charged $Fe^{2+}(aq)$ will readily react with the negatively charged $S_2O_8^{2-}(aq)$:

$$S_2O_8^{2-}(aq) + 2Fe^{2+}(aq) \rightarrow 2SO_4^{2-}(aq) + 2Fe^{3+}(aq)$$

The $Fe^{3+}(aq)$ so formed will now react with the negatively charged $I^-(aq)$:

$$2Fe^{3+}(aq) + 2I^-(aq) \rightarrow 2Fe^{2+}(aq) + I_2(aq)$$

Both of these reactions are redox reactions and the small quantity of iron(II) or iron(III) is constantly recycled by the two reactions.

In order to show that $Fe^{2+}(aq)/Fe^{3+}(aq)$ functions as a catalyst in this reaction, two experiments can be performed – one with the catalyst and one without. Starch solution can be used to detect the rate of formation of iodine.

45 What feature of transition metal compounds enables them to act as homogeneous catalysts?

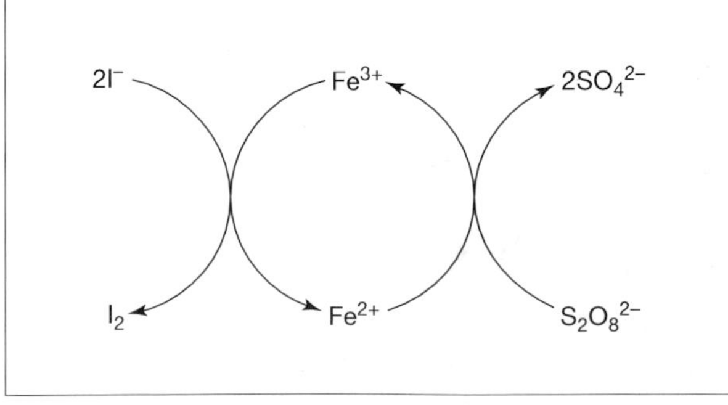

Figure 7 *The peroxodisulphate/iodide reaction is catalysed by iron(II) and iron(III) ions*

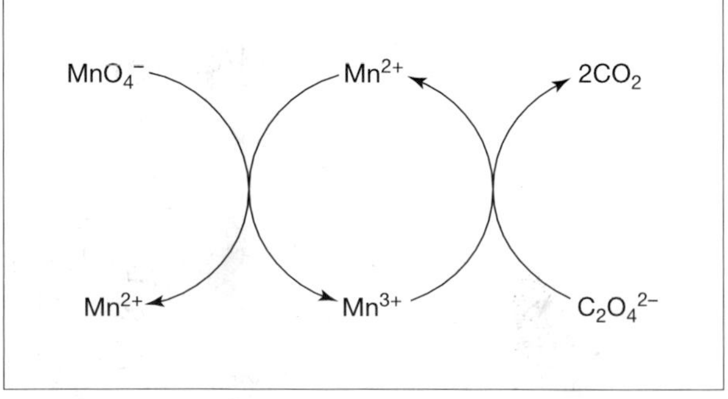

Figure 8 *The manganate(VII)/ethanedioate reaction is autocatalysed by Mn(II) ions*

The reaction between manganate(VII) ions and ethanedioate ions also involves a reaction between negative ions:

$$2MnO_4^-(aq) + 5C_2O_4^{2-}(aq) + 16H^+(aq) \rightarrow 2Mn^{2+}(aq) + 5CO_2(g) + 8H_2O(l)$$

The initial rate of the reaction is very slow, since both the reacting ions carry a negative charge, but as the concentration of the Mn^{2+}(aq) produced by the reaction increases, the rate of reaction rapidly increases.

The Mn^{2+}(aq) acts as an **autocatalyst** in the reaction.
The Mn^{2+} ions react with MnO_4^- ions to form Mn^{3+} ions, which then react with the ethanedioate ions regenerating Mn^{2+} ions.

46 Write equations to show these conversions

a) Mn(II) $\rightarrow$ Mn(III) b) Mn(III) $\rightarrow$ Mn(II).

47 The following reaction is catalysed by aqueous iron(II) sulphate:

$$S_2O_8^{2-}(aq) + 2I^-(aq) \rightarrow I_2(s) + 2SO_4^{2-}(aq)$$

a) Why is this reaction slow in the absence of the catalyst?

b) Use the following $E^\ominus$ values to suggest a possible explanation for the action of the iron(II) sulphate:

$$\tfrac{1}{2}S_2O_8^{2-}(aq) + e^- \rightleftharpoons SO_4^{2-}(aq) \qquad +2.01\,V$$

$$\tfrac{1}{2}I_2(s) + e^- \rightleftharpoons I^-(aq) \qquad +0.54\,V$$

$$Fe^{3+}(aq) + e^- \rightleftharpoons Fe^{2+}(aq) \qquad +0.77\,V$$

48 Explain the difference between a homogeneous and a heterogeneous catalyst.

Key Ideas 233 – 239

- **Transition metals have variable oxidation states which allows them to act as catalysts.**
- **Heterogeneous catalysts are in a different phase from the reactants.**
- **Heterogeneous catalysis occurs at the active sites on the surface of the solid catalyst.**
- **In heterogeneous catalysis adsorption, reaction and desorption occur on the surface of the catalyst.**
- **The efficiency of a heterogeneous catalyst depends upon a balance between the strength of adsorption and desorption.**
- **Homogeneous catalysts are in the same phase as the reactants.**
- **Homogeneous catalysis proceeds via an intermediate species usually involving a change in oxidation state of the transition metal ion catalyst.**

Unit 14 Questions

5

1 Transition metal ions form complexes by bonding with molecules or ions which act as ligands.

a) (i) What is meant by the term *ligand*? (1)
(ii) Give two examples of molecules or ions that can behave as ligands. (2)
b) (i) What type of bond is formed between the transition metal ion and the ligand? (1)
(ii) Explain how such a bond is formed. (2)

2 **a)** (i) Define a *reducing agent* and a *Lewis base* in terms of electrons. (2)
(ii) State whether the processes in the table below illustrate reduction, oxidation or neither of these:

	Process
1	$[CuCl_4]^{2-}(aq) \rightarrow CuCl(s)$
2	$AgCl(s) \rightarrow [Ag(NH_3)_2]^+(aq)$
3	$CrO_4^{2-}(aq) \rightarrow Cr_2O_7^{2-}(aq)$
4	$VO_2^+(aq) \rightarrow VO^{2+}(aq)$
5	$[Cr(H_2O)_2(OH)_4]^-(aq) \rightarrow CrO_4^{2-}(aq)$

(5)

b) Give the reagents you would use to carry out each of the conversions 2–4 above. (3)

3 The following are examples of transition metal complexes:
- $[CoCl_4]^{2-}(aq)$
- $[Ag(NH_3)_2]^+(aq)$
- $[Cu(H_2O)_2(NH_3)_4]^{2+}(aq)$

In each case give
a) The shape of the complex. (3)
b) The co-ordination number. (3)
c) The colour of the complex. (3)
d) The oxidation state of the metal ion. (3)

4 **a)** Explain how the presence of a catalyst increases the rate of some chemical reactions. (2)
b) Write an equation for a reaction that is catalysed by
(i) vanadium(V) oxide
(ii) iron(II) ions
(iii) manganese(II) ions. (3)

c) What feature of transition metal compounds and ions enables them to act as catalysts? (1)

5 a) Give the electronic configurations of
(i) a copper atom
(ii) a copper(I) ion
(iii) a copper(II) ion. (3)
b) Use your answers above to explain why copper(II) ions are described as transitional but copper(I) ions and copper atoms are not. (2)
c) Predict the colour of $[CuCl_2]^-(aq)$ and explain your prediction. (2)

6 Manganese is a transition metal.
a) State three characteristics of manganese, or its compounds, which illustrate this statement. (3)
b) (i) Write a half-equation to show the reduction of the manganate(VII) ion to manganese(II).
(ii) Write a half-equation to show the oxidation of iron(II) to iron(III).
(iii) Hence write an ionic equation to show the oxidation of iron(II) by manganate(VII). (3)
c) A medicinal iron-containing tablet weighing 0.700 g was dissolved in dilute sulphuric acid and the resulting solution titrated with 0.0200 M $KMnO_4$. Exactly 23.30 cm^3 of the $KMnO_4$ were required. Calculate:
(i) the number of moles of manganate(VII) used in the titration;
(ii) the number of moles of iron(II) present in the solution;
(iii) the mass of iron(II) present in the solution;
(iv) the percentage by mass of iron(II) in the tablet. (4)

7 a) (i) Explain the term *bidentate ligand.* (2)
(ii) 1,2-diaminoethane is an example of a bidentate ligand. Draw a diagram to show how this ligand will bond to a Cu^{2+} ion to form a complex with a co-ordination number of 6. (2)
b) A transition metal complex is found in the human body.
(i) Name this complex.
(ii) State the transition metal ion it contains.
(iii) What type of ligand is present in this complex?
(iv) What is the function of this complex in the human body? (4)

8 The ammonia molecule and the chloride ion can both act as ligands.
a) What feature do they both possess which enables them to act as ligands? (1)
b) Using ammonia or chloride ions as the ligand give examples of the following:
(i) a tetrahedral complex
(ii) an octahedral complex
(iii) a linear complex. (3)
c) The drug cisplatin contains both ammonia and chloride ions as ligands.
(i) Draw its structure.
(ii) What disease is cisplatin used to cure?
(iii) Why does the drug's name contain the term *cis*? (3)

1 Transition metal complexes

When transition metal compounds dissolve in water they form hexaqua ions. In this section the reactions of hexaqua ions are studied. This study includes reactions in which the water ligands are replaced by different ligands – **ligand substitution reactions** – and the acidity reactions of hexaqua ions in solution – **hydrolysis reactions**.

The formation of metal–aqua ions

Transition metal ions form complexes by co-ordinate bond formation with ligands. When a complex is formed the ligand behaves as a *Lewis base* and donates a lone pair of electrons. The transition metal ion acts as a *Lewis acid* and accepts a pair of electrons from the ligand.

In aqueous solution transition metal ions form metal–aqua ions with a co-ordination number of six. For example, anhydrous copper(II) sulphate is a white powder. When the powder is added to water it dissolves exothermically forming a blue solution:

$$\underset{\text{white}}{CuSO_4(s)} + 6H_2O(l) \rightarrow \underset{\text{blue}}{[Cu(H_2O)_6]^{2+}(aq)} + SO_4^{2-}(aq)$$

It is the hexaquacopper(II) complex ion that is blue. *Any* copper(II) compound that dissolves in water will contain $[Cu(H_2O)_6]^{2+}$ and the solution will be blue.

Figure 1 *Anhydrous copper(II) sulphate*

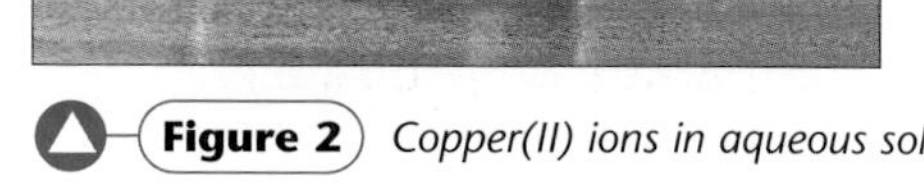

Figure 2 *Copper(II) ions in aqueous solution*

In some cases these aqua ions are present in solid transition metal compounds in the crystalline state. The colour of the crystals is again due to the hexaqua ion. Examples include hydrated copper(II) sulphate, $CuSO_4.5H_2O$, hydrated iron(II) sulphate, $FeSO_4.7H_2O$ and hydrated cobalt(II) chloride, $CoCl_2.6H_2O$.

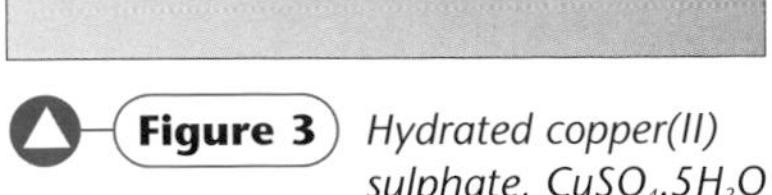

Figure 3 *Hydrated copper(II) sulphate, $CuSO_4.5H_2O$*

Figure 4 *Hydrated iron(II) sulphate, $FeSO_4.7H_2O$*

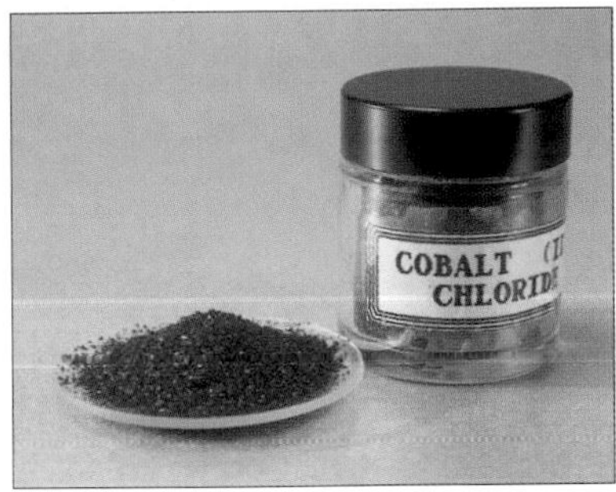

Figure 5 *Hydrated cobalt(II) chloride, $CoCl_2.6H_2O$*

1 If the systematic name for $CuSO_4.5H_2O$ is copper(II) sulphate pentahydrate, give the systematic names for a) $FeSO_4.7H_2O$ b) $CoCl_2.6H_2O$.

In this unit we will consider the reactions of some di-positive and tri-positive transition metal–aqua ions in solution. Aluminium is included even though it is not a transition metal because it does form hexaqua complexes.

Di-positive transition metal–aqua ions include:

$[Fe(H_2O)_6]^{2+}$	$[Cu(H_2O)_6]^{2+}$	$[Co(H_2O)_6]^{2+}$
pale green	blue	pink

Tri-positive transition metal–aqua ions include:

$[Fe(H_2O)_6]^{3+}$	$[Cr(H_2O)_6]^{3+}$	$[Al(H_2O)_6]^{3+}$	$[V(H_2O)_6]^{3+}$
yellow/orange	blue/green	colourless	green

2 Anhydrous cobalt(II) chloride is blue.

a) Write an equation to show how it reacts with water.

b) What colour change would you see during this reaction?

A transition metal–aqua ion can undergo two different types of reaction.

1 **Substitution reactions** in which the co-ordinate bonds are broken and the ligands are replaced by different ligands, e.g. NH_3, Cl^- or CN^-.

2 **Hydrolysis reactions** in which the O—H bond in the water ligands is broken and $H^+(aq)$ ions are released into solution.

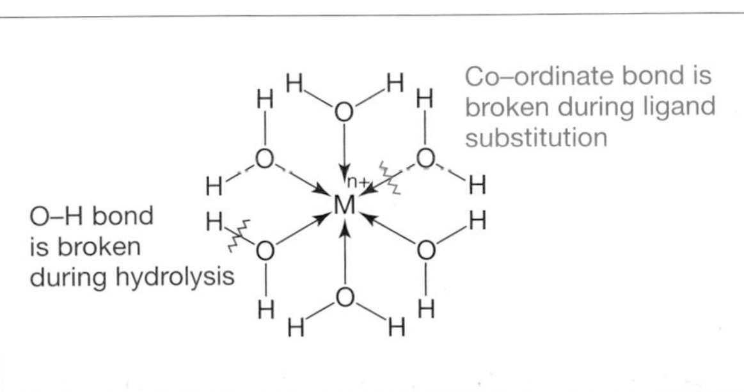

Figure 6 *Structure of metal–aqua ion to show different bonds broken in the two types of reaction*

Ligand substitution reactions

A ligand substitution reaction occurs when one or more of the ligands in the complex are replaced by a different ligand.

There are several features of ligand substitution reactions that need to be considered.

1 The substitution occurs step-wise

In other words, the ligands are replaced one at a time.

Substitution may be complete (all of the ligands are replaced) or incomplete (only some of the ligands are replaced). For example when excess aqueous ammonia is added to an aqueous solution of a cobalt(II) salt, all six water ligands are replaced by ammonia ligands:

$$[Co(H_2O)_6]^{2+} + 6NH_3 \rightleftharpoons [Co(NH_3)_6]^{2+} + 6H_2O$$

But when excess aqueous ammonia is added to an aqueous solution of a copper(II) salt only four of water ligands are replaced:

$$[Cu(H_2O)_6]^{2+} + 4NH_3 \rightleftharpoons [Cu(NH_3)_4(H_2O)_2]^{2+} + 4H_2O$$

When aqueous ammonia is added the metal hydroxide is formed first, but it dissolves in excess ammonia to form the ammine complex (see page 253).

2 Ligand substitution reactions are reversible

For example:

$$[Co(H_2O)_6]^{2+} + 4Cl^- \rightleftharpoons [CoCl_4]^{2-} + 6H_2O$$

When concentrated hydrochloric acid is added to an aqueous solution of a cobalt(II) salt the following reaction occurs and the solution changes gradually from pink to blue as the water ligands are replaced by chloride ion ligands:

$$\underset{\text{pink}}{[Co(H_2O)_6]^{2+}} + 4Cl^- \rightarrow \underset{\text{blue}}{[CoCl_4]^{2-}} + 6H_2O$$

However, on the addition of excess water the solution reverts to pink:

$$[CoCl_4]^{2-} + 6H_2O \rightarrow [Co(H_2O)_6]^{2+} + 4Cl^-$$

3 Write the equation to show the reversible reaction between the hexaquachromium(III) ion and the hexamminechromium(III) ion.

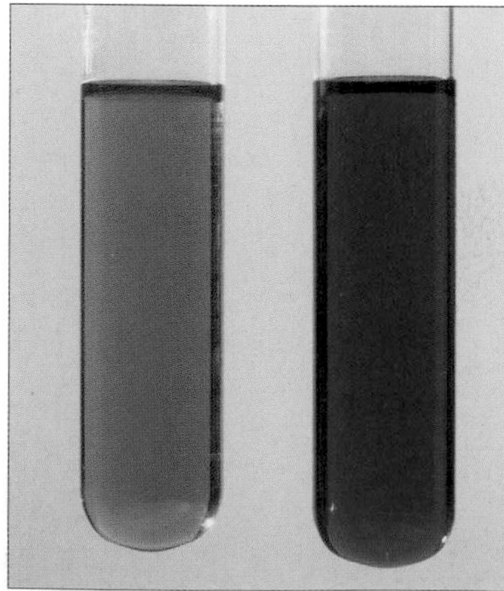

Figure 7 *The complexes $[Co(H_2O)_6]^{2+}$ and $[CoCl_4]^{2-}$*

3 The effect on co-ordination number and shape of the complex

When the ligands have different sizes then ligand substitution can result in a change in co-ordination number and hence in the shape (see page 217).

The chloride ligand is larger than a water ligand and substitution of water by chloride ions results in a change in co-ordination number and shape (see Figure 7 and Table 1).

Ion	Co-ordination no.	Shape
$[Co(H_2O)_6]^{2+}$	6	octahedral
$[CoCl_4]^{2-}$	4	tetrahedral

Table 1

Water and ammonia ligands are of a similar size and they are both neutral. Ligand exchange occurs *without* a change in co-ordination number. Since there is no change in co-ordination number there is no change in the shape of the complex. For example:

$$[Co(H_2O)_6]^{2+} + 6NH_3 \rightleftharpoons [Co(NH_3)_6]^{2+} + 6H_2O$$

4 Write an equation for a reaction of $[Cu(H_2O)_6]^{2+}$ to show

a) a change in co-ordination number

b) no change in co-ordination number.

4 The effect on colour

The change in ligand results in a change in colour (see page 219). Some examples are given below:

$$\underset{\text{pink}}{[Co(H_2O)_6]^{2+}} + 4Cl^- \rightleftharpoons \underset{\text{blue}}{[CoCl_4]^{2-}} + 6H_2O$$

$$\underset{\text{blue/green}}{[Cr(H_2O)_6]^{3+}} + 6NH_3 \rightleftharpoons \underset{\text{purple}}{[Cr(NH_3)_6]^{3+}} + 6H_2O$$

$$\underset{\text{blue}}{[Cu(H_2O)_6]^{2+}} + 4NH_3 \rightleftharpoons \underset{\text{deep blue}}{[Cu(NH_3)_4(H_2O)_2]^{2+}} + 4H_2O$$

5 a) What is the colour of $[CuCl_4]^{2-}$?

b) Write an equation for its formation from the hexaqua ion.

Figure 8 *The complex $[Cu(NH_3)_4(H_2O)_2]^{2+}$*

5 The effect on oxidation state

When the cobalt(II) hexammine complex is allowed to stand in air an oxidation reaction occurs and the solution turns brown (addition of hydrogen peroxide as an oxidising agent can be used to speed up the reaction).

$$[Co(NH_3)_6]^{2+} \rightarrow [Co(NH_3)_6]^{3+} + e^-$$

pale yellow/brown   brown

Hexamminecobalt(II) rapidly oxidises to hexamminecobalt(III). This reaction is an example of how a change in ligand can alter the relative stability of oxidation states. Hexaquacobalt(II) is stable with respect to oxidation to hexaquacobalt(III) but hexamminecobalt(II) is unstable with respect to oxidation to hexamminecobalt(III).

6 Give an example of a) an anionic ligand b) a neutral ligand.

7 Give an example of a) a cationic complex b) an anionic complex.

A summary of the complexes met so far in this section is given in Table 2.

Transition metal		Hexaqua ion	Hexammine ion	Tetrachloro ion
copper	formula	$[Cu(H_2O)_6]^{2+}$	$[Cu(NH_3)_4(H_2O)_2]^{2+}$	$[CuCl_4]^{2-}$
	shape	octahedral	octahedral	tetrahedral
	colour	blue	deep blue	yellow/green
cobalt	formula	$[Co(H_2O)_6]^{2+}$	$[Co(NH_3)_6]^{2+}$	$[CoCl_4]^{2-}$
	shape	octahedral	octahedral	tetrahedral
	colour	pink	pale yellow	blue
	formula		$[Co(NH_3)_6]^{3+}$	
	shape		octahedral	
	colour		brown	
chromium	formula	$[Cr(H_2O)_6]^{3+}$	$[Cr(NH_3)_6]^{3+}$	
	shape	octahedral	octahedral	
	colour	blue/green	purple	

Table 2

8 Explain, with equations, the following observations.

a) White anhydrous copper(II) sulphate turns blue on the addition of water.

b) A pink solution of cobalt(II) chloride forms a pale yellow solution on addition of excess ammonia solution which rapidly darkens on exposure to air.

9 A blue solution X turns green on addition of concentrated hydrochloric acid. Identify the ion present in the blue solution X and explain why it turns green.

6 The effect on stability

When the substitution is by a bidentate or multidentate ligand then the new complex formed will have a greater stability. The reason for this greater stability is because the reaction results in an increase in entropy.

e.g. $[Cu(H_2O)_6]^{2+} + EDTA^{4-} \rightleftharpoons [Cu(EDTA)]^{2-} + 6H_2O$

The six water ligands are replaced by one EDTA ligand and this results in an increase in the number of particles in solution and hence an increase in entropy.

The concentration of metal ions in solution can be determined by titration with a standard solution of EDTA. In all cases the reacting ratio is 1 : 1. A worked example is shown below.

When 25 cm^3 of a copper(II) solution were titrated with 0.100 M EDTA, 24.00 cm^3 of EDTA were needed. Calculate the concentration of the copper(II) solution.

$$[Cu(H_2O)_6]^{2+} + EDTA^{4-} \rightleftharpoons [Cu(EDTA)]^{2-} + 6H_2O$$

moles of EDTA = $MV/1000$ = $(0.100 \times 24.00)/1000$ = 0.0024 mol

so moles of Cu^{2+}(aq) = 0.0024

Concentration of Cu^{2+}(aq) = $(\text{moles} \times 1000)/V$ = $(0.0024 \times 1000)/25$ = 0.096 M

In EDTA titrations the solutions are buffered to a pH of about 10 since the EDTA–metal complexes are less stable at low pH.

10 a) Explain why EDTA is described as a multidentate ligand.

b) Give one commercial use of EDTA.

Key Ideas 242 – 247

- **Transition metal hexaqua ions undergo ligand substitution reactions whereby the water ligands are replaced by chloride or ammonia ligands.**
- **These ligand substitution reactions are reversible.**
- **The size of the ligand determines the co-ordination number and the shape of the complex.**
- **The ligand and the oxidation state of the central metal ion determines the colour of the complex.**
- **The ligand determines the stability of the complex.**

2 Acidity reactions

In solution, tri-positive metal hexaqua ions react with the solvent water molecules to produce an acidic solution. These solutions contain $H^+(aq)$ ions and thus behave as Brønsted–Lowry acids, showing all the characteristic reactions. This acidity can be explained in terms of the polarising power of the tri-positive metal ion.

Hydrolysis

In 1988 twenty tonnes of aluminium sulphate were accidentally tipped into the drinking water supply in Camelford, Cornwall. Aluminium salts are used in water treatment but their presence in water makes it acidic.

When studying periodicity you will have met the reaction of anhydrous aluminium chloride $AlCl_3$ with water (see page 184). Anhydrous aluminium chloride dissolves exothermically in water to form a hexaqua ion:

$$AlCl_3(s) + 6H_2O(l) \rightarrow [Al(H_2O)_6]^{3+}(aq) + 3Cl^-(aq)$$

The $[Al(H_2O)_6]^{3+}$ ion formed is an example of a metal–aqua ion complex, which reacts with water to form an acidic solution (pH ≈ 3):

$$[Al(H_2O)_6]^{3+} + H_2O \rightleftharpoons [Al(H_2O)_5(OH)]^{2+} + H_3O^+$$

This reaction is a **hydrolysis** reaction. In solution all tri-positive metal hexaqua ions react with the solvent water molecules to produce acidic solutions. In this study these include $[Cr(H_2O)_6]^{3+}$, $[Fe(H_2O)_6]^{3+}$ and $[V(H_2O)_6]^{3+}$ as well as $[Al(H_2O)_6]^{3+}$.

Explaining hydrolysis

11 State the colours of these tri-positive metal–hexaqua ions.

Using M to represent any tri-positive metal ion the equation for the reaction with water is:

$$[M(H_2O)_6]^{3+} + H_2O \rightleftharpoons [M(H_2O)_5(OH)]^{2+} + H_3O^+$$

Note that this is an equilibrium reaction. The equilibrium position lies very much to the left-hand side, hence the pH of the resulting solutions is about 3. The principal transition metal species present in the solution is the $[M(H_2O)_6]^{3+}$ ion.

Tri-positive metal ions are small and therefore have a large charge/size ratio and are very *polarising*.

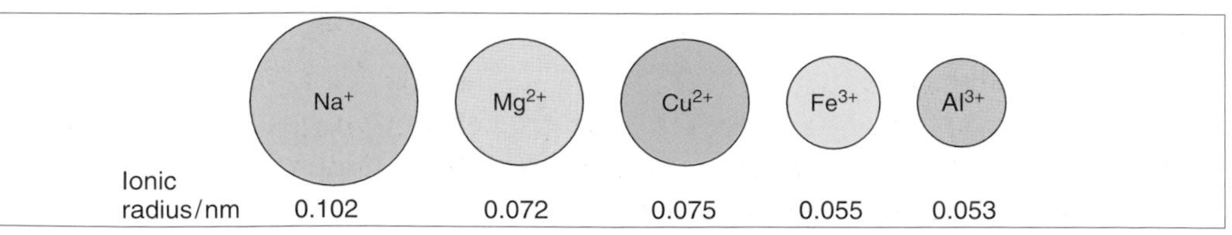

Figure 1 *Table to show the sizes of some cations*

The water ligands are polarised to such an extent that the O–H bond in the water molecule is weakened sufficiently for a solvent water molecule to accept a hydrogen from the ligand. The metal–aqua ion can thus donate a proton to a solvent molecule. The metal–aqua ion behaves as a Brønsted–Lowry acid.

Figure 2 *The loss of a proton from a polarised ligand*

Q 12 Write an equation to show the acidity reaction of $[Cr(H_2O)_6]^{3+}$

Further hydrolysis steps are possible in the presence of a base:

$$[M(H_2O)_5(OH)]^{2+} + H_2O \rightleftharpoons [M(H_2O)_4(OH)_2]^{+} + H_3O^{+}$$

$$[M(H_2O)_4(OH)_2]^{+} + H_2O \rightleftharpoons [M(H_2O)_3(OH)_3] + H_3O^{+}$$

These further steps can only happen if the equilibria are pulled over to the right-hand side. This will happen if a reagent is added that removes the H_3O^+ ions from the reaction causing the equilibria to shift to the right. (By Le Chatelier's Principle the equilibria will shift to oppose the change i.e. to replace the ions that have been removed).

Addition of a base such as NaOH, NH_3 or Na_2CO_3 or a reactive metal such as magnesium or zinc will cause the three hydrolysis reactions to be shifted to the right-hand side leading to the formation of the metal hydroxide precipitate, $[M(H_2O)_3(OH)_3]$.

Di-positive transition metal–aqua ions are much *weaker* acids than the tri-positive metal–aqua ions since the charge/size ratio is much smaller.

$$[M(H_2O)_6]^{2+} + H_2O \rightleftharpoons [M(H_2O)_5(OH)]^{+} + H_3O^{+}$$

This equilibrium lies much more to the left-hand side compared to the reaction of tri-positive aqua ions, so di-positive metal ions in solution are only very weakly acidic.

13 Explain why a solution of iron(II) chloride is much less acidic than a solution of iron(III) chloride.

Reactions of metal–aqua ions with sodium hydroxide

When an aqueous solution of sodium hydroxide is added to a tri-positive metal–aqua ion the three hydrolysis steps shown above occur, leading to the precipitation of the metal hydroxide. The hydroxide ions remove the H_3O^+ ions from the equilibrium, as they react together to form water:

$$H_3O^{+} + OH^{-} \rightarrow 2H_2O$$

When sodium hydroxide solution is added to an aqueous solution of chromium(III) sulphate a grey/green precipitate is observed due to the formation of chromium(III) hydroxide.

The three hydrolysis steps for the hexaqua chromium(III) ion are shown below:

$$[Cr(H_2O)_6]^{3+} + H_2O \rightleftharpoons [Cr(H_2O)_5(OH)]^{2+} + H_3O^+$$

$$[Cr(H_2O)_5(OH)]^{2+} + H_2O \rightleftharpoons [Cr(H_2O)_4(OH)_2]^+ + H_3O^+$$

$$[Cr(H_2O)_4(OH)_2]^+ + H_2O \rightleftharpoons \underset{\text{grey/green ppt}}{[Cr(H_2O)_3(OH)_3]} + H_3O^+$$

The overall equation for the reaction is:

$$[Cr(H_2O)_6]^{3+} + 3H_2O \rightleftharpoons [Cr(H_2O)_3(OH)_3] + 3H_3O^+$$

This can be simplified to:

$$Cr^{3+}(aq) + 3OH^-(aq) \rightleftharpoons Cr(OH)_3(s)$$

These are *reversible* reactions and the addition of a strong acid will reverse the reactions leading to the formation of the metal–hexaqua ion:

$$[Cr(H_2O)_3(OH)_3] + 3H_3O^+ \rightleftharpoons [Cr(H_2O)_6]^{3+} + 3H_2O$$

During this reaction the grey/green precipitate of chromium(III) hydroxide dissolves, forming the blue/green solution of the hexaqua ion.

Similar reactions occur with iron(III) and aluminium(III) solutions where the precipitates are iron(III) hydroxide and aluminium hydroxide respectively.

$$\underset{\text{yellow}}{[Fe(H_2O)_6]^{3+}} + 3H_2O \rightleftharpoons \underset{\text{red/brown ppt}}{[Fe(H_2O)_3(OH)_3]} + 3H_3O^+$$

$$\underset{\text{colourless}}{[Al(H_2O)_6]^{3+}} + 3H_2O \rightleftharpoons \underset{\text{white ppt}}{[Al(H_2O)_3(OH)_3]} + 3H_3O^+$$

These reactions are also reversed by the addition of acid.

Figure 3 *The formation of hydroxides, $M(OH)_3$*

14 Write simplified equations to show the formation of

a) iron(III) hydroxide and b) aluminium hydroxide from the corresponding aqueous ions.

15 What would you observe when a) iron(III) hydroxide and b) aluminium hydroxide are treated with excess dilute sulphuric acid?

Amphoteric hydroxides

Aluminium hydroxide and chromium(III) hydroxide are classified as *amphoteric* since they will react with both acids and bases.

Addition of an acid to the hydroxides results in the formation of the hexaqua ions as described above:

$$[Al(H_2O)_3(OH)_3] + 3H_3O^+ \rightleftharpoons [Al(H_2O)_6]^{3+} + 3H_2O$$

$$[Cr(H_2O)_3(OH)_3] + 3H_3O^+ \rightleftharpoons [Cr(H_2O)_6]^{3+} + 3H_2O$$

In the presence of *excess* sodium hydroxide solution the chromium and aluminium hydroxide precipitates will again dissolve but the products formed this time are hydroxy complexes.

The white precipitate of aluminium hydroxide dissolves to form a colourless solution:

$$[Al(H_2O)_3(OH)_3] + OH^- \rightleftharpoons [Al(H_2O)_2(OH)_4]^- + H_2O$$

colourless solution

or $$Al(OH)_3 + OH^- \rightleftharpoons [Al(OH)_4]^-$$

The grey/green precipitate of chromium(III) hydroxide dissolves to form a green solution:

$$[Cr(H_2O)_3(OH)_3] + OH^- \rightleftharpoons [Cr(H_2O)_2(OH)_4]^- + H_2O$$

green solution

If a large excess of *concentrated* sodium hydroxide solution is added then the hydrolysis reactions continue to form $[Al(H_2O)(OH)_5]^{2-}$ and $[Al(OH)_6]^{3-}$ from aluminium hydroxide and $[Cr(H_2O)(OH)_5]^{2-}$ and $[Cr(OH)_6]^{3-}$ from chromium(III) hydroxide.

16 Write equations to show the formation of $[Al(OH)_6]^{3-}$ and $[Cr(OH)_6]^{3-}$ from the corresponding hydroxides.

Under normal laboratory conditions iron(III) hydroxide does *not* dissolve in excess sodium hydroxide solution but all metal hydroxides will eventually dissolve in sodium hydroxide solution if the concentration of the latter is great enough.

Reactions of sodium hydroxide with di-positive aqua ions

With di-positive metal–aqua ions, the addition of sodium hydroxide solution results in the formation of the metal hydroxide precipitate. Again the hydroxide ions will react with the H_3O^+ ions and shift the equilibria to the right-hand side leading to the formation of the metal hydroxide precipitate.

The equations for the hydrolysis reactions are:

$$[M(H_2O)_6]^{2+} + H_2O \rightleftharpoons [M(H_2O)_5(OH)]^+ + H_3O^+$$

$$[M(H_2O)_5(OH)]^+ + H_2O \rightleftharpoons [M(H_2O)_4(OH)_2] + H_3O^+$$

The overall equation for this reaction is:

$$[M(H_2O)_6]^{2+} + 2H_2O \rightleftharpoons [M(H_2O)_4(OH)_2] + 2H_3O^+$$

This can be simplified to:

$$M^{2+}(aq) + 2OH^-(aq) \rightarrow M(OH)_2(s)$$

When sodium hydroxide solution is added to an aqueous solution containing copper(II) ions a pale blue precipitate of copper(II) hydroxide forms:

$$[Cu(H_2O)_6]^{2+} + H_2O \rightleftharpoons [Cu(H_2O)_5(OH)]^+ + H_3O^+$$

blue solution

$$[Cu(H_2O)_5(OH)]^+ + H_2O \rightleftharpoons [Cu(H_2O)_4(OH)_2] + H_3O^+$$

pale blue ppt

17 Write an overall equation for this reaction.

When sodium hydroxide solution is added to an aqueous solution containing iron(II) ions a green precipitate of iron(II) hydroxide forms. The overall equation for this reaction is:

$$[Fe(H_2O)_6]^{2+} + 2H_2O \rightleftharpoons [Fe(H_2O)_4(OH)_2] + 2H_3O^+$$

pale green solution — green ppt

or $Fe^{2+}(aq) + 2OH^-(aq) \rightarrow Fe(OH)_2(s)$

On standing, the iron(II) hydroxide precipitate turns brown duc to aerial oxidation to iron(III) hydroxide.

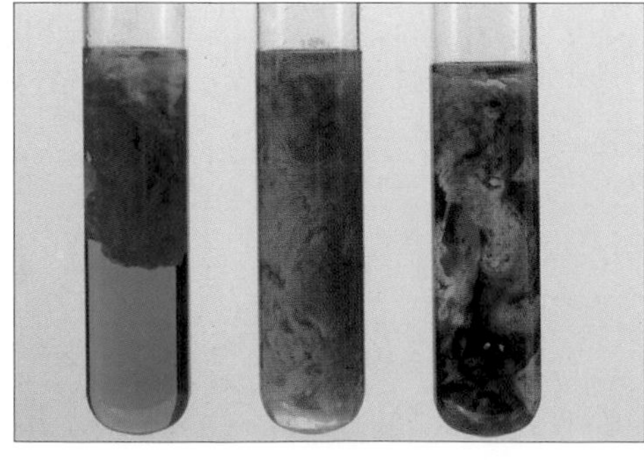

Figure 4 *The formation of hydroxides, $M(OH)_2$*

18 A pink solution containing Co^{2+}(aq) reacts with sodium hydroxide solution to form a blue precipitate, A. On exposure to air this precipitate turns a beige colour as compound B is formed by oxidation. Identify A and B and write an equation for the formation of A.

Metal–aqua ion	Addition of NaOH solution	Addition of excess NaOH solution	On standing in air
$[Al(H_2O)_6]^{3+}$ colourless solution	$[Al(H_2O)_3(OH)_3]$ white ppt	$[Al(H_2O)_2(OH)_4]^-$ colourless solution	no change
$[Cr(H_2O)_6]^{3+}$ blue/green solution	$[Cr(H_2O)_3(OH)_3]$ grey/green ppt	$[Cr(H_2O)_2(OH)_4]^-$ green solution	no change
$[Fe(H_2O)_6]^{3+}$ yellow solution	$[Fe(H_2O)_3(OH)_3]$ red/brown ppt	no change	no change
$[Cu(H_2O)_6]^{2+}$ blue solution	$[Cu(H_2O)_4(OH)_2]$ blue ppt	no change	no change
$[Fe(H_2O)_6]^{2+}$ pale green solution	$[Fe(H_2O)_4(OH)_2]$ green ppt	no change	$[Fe(H_2O)_3(OH)_3]$ red/brown ppt
$[Co(H_2O)_6]^{2+}$ pink solution	$[Co(H_2O)_4(OH)_2]$ blue ppt	no change	$[Co(H_2O)_3(OH)_3]$ beige ppt

Table 1 *A summary of the reactions of metal–aqua ions with NaOH(aq)*

Reactions of metal–aqua ions with aqueous ammonia

Aqueous ammonia is a weakly alkaline solution and when added to metal–aqua complexes the metal hydroxides precipitate. The precipitates formed are the same as with the reaction with sodium hydroxide solution.
In water ammonia molecules partially ionise:

$$NH_3 + H_2O \rightleftharpoons NH_4^+ + OH^-$$

The hydroxide ions produced result in the hydrolysis equilibrium reaction being pulled over to the right-hand side as H_3O^+ ions are removed. This leads to the formation of the metal hydroxides.

$$H_3O^+ + OH^- \rightarrow 2H_2O$$

or $$NH_3 + H_3O^+ \rightarrow NH_4^+ + H_2O$$

The equations for the reactions for the tri-positive metal–aqua ions are summarised below using chromium(III) as the example:

$$[Cr(H_2O)_6]^{3+} + 3H_2O \rightleftharpoons \underset{\text{grey/green ppt}}{[Cr(H_2O)_3(OH)_3]} + 3H_3O^+$$

or $$[Cr(H_2O)_6]^{3+} + 3NH_3 \rightleftharpoons [Cr(H_2O)_3(OH)_3] + 3NH_4^+$$

The equations for the reactions for the di-positive metal–aqua ions are summarised below using cobalt(II) as the example:

$$[Co(H_2O)_6]^{2+} + 2H_2O \rightleftharpoons \underset{\text{blue ppt}}{[Co(H_2O)_4(OH)_2]} + 2H_3O^+$$

or $$[Co(H_2O)_6]^{2+} + 2NH_3 \rightleftharpoons [Co(H_2O)_4(OH)_2] + 2NH_4^+$$

Ammonia being a weak base does *not* cause a further hydrolysis step with the metal hydroxide precipitates. However some of the metal hydroxide precipitates will dissolve in excess ammonia solution due to the formation of **ammine** complexes. In these reactions the ammonia molecules act as ligands and the reactions occurring are ligand substitution reactions, not hydrolysis (see page 244). Table 2 below shows which metal ions do or do not form ammine complexes.

For example, if a solution of copper(II) sulphate is treated with aqueous ammonia added drop-wise until present in excess the following observations are made. A blue precipitate forms which dissolves in excess forming a deep blue solution. The equations for the reactions occurring are:

$$[Cu(H_2O)_6]^{2+} + 2NH_3 \rightleftharpoons [Cu(H_2O)_4(OH)_2] + 2NH_4^+$$

blue solution — blue ppt

$$[Cu(H_2O)_4(OH)_2] + 4NH_3 \rightleftharpoons [Cu(H_2O)_2(NH_3)_4]^{2+} + 2H_2O + 2OH^-$$

deep blue solution

The overall equation is:

$$[Cu(H_2O)_6]^{2+} + 4NH_3 \rightleftharpoons [Cu(H_2O)_2(NH_3)_4]^{2+} + 4H_2O$$

If a solution of iron(II) sulphate is treated with aqueous ammonia added drop-wise until present in excess the following observations are made. A green precipitate forms which does not dissolve in excess (since iron(II) does not form ammine complexes).

$$[Fe(H_2O)_6]^{2+} + 2NH_3 \rightleftharpoons [Fe(H_2O)_4(OH)_2] + 2NH_4^+$$

Metal–aqua ion	Addition of NH_3 solution	Addition of excess NH_3 solution	On standing in air
$[Al(H_2O)_6]^{3+}$	$[Al(H_2O)_3(OH)_3]$ white ppt	no change	no change
$[Cr(H_2O)_6]^{3+}$	$[Cr(H_2O)_3(OH)_3]$ grey/green ppt	$[Cr(NH_3)_6]^{3+}$ purple solution	no change
$[Fe(H_2O)_6]^{3+}$	$[Fe(H_2O)_3(OH)_3]$ red/brown ppt	no change	no change
$[Cu(H_2O)_6]^{2+}$	$[Cu(H_2O)_4(OH)_2]$ blue ppt	$[Cu(NH_3)_4(H_2O)_2]^{2+}$ deep blue solution	no change
$[Fe(H_2O)_6]^{2+}$	$[Fe(H_2O)_4(OH)_2]$ green ppt	no change	$[Fe(H_2O)_3(OH)_3]$ red/brown ppt
$[Co(H_2O)_6]^{2+}$	$[Co(H_2O)_4(OH)_2]$ blue ppt	$[Co(NH_3)_6]^{2+}$ pale yellow solution	$[Co(NH_3)_6]^{3+}$ brown solution

Table 2 *A summary of the reactions of metal–aqua ions with ammonia solution*

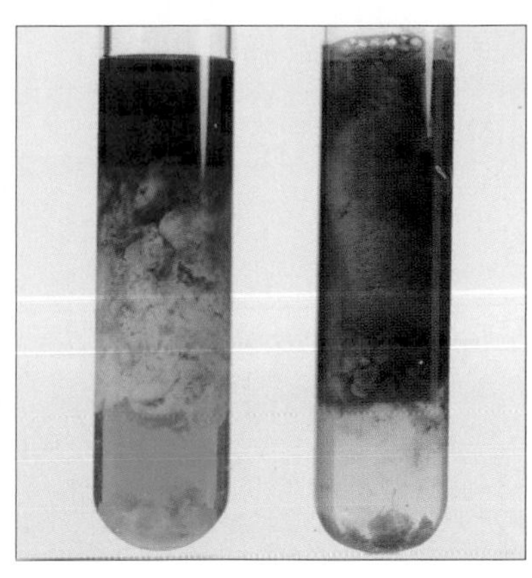

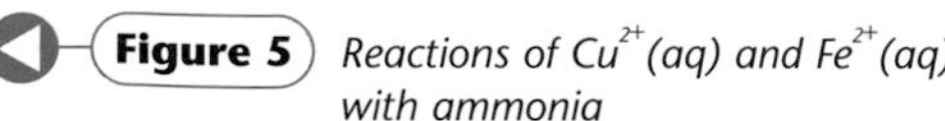

Figure 5 *Reactions of $Cu^{2+}(aq)$ and $Fe^{2+}(aq)$ with ammonia*

19 **What would you observe if aqueous ammonia was added to a solution of aluminium chloride until present in excess?**

20 **A green solution X is treated with excess aqueous ammonia solution. Initially a green precipitate Y forms which slowly dissolves to form a purple solution Z. Identify by formulae X, Y and Z.**

Reactions of metal–aqua ions with sodium carbonate

When a solution of chromium(III) nitrate is treated with sodium carbonate solution vigorous effervescence and a grey/green precipitate are observed. The precipitate does not dissolve in excess sodium carbonate solution.

The acidic, tri-positive metal–aqua ions, like chromium, react with sodium carbonate to form the metal hydroxide precipitate and carbon dioxide.

The reaction is another example of hydrolysis.

$$[Cr(H_2O)_6]^{3+} + H_2O \rightleftharpoons [Cr(H_2O)_5(OH)]^{2+} + H_3O^+$$

The H_3O^+ ions released from the hexaqua ion react with the carbonate ions to form carbon dioxide:

$$2H_3O^+ + CO_3^{2-} \rightarrow 3H_2O + CO_2$$

This results in the hydrolysis equilibrium reaction being pulled to the right-hand side, forming the metal hydroxide precipitate:

$$[Cr(H_2O)_6]^{3+} + 3H_2O \rightleftharpoons \underset{\text{grey/green ppt}}{[Cr(H_2O)_3(OH)_3]} + 3H_3O^+$$

The overall equation for the reaction of chromium(III) and carbonate ions is:

$$2[Cr(H_2O)_6]^{3+} + 3CO_3^{2-} \rightleftharpoons 2[Cr(H_2O)_3(OH)_3] + 3CO_2 + 3H_2O$$

Similar reactions occur with aluminium(III) and iron(III):

$$2[Al(H_2O)_6]^{3+} + 3CO_3^{2-} \rightleftharpoons \underset{\text{white ppt}}{2[Al(H_2O)_3(OH)_3]} + 3CO_2 + 3H_2O$$

$$2[Fe(H_2O)_6]^{3+} + 3CO_3^{2-} \rightleftharpoons \underset{\text{red/brown ppt}}{2[Fe(H_2O)_3(OH)_3]} + 3CO_2 + 3H_2O$$

The di-positive metal–aqua ions are weaker acids than carbonic acid and as a result they do *not* release carbon dioxide from sodium carbonate. Instead they react with sodium carbonate solution to form *metal carbonate* precipitates.

The general equation for this type of reaction is:

$$M^{2+}(aq) + CO_3^{2-}(aq) \rightarrow MCO_3(s)$$

When solutions of cobalt(II), copper(II) and iron(II) are treated separately with sodium carbonate solution they form coloured precipitates as shown below:

$$Co^{2+}(aq) + CO_3^{2-}(aq) \rightarrow \underset{\text{mauve/lilac}}{CoCO_3(s)}$$

$$Cu^{2+}(aq) + CO_3^{2-}(aq) \rightarrow \underset{\text{green}}{CuCO_3(s)}$$

$$Fe^{2+}(aq) + CO_3^{2-}(aq) \rightarrow \underset{\text{green}}{FeCO_3(s)}$$

Metal–aqua ion	Addition of Na_2CO_3 solution
$[Al(H_2O)_6]^{3+}$	$[Al(H_2O)_3(OH)_3] + CO_2$ white ppt
$[Cr(H_2O)_6]^{3+}$	$[Cr(H_2O)_3(OH)_3] + CO_2$ grey/green ppt
$[Fe(H_2O)_6]^{3+}$	$[Fe(H_2O)_3(OH)_3] + CO_2$ red/brown ppt
$[Cu(H_2O)_6]^{2+}$	$CuCO_3$ green ppt
$[Fe(H_2O)_6]^{2+}$	$FeCO_3$ green ppt
$[Co(H_2O)_6]^{2+}$	$CoCO_3$ mauve/lilac ppt

Table 3 *A summary of the reactions of metal–aqua ions with sodium carbonate*

21 Explain how the addition of sodium carbonate solution to a mixture of iron(II) and iron(III) chlorides could be used to detect the presence of iron(III) ions in the mixture.

22 Use your knowledge of transition metal chemistry to predict the reaction of Sc^{3+}(aq) ions with sodium carbonate solution. Write an equation (or equations) for the reaction described.

A summary of all the reactions of Al^{3+}(aq), Cu^{2+}(aq), Co^{2+}(aq), Cr^{3+}(aq), Fe^{2+}(aq), and Fe^{3+}(aq) is given in Appendix B.

Reactions of metal–aqua ions with metals

Tri-positive metal ions in solution are sufficiently acidic to react with metals such as magnesium and zinc forming a metal hydroxide precipitate and hydrogen gas.

For example, a colourless solution of aluminium chloride reacts with magnesium to produce effervescence and a white precipitate.

The magnesium will react with the H_3O^+ ions in solution to form hydrogen:

$$2H_3O^+ + Mg \rightarrow Mg^{2+} + 2H_2O + H_2$$

The removal of the H_3O^+ ions from the equilibrium causes further hydrolysis and the hydroxide is precipitated:

$$[Al(H_2O)_6]^{3+} + 3H_2O \rightleftharpoons \underset{\text{white ppt}}{[Al(H_2O)_3(OH)_3]} + 3H_3O^+$$

The overall equation for the reaction of aluminium ions and magnesium is:

$$2[Al(H_2O)_6]^{3+} + 3Mg \rightleftharpoons 2[Al(H_2O)_3(OH)_3] + 3Mg^{2+} + 3H_2$$

23 **Using your knowledge of the reactions of transition metal ions with bases explain how the following cations could be separated from the mixture containing them.**

a) **Fe^{3+}(aq) and Al^{3+}(aq)** **b)** **Al^{3+}(aq) and Cr^{3+}(aq).**

24 **a)** **Give the formula of the principal aluminium species present in an aqueous solution of aluminium sulphate.**

b) **Write an equation to show why this solution is acidic.**

c) **When zinc powder is added to aluminium sulphate solution a gas is evolved and a white precipitate formed. Identify the gas and the precipitate and write equations for their formation.**

Key Ideas 248 – 257

- **Transition metal ions form aqua ions in solution.**
- **Tri-positive transition metal–aqua ions are acidic in solution. They undergo a hydrolysis reaction releasing H^+ ions into solution.**
- **The extent of the hydrolysis reaction depends upon the polarising power of the metal ion.**
- **Tri-positive metal ions are more polarising than di-positive metal ions and therefore solutions of tri-positive metal–aqua ions are more acidic.**
- **Tri-positive metal–aqua ions react with bases to precipitate the metal hydroxides.**
- **Amphoteric hydroxides dissolve in acids and bases.**
- **Di-positive metal–aqua ions react with NaOH and NH_3 to precipitate the metal hydroxides but with sodium carbonate the metal carbonate is formed.**

Unit 15 Questions

3

1. A pink solution, **A**, when treated with excess concentrated hydrochloric acid, formed a blue solution, **B**. The drop-wise addition of a dilute ammonia solution to **A** resulted in a blue precipitate, **C**. If excess ammonia solution was then added the precipitate dissolved and a pale yellow solution, **D**, formed.
   - **a)** Identify, by formula, each of the species **A–D**. (4)
   - **b)** Write equations for the reactions described. (3)
   - **c)** Solution **D** rapidly turns dark brown on exposure to air. Explain this observation. (2)
   - **d)** Solution **B** turns pink when excess water is added. Explain this observation. (2)

2. The scheme below illustrates some reactions of metal–aqua ions.
   - **a)** For each reaction give one example of a metal whose ion undergoes such a reaction. (6)

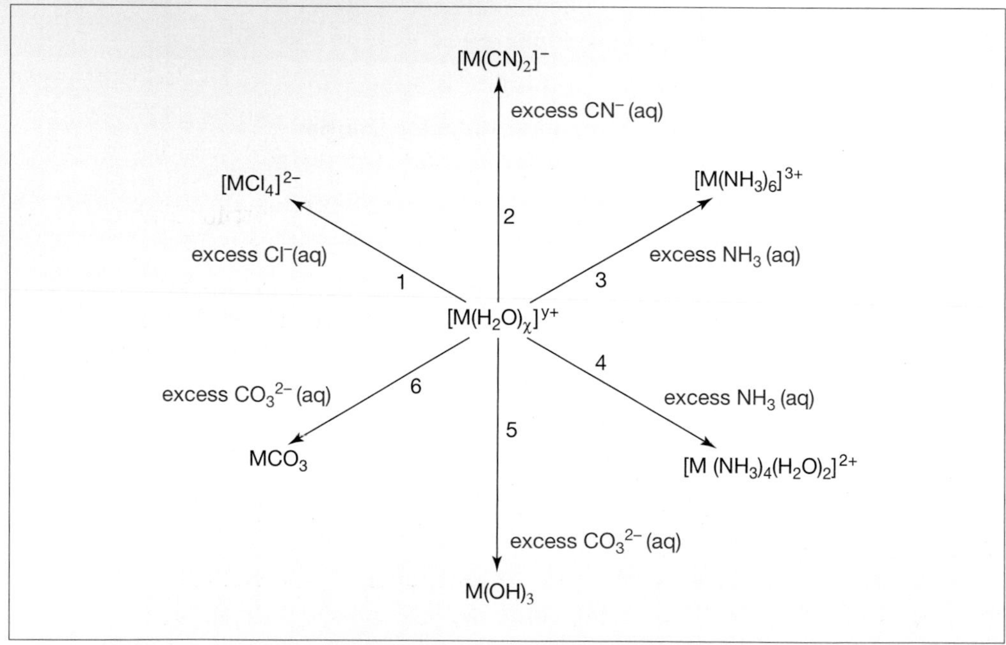

Figure 1

   - **b)** State the shapes of the complex ions formed in reactions 1,2 and 3. (3)
   - **c)** Give one use of the complex formed in reaction 2. (1)
   - **d)** Explain why the addition of excess sodium carbonate to a solution of a metal–aqua ion can lead to the formation of different products as in reactions 5 and 6. (4)

3 a) A student carries out a series of test tube reactions using a solution of chromium(III) sulphate. What would be observed during these reactions?
(i) A solution of ammonia is added drop-wise until present in excess.
(ii) A solution of sodium hydroxide is added drop-wise until present in excess. The resulting solution is then treated with hydrogen peroxide.
(iii) A solution of sodium carbonate is added drop-wise until present in excess. (9)

b) What do the reactions in a) have in common? (4)

c) Chromium(III) hydroxide is amphoteric. Explain the term *amphoteric* and illustrate your answer with two equations from chromium(III) chemistry. (3)

4 a) (i) Describe the observations made when a sample of anhydrous copper(II) sulphate is added to an excess of water.
(ii) Give the formula and shape of the copper(II) species present in the resulting aqueous solution. (4)

b) Give the formulae and colour of the copper(II) species formed when the aqueous solution in a) is treated with
(i) a few drops of aqueous ammonia
(ii) excess aqueous ammonia
(iii) excess concentrated sodium chloride solution. (6)

5 Identify the species, **A** to **H**, responsible for the observations described below:

a) Metal **A** dissolves in potassium hydroxide solution to form a colourless solution **B**. When dilute sulphuric acid is added dropwise to **B** a white solid **C** precipitates which dissolves in excess acid forming solution **D**. (4)

b) A blue anhydrous solid **E** dissolves in water producing a pink solution **F**. One portion of **F** is acidified with dilute nitric acid followed by the addition of a few drops of barium nitrate solution; a white precipitate, **G** results. A second portion of **F** reacts with concentrated hydrochloric acid to form a blue solution containing the complex ion **H**. (4)

6 a) Explain why a solution of iron(III) chloride is more acidic than a solution of iron(II) chloride. (5)

b) Explain the following observations and write equations for the reactions described.
(i) When a solution of iron(II) is treated with sodium hydroxide solution a green precipitate is formed which turns brown where it comes into contact with air.
(ii) When a solution of iron(III) is treated with sodium carbonate solution the mixture effervesces and a brown precipitate is formed. (8)

Module 5 Questions

1 Ammonium vanadate(V) NH_4VO_3 dissolves in dilute sulphuric acid to produce an orange solution containing the VO_2^+(aq) ion. Using granulated zinc, this ion is reduced through various stages to produce a blue solution containing VO^{2+}(aq) ions, then a green solution containing V^{3+}(aq) ions and finally a purple solution containing V^{2+}(aq) ions. During these stages the Zn is converted into Zn^{2+}(aq).

a) Give two characteristic properties of a transition metal shown by vanadium in this sequence of reactions. (2)

b) Write an ionic equation for the conversion of VO_3^-(aq) into VO_2^+(aq) on acidification and explain briefly why this reaction is *not* a redox reaction. (2)

c) Give half-equations for the oxidation of Zn to Zn^{2+}(aq) and for the reduction of VO_3^-(aq) to V^{2+}(aq). Use these equations to produce a redox equation for the reduction of VO_3^-(aq) to V^{2+}(aq) by granulated zinc. (3)

2 **a)** (i) Draw a Born–Haber cycle for the process:

Na(s) + water → Na^+(aq)

Label the following enthalpy changes on your diagram.

Enthalpy of atomisation = +109 kJ mol^{-1}.

Enthalpy of hydration = –406 kJ mol^{-1}.

First ionisation enthalpy = +494 kJ mol^{-1}.

(ii) Use the values given above to calculate the enthalpy change when sodium reacts with water.

(iii) The first ionisation enthalpy of lithium is +520 kJ mol^{-1} and its enthalpy of hydration is –510 kJ mol^{-1}. Explain the difference in magnitude of these values compared to those of sodium. (7)

b) What would you observe when sodium reacts with water? (5)

c)

	$\Delta H_f^{\ominus}$/kJ mol^{-1}	$S^{\ominus}$/ J K^{-1} mol^{-1}
Li_2CO_3(s)	–1216	90
Li_2O(s)	–596	39
CO_2(g)	–394	214
Na_2CO_3(s)	–1131	136
Na_2O(s)	–416	73

Table 1

(i) Use the data given in Table 1 to calculate the free enthalpy change at 298 K for the reactions:

$$Li_2CO_3(s) \rightarrow Li_2O(s) + CO_2(g)$$

$$Na_2CO_3(s) \rightarrow Na_2O(s) + CO_2(g)$$

(ii) Calculate the temperature at which each reaction becomes feasible. Comment on your results. (17)

3 a) State and explain the trend in melting points of the oxides of the Period 3 elements, Na to S, in terms of their bonding and structure. (12)

b) The pH values obtained when 0.1 mol of each of the following oxides is added to water are:

Na_2O	MgO	Al_2O_3	SiO_2	P_4O_{10}	SO_3
13	9	7	7	3	1

Table 2

(i) Explain in terms of bonding the trend in pH given above.
(ii) Write equations for the oxides that react with water. (11)

4 a) Outline a plan of an experiment to determine the percentage of iron(II) ions in a medicinal tablet which consists mainly of hydrated iron(II) sulphate mixed with an inert filler. You should include equations for any reactions that are involved and show how you would calculate the result. (17)

b) 25.0 cm^3 of $FeCl_2(aq)$ were acidified with excess dilute sulphuric acid. The solution required 20.00 cm^3 of 0.010 M potassium dichromate(VI) solution for complete oxidation. Calculate the concentration of the iron(II) chloride solution. Explain why potassium manganate(VII) should not be used as the oxidant in this reaction. (5)

5 a) Describe, with the aid of a labelled diagram, how you could measure the standard electrode potential of silver.
Write an equation for the spontaneous cell reaction given that

$$Ag^+(aq) + e^- \rightleftharpoons Ag(s) \qquad E^\ominus = +0.80\,V$$ (14)

b) A half-cell is constructed from a strip of cobalt metal in a 1.0 M solution of cobalt(II) chloride. This is connected to another half-cell consisting of a strip of platinum metal in a 1.0 M solution of hydrochloric acid through which chlorine, at a pressure of 100 kPa, is bubbled. The $E^\ominus$ total of the cell is +1.63 V. Cobalt acts as the negative electrode.
Given that

$$\tfrac{1}{2}Cl_2(g) + e^- \rightleftharpoons Cl^-(aq) \qquad E^\ominus = +1.36\,V$$

(i) Calculate the $E^\ominus$ value for the cobalt electrode.
(ii) Write the equation for the spontaneous cell reaction.
(iii) Predict the effect on the $E^\ominus_{total}$ of increasing the pressure of chlorine gas. (8)

6 a) Use the complex ions of copper to explain the meaning of the terms *ligand* and *co-ordination number*. (4)

b) Discuss, with examples, how the change of ligand can affect
(i) the shape of the complex ion
(ii) the colour of the complex
(iii) the stability of a complex ion with respect to oxidation. (13)

c) The diagram below shows the apparatus that could be used to measure the standard electrode potential of copper.

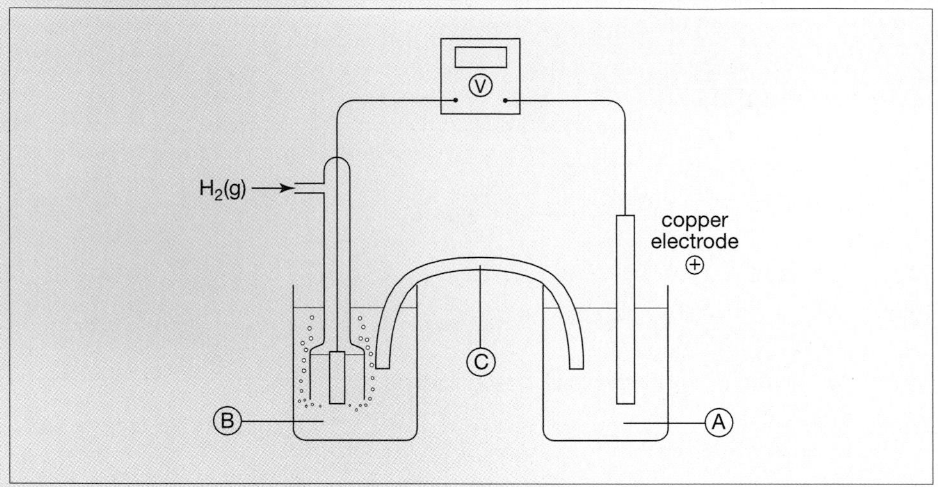

Figure 1

(i) Name the solutions that could be used in A, B and C, specifying the concentrations, where appropriate.
(ii) What is the function of the salt bridge?
(iii) In which direction will the electrons flow in the external circuit? (6)

7 a) Explain why transition metal ions become hydrated in water. (4)

b) Use $[Cr(H_2O)_6]^{3+}$ to illustrate what is meant by
(i) a ligand substitution reaction
(ii) a hydrolysis reaction. (6)

c) Write equations and state what you would observe in each of the following reactions.
(i) Concentrated ammonia solution is added drop-wise until in excess to an aqueous solution of cobalt(II) sulphate. The resulting solution is allowed to stand in air.
(ii) Concentrated hydrochloric acid is added in excess to an aqueous solution of copper(II) sulphate.
(iii) Sodium carbonate solution is added drop-wise until in excess to an aqueous solution of chromium(III) sulphate. (14)

8 a) Distinguish between the terms *homogeneous* and *heterogeneous* as applied to catalysts. (2)

b) Transition metals and their compounds can act as homogeneous and heterogeneous catalysts. Illustrate this statement with one example of each. (2)

c) Discuss how a heterogeneous catalyst increases the rate of reaction. Why are some of these catalysts more effective than others? (10)

d) A catalytic converter consists of a *honeycombed ceramic support* coated with a layer of *powdered* metal. Cars fitted with catalytic converters must use *unleaded* petrol. Explain the significance of the terms in italics. (4)

9 **a)** Describe the bonding and structure in the anhydrous chlorides of sodium, aluminium and silicon. (7)

b) Distinguish between the terms *hydration* and *hydrolysis*. Illustrate your answer with reference to the changes that occur when sodium chloride and aluminium chloride are added separately to water. In each case describe what would be observed, identify the products and comment on the pH of the solution formed. (11)

c) When an aqueous solution of sodium carbonate is added to a solution of aluminium chloride a white precipitate, **A**, and a colourless gas, **B**, are formed. Compound **A** is insoluble in excess sodium carbonate solution but dissolves in excess sodium hydroxide solution to form species **C**. Compound **A** dissolves in excess dilute hydrochloric acid to form species **D**.

(i) Identify **A** to **D** and write equations for the reactions occurring.

(ii) Compound **A** is amphoteric. What evidence is provided in the passage above to confirm this statement? (8)

10 **a)** Draw a Born–Haber cycle for the formation of the hypothetical ionic solid CaCl. Name the enthalpy changes which occur at each step in the cycle. (9)

b) Use this cycle, and the data below, to calculate the standard enthalpy of formation of CaCl(s). (2)

Process	ΔH/kJ mol^{-1}
Ca → Ca(g)	+190
Ca(g) → Ca^+(g)	+590
$\frac{1}{2}Cl_2$(g) → Cl(g)	+121
Cl(g) → Cl^-(g)	−364
Ca^+(g) + Cl^-(g) → CaCl(s)	+760

Figure 2

c) Compare your answer in **b)** with the standard enthalpy of formation of $CaCl_2$ which is −780 kJ mol^{-1}. What enthalpy changes contribute to the difference in the values? Is it possible to prepare CaCl(s)? (7)

1 Synoptic assessment

One requirement of the A2 Chemistry course is that there must be a **synoptic** element. Modules 5 and 6 both include synoptic questions. The synoptic element requires the drawing together of knowledge, understanding and skills learned in different parts of the AS and A2 course.

This means that all of the Chemistry studied in AS and in Module 4 of the A2 course can be required for answering questions in the Module 5 and Module 6 examinations.

This may seem a daunting prospect but as you will have found most of the chemistry studied at AS is revisited in A2 chemistry. Examples include kinetics, equilibria, energetics, periodicity and some aspects of organic chemistry. The concepts of electronic structure and bonding play an important part in the understanding of the chemistry in A2 and questions to retest your knowledge of these areas of chemistry have specifically been included throughout this text.

The Module 5 examination paper will have some synoptic questions involving the AS modules and Module 4. The questions can be short structured ones, or 'essay' type questions. One aspect of the synoptic element in A2 Chemistry requires the ability to make connections between different areas of chemistry. One method of examining this aspect of the synoptic element could be by basing questions on one particular compound and the links with different areas of the syllabus. Some examples are shown below.

Sulphuric acid

The areas of study that should be linked include:

- Manufacture by the Contact process: this involves understanding of equilibria, Le Chatelier's Principle and catalysis. (Modules 2, 4 and 5)
- Sulphuric acid as a typical strong acid. The acid as a proton donor as part of the Brønsted–Lowry theory of acidity. (Module 4)
- Concentrated sulphuric acid as a strong non-volatile acid – its reactions with solid halides. (Module 2)
- Concentrated sulphuric acid as an oxidising agent, as shown by its reactions with solid ionic halides. (Module 2)
- Sulphuric acid as a catalyst – mechanism of the nitration of benzene (Module 4) – and in esterification reactions. (Module 4)
- Sulphuric acid as an electrophile – mechanism of the reaction with alkenes. (Module 3)
- Dilute sulphuric acid as the acidifying acid in manganate(VII) titrations. (Module 5)

Ammonia

The areas of study that should be linked include:

- Manufacture by the Haber Process: this involves understanding of equilibria, Le Chatelier's Principle and catalysis. (Modules 2, 4 and 5)
- The shape of the molecule – including the effect of the lone pair. (Module 1)
- Hydrogen bonding in ammonia. (Module 1)
- Ammonia as a Brønsted–Lowry weak base. (Module 4)
- Ammonia as a ligand in transition metal complexes. (Module 5)
- Ammonia as a nucleophile – nucleophilic substitution reactions with haloalkanes (Modules 3 and 4) and nucleophilic addition–elimination reactions with acyl groups. (Module 4)

Aluminium chloride

The areas of study that should be linked include:

- Aluminium chloride as a covalent molecule – discussion of ionic and covalent bonding, including electronegativity and polarisation caused by the aluminium ion. (Module 1)
- The shape of the molecule, including dimer formation and co-ordinate bonding. (Module 1 and 5)
- The reaction of aluminium chloride with water as a chloride of a Period 3 element. (Module 5)
- Formation of complexes and hexaquo acidity of aluminium ions in solution. (Modules 4 and 5)
- Aluminium chloride as a Lewis acid – as a catalyst in acylation and alkylation reactions with benzene (Friedel–Crafts reactions). (Module 4)

Module 6 will be examined using **objective questions**, all of which will be synoptic on all of the modules in AS and A2. These will be multiple choice questions and either matching pairs questions or multiple completion questions. Since you are unfamiliar with this type of assessment some worked examples are given below.

Multiple choice questions

When answering these questions you must consider the four alternatives and choose the correct answer by a letter A–D.

Examples

1 Which of the following has the greatest first ionisation energy?

A. hydrogen
B. helium
C. lithium
D. fluorine.

To answer this question you need to remember the trends in ionisation energies from Module 1. Across a period there is an increase in ionisation energy as the nuclear charge increases. Down a group the ionisation energy decreases, since the outer electron is further from the nucleus. If you look at a copy of the periodic table the answer is **B; helium**. This has the highest first ionisation energy of any element, since the electron is removed from the lowest energy level (1s) and a helium atom has twice the nuclear charge of a hydrogen atom.

2 Which of the following is present in 1mol of $CaCl_2(s)$?

A. 3 mol of atoms
B. 1 mol of molecules
C. 1 mol of positive ions
D. 1 mol of negative ions.

The topic on moles was initially studied in Module 1 and calcium is a Group 2 element. Calcium chloride is ionic. Its formula is $Ca^{2+}(Cl^-)_2$ so it contains one mole of calcium ions and two moles of chloride ions.

The answer is therefore **C**.

3 The rate equation for the reaction between X and Y is

rate = $k[X]^{1/2}[Y]$

Which statement is incorrect?

A. The order of reaction with respect to X is 0.5.
B. The order of reaction with respect to Y is 1.
C. The rate of reaction is halved when the concentration of X is halved.
D. The rate of reaction is doubled when the concentration of Y is doubled.

This is a Module 4 question. The response **C** is an incorrect statement. If the rate of reaction is halved when the concentration of a reactant is halved then the order of reaction with respect to that reactant is first order. The order of reaction with respect to X is 0.5. If [X] is halved then the rate is reduced by a factor of $0.5^{0.5} = 0.7$.

4 0.160g of an unknown chloride, X, precipitates 0.188g of silver bromide. The percentage of bromide ions in this unknown is

A. 2
B. 5
C. 20
D. 50

The M_r of AgBr is 188 so 0.188 g is equal to 0.001 mol.

0.001 mol of bromide ions = 0.001 × 80 = 0.080 g

The % of bromide in X = 0.080/0.160 × 100 = 50%

The answer is **D.**

5 Which of the following is the major product formed when propene reacts with concentrated sulphuric acid and the product is hydrolysed?

A. $CH_3CH_2CH_2OH$
B. $HOCH_2CH_2CH_2OH$
C. $CH_3CH(OH)CH_3$
D. $CH_3CH(OH)CH_2OH$

The reactions of the alkenes were studied in Module 3. Indirect hydrolysis of an alkene with one double bond produces an alcohol, not a diol, so answers B and D can be eliminated. The secondary carbocation intermediate is more stable than the primary carbocation intermediate and this will result in the major product, which is a secondary alcohol. The answer is **C**.

Matching pairs questions

In this type of question a group of four or five questions is accompanied by a set of alternative answers A–D. Within each group of questions the answers A –D may be used once, more than once, or not at all.

Example

Questions 6–9

Choose from the list A–D the type of reaction taking place in each of questions 6–9.

A. free-radical substitution
B. nucleophilic substitution
C. elimination
D. electrophilic substitution.

6 The reaction of concentrated ethanolic KOH with 2-bromopropane to give propene.

7 The reaction of methylbenzene with chlorine to produce (choromethyl)benzene.

8 The formation of propan-2-ol from 2-bromopropane and aqueous KOH.

9 The reaction between 2-bromopropane and ethanolic KCN.

Three of these reactions involve the haloalkane, 2-bromopropane. The reactions of haloalkanes were studied in Module 3. The formation of an alcohol (propan-2-ol) and a nitrile (using KCN) from a haloalkane are both nucleophilic substitution reactions while the formation of an alkene (propene) occurs via elimination.

Methylbenzene is an aromatic molecule and substitution into the benzene ring involves an electrophile but the reaction described above is of the methyl side chain, acting like an alkane. This reaction is free radical substitution not electrophilic substitution.

The answers are:

6 C
7 A
8 B
9 B

D is a distracter; it is not one of the answers.

Multiple completion questions

In these questions four responses are given to each question. You have to decide how many are correct and answer with the letter A–D using the key below:

Answer **A** if (i), (ii) and (iii) only are correct
Answer **B** if (i) and (iii) only are correct
Answer **C** if (ii) and (iv) only are correct
Answer **D** if only (iv) is correct

Table 1 summarises these responses:

A	B	C	D
(i), (ii) and (iii) only are correct	(i) and (iii) only are correct	(ii) and (iv) only are correct	(iv) only is correct

Table 1

Examples

10 Which of the following processes involve(s) a negative enthalpy change?

(i) $Na(s) \rightarrow Na(g)$
(ii) $Cl(g) + e^- \rightarrow Cl^-(g)$
(iii) $Cl_2(l) \rightarrow Cl_2(g)$
(iv) $Na^+(g) + Cl^-(g) \rightarrow NaCl(s)$

These equations are part of the Born–Haber cycle for the formation of sodium chloride studied in Module 5. The reactions that are exothermic are (ii), electron affinity and (iv), lattice enthalpy. The other two responses are endothermic reactions involving the change of state from a solid to a gas and a liquid to a gas. Since (ii) and (iv) only are correct the answer is **C**.

11 Which of the following statements about the Maxwell-Boltzmann curve for the distribution of the energies of particles in a gas is/are correct?

(i) The vertical axis is proportional to the number of molecules with a certain energy.
(ii) The curve is symmetrical in shape.
(iii) There is a very small number of molecules with very high energies.
(iv) The peak shifts to the left if the temperature is increased.

The Maxwell-Boltzmann energy distribution curves were studied in Module 2. The vertical axis represents the number of molecules with a given energy. The horizontal axis represents the increase in energy. The curve is asymmetrical and the peak shifts to a higher energy if the temperature is increased. Using this information only (i) and (iii) are correct so the correct response is **B**.

12 A buffer solution is formed by mixing ethanoic acid with sodium ethanoate. Which of these statements is/are true?

(i) When hydrogen ions are added to the buffer the concentration of ethanoate ions decreases.
(ii) The buffer solution has a pH less than 7.
(iii) The total concentration of ethanoate ions is the same as the concentration of sodium ethanoate.
(iv) The buffer is effective because both ethanoic acid and sodium ethanoate are completely ionised.

Buffers were studied in Module 4. An acid buffer consists of a weak acid and its salt. The salt is fully ionised but the acid is weak. In fact, due to excess ethanoate ions from the fully ionised salt, the equilibrium shifts so far to the left that the acid is effectively undissociated so the total concentration of ethanoate ions is from the salt. Addition of H^+ ions will, by Le Chatelier's Principle, also shift the equilibrium to the left and further reduce the dissociation of the acid.

$$CH_3COOH(aq) \rightleftharpoons \underset{\text{excess}}{CH_3COO^-(aq)} + H^+(aq)$$

Using this information you can answer the question. Response (iv) is wrong because the acid is not fully ionised. Response (ii) is correct – this is an acid buffer with a pH of less than 7. If (ii) is correct and (iv) is wrong then the answer must be **A**.

13 Which of the following exhibit hydrogen bonding?

(i) ammonia
(ii) hydrogen bromide
(iii) protein molecules
(iv) sulphur dioxide.

Hydrogen bonding was introduced in Module 1. It is the strongest type of intermolecular bonding requiring the molecules to possess a hydrogen atom and one of the electronegative atoms F, O or N. These requirements are met by ammonia and protein molecules only so the answer is **B**.

14 The properties of the hydrogen halides, HX, show trends as Group 7 is descended. Which of the following trends is/are correct?

(i) They become stronger oxidising agents.
(ii) Their boiling points increase in a regular manner.
(iii) The polarity of the molecules increases.
(iv) They become stronger reducing agents.

The trends in Group 7 were studied in Module 2. The key feature of the halides is that they become stronger reducing agents down the Group so response (iv) is correct. Now consider response (ii). HF has the highest boiling point, due to hydrogen bonding, but from HCl to HI the boiling points increase gradually. Response (ii) is incorrect so the only alternative is **D**. You do not need to recall the trend in polarity to answer this question.

Module 6 Synoptic assessment questions

1 The following reaction scheme occurs in nature

A (H—C(H)(COOH)—C(H)(COOH)—H) —Step 1→ B (HOOC(H)C=C(H)COOH) —Step 2→ C (H—C(OH)(COOH)—C(H)(COOH)—H) —Step 3→ D (O=C(COOH)—C(H)(H)—COOH)

a) (i) Give the systematic names for compounds B and C and discuss the types of stereoisomerism shown by compounds.

(ii) Compound C can be synthesised from compound B in the laboratory. How would this product differ from that produced naturally? Explain your answer. (14)

b) Outline how steps 2 and 3 can be brought about in the laboratory. Write equations and state the reagents required, including any essential reaction conditions. (7)

(Module 3: Units 11, 13 and 15; Module 4: Units 4, 5 and 10)

2 **a)** (i) Draw a dot/cross diagram to show the arrangement of outer electrons in a water molecule. State the shape of this molecule and the bond angle H—O—H.

(ii) Draw a diagram to show the arrangement of water molecules in ice.

(iii) Explain why the bond angles in the water molecules in ice are greater than the bond angle you have stated above. (10)

b) Write an equation to show how anhydrous aluminium chloride reacts with water. Explain why the resulting solution is acidic. (3)

c) (i) Define the terms *Brønsted–Lowry acid* and *Brønsted–Lowry base*.

(ii) Write equations, one in each case, to show water behaving as a Brønsted–Lowry acid and a Brønsted–Lowry base. (3)

(Module 1: Unit 2; Module 4: Unit 3; Module 5: Units 12 and 15)

3 **a)** Naturally occurring iron consists of four isotopes: ^{54}Fe, ^{56}Fe, ^{57}Fe and ^{58}Fe.The relative abundances are 5.82 : 91.66 : 2.19 : 0.33 respectively.

(i) Sketch the appearance of the mass spectrum of iron for the Fe^{+} species.

(ii) Use the data to calculate the accurate relative atomic mass of iron. (6)

b) The commonly occurring ions of iron are $^{56}Fe^{2+}$ and $^{56}Fe^{3+}$.
   (i) State the number of protons, neutrons and electrons in each species.
   (ii) Write the electronic configuration for each ion and explain why they are classified as transition metal ions. (5)

c) Iron and its compounds can act as *heterogeneous* and *homogeneous* catalysts. Give one example of each type of catalyst, explaining clearly the differences between the two types. (7)

d) (i) Explain the role of iron in the transport of oxygen in the body.
   (ii) Give a source of carbon monoxide pollution. Why is carbon monoxide classified as toxic? (4)

(Module 1: Unit 1; Module 5: Unit 14)

4 Petrol, which is mainly octane, can be obtained from the *fractional distillation* of crude oil. Alternative methods are being sought since crude oil is a *finite resource* and provides important feedstocks for the petrochemical industry. One solution could be to manufacture petrol on an industrial scale from coal by the following reactions:

$$C(s) + H_2O(g) \rightleftharpoons CO(g) + H_2(g) \quad \text{Reaction 1 (endothermic)}$$
$$8CO(g) + 17H_2(g) \rightleftharpoons C_8H_{18}(g) + 8H_2O(g) \quad \text{Reaction 2 (exothermic)}$$

The standard enthalpies of formation for the reactants and products of these reactions are given in the table below:

Product	$H_2O(g)$	$CO(g)$	$C_8H_{18}(g)$	$H_2(g)$	$C(s)$
$\Delta H^\circ f$ /kJ mol^{-1}	-242	-111	-169	0	0

a) Explain the meanings of the terms in italics in the above passage. (4)

b) Use the data in the table to calculate the enthalpy change for (i) Reaction 1 (ii) Reaction 2. (6)

c) Predict the optimum conditions required to produce petrol by this two-stage process. Explain the reasoning behind your predictions. (11)

d) Discuss any hazards and pollution problems which may influence the use of this process on a large scale. (3)

(Module 3: Unit 12; Module 2: Units 5 and 7; Module 4: Unit 2)

5 Describe briefly how each of the following can be estimated using volumetric analysis. In each case state the standardised volumetric reagent required, the indicator (if any) and any essential conditions or other reagents necessary for the titration.

a) The percentage of sodium carbonate in a sample of washing soda.

b) The amount of available chlorine in a sample of bleach.

c) The percentage of iron in an iron tablet. (9)

(Module 1: Unit 4; Module 2: Unit 9; Module 4: Unit 3; Module 5: Unit 14)

6 'The shapes of molecules and complex ions are determined by the repulsions between electron pairs around the central atom or ion.'

a) Discuss this statement with reference to the following: BF_3, $[Cu(H_2O)_6]^{2+}$, PF_5, $[CoCl_4]^{2-}$ and PCl_3. (12)

b) Deduce the shapes of, and bonding in: ICl_2^-, PF_6^-, NH_4^+ and $[Zn(NH_3)_4]^{2+}$. (8)

(Module 1: Unit 2; Module 5: Unit 14)

Multiple choice questions

In each of questions 7–10 a question is followed by four alternative responses. Choose the correct answer A–D.

7 Which of the following is the correct set of conditions to measure the standard enthalpy of formation of ethane?

A. 10 kPa and 298 K
B. 10 kPa and 273 K
C. 100 kPa and 273 K
D. 100 kPa and 298 K

8 The K_a value for methanoic acid at 298 K is 2×10^{-4} mol dm^{-3}. Which of the following is the hydrogen ion concentration of 0.5 M methanoic acid at this temperature?

A. 1×10^{-4}
B. 4×10^{-4}
C. 1×10^{-2}
D. 2×10^{-2}

9 Which one of the following produces an acidic solution when dissolved in water?

A. $NaHCO_3$
B. $FeCl_3$
C. SiO_2
D. CaO

10 The oxidation of ethanedioate ions can be represented by the half equation:

$$C_2O_4^{2-}(aq) \rightleftharpoons 2CO_2(g) + 2e^-$$

What volume, in cm^3, of 0.02 M $KMnO_4$ is required to completely oxidise a solution containing 0.02 mol of ethandioate ions?

A. 40
B. 100
C. 140
D. 400

Matching pairs questions

In questions 11–14 a group of questions is followed by a set of alternative answers A–D. Within each group of questions each letter may be used once, more than once, or not at all.
Select from the list A–D the appropriate observation in the reactions described.

A. a white precipitate
B. a yellow precipitate
C. a green solution
D. a red-brown precipitate

The reaction between:

(11) aqueous iron(III) chloride and excess aqueous sodium hydroxide

(12) propan-2-ol and acidified potassium dichromate(VI) solution

(13) aqueous sodium iodide and aqueous silver nitrate

(14) aqueous chromium(III) sulphate and excess aqueous sodium hydroxide.

Multiple completion questions

Summarised directions for recording responses:

A	B	C	D
(i), (ii) and (iii) only are correct	(i) and (iii) only are correct	(ii) and (iv) only are correct	(iv) only is correct

(15) Which of the following statements about ionic compounds is/are always correct?
(i) They have relatively high melting points.
(ii) They conduct electricity when dissolved in water.
(iii) They conduct electricity when molten.
(iv) Energy is produced when they melt.

(16) Which of the following will increase the yield of SO_3?
$$2SO_2(g) + O_2(g) \rightleftharpoons 2SO_3(g) \quad \Delta H = -189\,kJmol^{-1}$$
(i) The addition of a catalyst.
(ii) An increase in temperature.
(iii) A decrease in pressure.
(iv) An increase in the concentration of oxygen.

(17) Which of the following statements about sodium carbonate is/are true?
(i) It produces effervescence when added to aqueous aluminium sulphate.
(ii) It precipitates iron(III)hydroxide when added to aqueous iron(III) chloride.
(iii) It precipitates cobalt(II)carbonate when added to aqueous cobalt(II)nitrate.
(iv) It produces effervescence when added to iron(II)chloride.

(18) Which of the following can behave as a Brønsted–Lowry acid in aqueous solution?
(i) SO_4^{2-}
(ii) HSO_4^-
(iii) NH_3
(iv) NH_4^+

(19) Which of the following reactions involve the addition of a nucleophile?
(i) propanone with HCN
(ii) propene with HBr
(iii) propanal with $NaBH_4$
(iv) propane with Cl_2

Answers: Module 4

Unit 1 Kinetics

Pages 4 – 13

1 It would be three times as fast.

2 Doubling concentration of the iodate or increasing concentration of the acid by a factor of four.

3 a) Reaction is zero order w.r.t. X.

b) Second order w.r.t. Y: quadruples the rate.

4 1.28×10^{-1} mol dm^{-3} s^{-1}

5 $k = r/([A][B]) = (\text{mol dm}^{-3}\ \text{s}^{-1})/(\text{mol dm}^{-3})^2 = \text{mol}^{-1}\ \text{dm}^3\ \text{s}^{-1}$

6 $k = r/[X]^2[Y] = (9.60 \times 10^{-4})/(0.40)^2(0.40)$
$= 1.5 \times 10^{-2}\ \text{mol}^{-2}\ \text{dm}^6\ \text{s}^{-1}$

Unit 1 End-of-unit questions Page 14

1 a) (i) First order (1) (ii) first order (1).

b) (i) Second order (1) (ii) sum of the two orders (1).

c) Nucleophilic substitution (1).

2 a) Run 2 = 4.8×10^{-5} mol dm^{-3} s^{-1}(1).
run 3 = 0.01 mol dm^{-3}(1).
run 4 = 1.28×10^{-4} mol dm^{-3} s^{-1}(1).

b) (i) $k = r/[X][Y]^2$ (1) $= (1.6 \times 10^{-5})/(0.01)(0.02)^2 = 4$ (1).
units: mol^{-2} dm^6 s^{-1}(1).
(ii) Increase (1).
(iii) No change (1).

3 a)

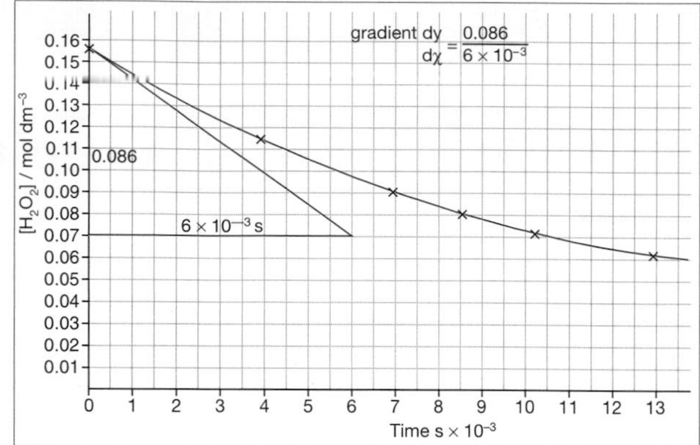

Rate = 14.33 mol dm^{-3} s^{-1}

b) Manganese(IV) oxide.

4 a) Benzene diazonium chloride in a suitable vessel (conical flask) (1) in a water bath at 50°C (1) connected to a graduated syringe (1).

b) By inspection the initial rate is halved when the initial concentration is halved (1) – hence first order w.r.t. A (1).

c) Rate increases (1) since more particles (1) will have energy in excess of E_a (1).

Unit 2 Equilibria

Pages 16 – 31

1 All of the reactants and products are in the same physical state (phase).

2 It would change colour from orange to yellow. OH^- ions remove H^+ ions as H_2O: equilibrium shifts to the left.

3 At lower temps the rate of reaction is too slow. 400°C is a compromise temp. producing a reasonable yield at a reasonable rate.

4 a) $K_c = \frac{[PCl_3][Cl_2]}{[PCl_5]}$ mol dm^{-3}

b) $K_c = \frac{[NH_3]^2}{[N_2][H_2]^3}$ mol^{-2} dm^6

5 Reaction of nitrogen and oxygen, since it has the smallest K_c value.

6 This is the reverse of the N_2O_4(g) reaction and hence $K_c = 1/0.05 = 20$ dm^3 mol^{-1}.

7 a) As temp. increases K_c becomes larger and reaction must shift to right. Increasing temp. favours endothermic reactions: hence endothermic.

b) Reaction of N_2 and O_2 occurs at the high temps in the engine. Exhaust gases contain NO which is oxidised to NO_2 which will contribute to acid rain.

8 $K_c = \frac{[HI]^2}{[H_2][I_2]} = \frac{(17.15)^2}{(2.265)(2.840)} = 45.72$

9 $CH_3COOH + CH_3CH_2OH \rightleftharpoons CH_3COOCH_2CH_3 + H_2O$

initial moles	1	0.50	0	0
at equil	0.586	0.086	0.414	0.414

$K_c = \frac{[CH_3COOCH_2CH_3][H_2O]}{[CH_3COOH][CH_3CH_2OH]} = \frac{(0.414)(0.414)}{(0.586)(0.086)} = 3.4$

10 $K_c = \frac{[NH_3]^2}{[N_2][H_2]^3}$

$[NH_3]^2 = K_c[N_2][H_2]^3 = 2 \times 2 \times 2^3 = 32$

$\therefore [NH_3] = 5.66$ mol dm^{-3}

11 $CH_3COOH + CH_3CH_2OH \rightleftharpoons CH_3COOCH_2CH_3 + H_2O$

initial moles	60/60 = 1	8.28/46 = 0.18	0	0
at equil	0.829	0.009	0.171	0.171

(49.74/60 = 0.829 moles of acid remaining i.e. 0.171 moles reacted)

$K_c = \frac{(0.171)(0.171)}{(0.829)(0.009)} = 3.92$

12 a) $PCl_5 \rightleftharpoons PCl_3 + Cl_2$

b) $K_c = \frac{[PCl_3][Cl_2]}{[PCl_5]}$ units: mol dm^{-3}

c) $PCl_5 \rightleftharpoons PCl_3 + Cl_2$

initial moles	0.01	0	0
at equil	0.0042	0.0058	0.0058
conc at equil (V = 1)	0.0042	0.0058	0.0058

$$K_c = \frac{(0.0058)(0.0058)}{(0.0042)} = 8.00 \times 10^{-3} \text{mol dm}^{-3}$$

13 $CO(g) + Cl_2(g) \rightleftharpoons COCl_2(g)$

initial moles	2	5	0
equil	1	4	1
concentration (V=10)	1/10	4/10	1/10

$$K_c = \frac{[COCl_2]}{[CO][Cl_2]} = \frac{(0.1)}{(0.1)(0.4)} = 2.5\,\text{dm}^3\text{ mol}^{-1}$$

14 $K_p = \frac{(PNH_3)^2}{(PN_2)(PH_2)^3}$

$(PNH_3)^2 = K_p(PN_2)(PH_2)^3 = 3.5 \times 10^{-4} \times 20 \times (40)^3$

$= 448$ $PNH_3 = 21.17\,\text{kPa}$

15 This is the reverse of the Haber Process. At 700 K the reciprocal of K_p for the Haber Process is $1/(7.8 \times 10^{-6}) = 1.282 \times 10^5\,\text{kPa}^2$

16 a) $K_p = \frac{(PHI)^2}{(PH_2)(PI_2)}$

b) $K_p = \frac{(1400)^2}{(250)(160)} = 49$

c) Forward reaction is exothermic and hence reaction is favoured by low temps. If K_p decreases then equilibrium has shifted to the left. Temp. X must be higher temp

17 $K_p = \frac{(PPCl_3)(PCl_2)}{(PPCl_5)} = \frac{20 \times 20}{80} = 5\,\text{kPa}$

18 $2SO_2 + O_2 \rightleftharpoons 2SO_3$

initial moles	12	6	0
at equil	1.2	0.6	10.8

Total moles at equilibrium = 12.6

Mole fraction partial pressure

SO_2	1.2/12.6	1.2/12.6 × 200 = 19.05
O_2	0.6/12.6	0.6/12.6 × 200 = 9.52
SO_3	10.8/12.6	10.8/12.6 × 200 = 171.43

$$K_p = \frac{(PSO_3)^2}{(PSO_2)^2(PO_2)} = \frac{(171.43)^2}{(19.05)^2(9.52)} = 8.51\,\text{kPa}^{-1}$$

Unit 2 End-of-unit questions Page 32

1

	Effect on position of equilibrium	Effect on rate at which equilibrium is attained
A high pressure	moves to the right (1)	increases (1)
A high temperature	moves to the left (1)	increases (1)
The presence of a catalyst	none (1)	increases (1)

2 a) Equilibrium shifts to the left (1). Increasing temp. favours endothermic reaction (1). Hence, the forward reaction is exothermic – ΔH is negative (1).

b) Yield increases (1); reaction involving decrease in gaseous moles (1) is favoured (1).

c) (i) $K_p = \frac{(PN_2O_4)}{(PNO_2)^2}$ Units Pa^{-1} (1).

(ii) Partial pressures

NO_2 0.23 × 200 = 46 kPa (1).

N_2O_4 0.77 × 200 = 154 kPa (1).

$K_p = \frac{(154)}{(46)^2} = 7.28 \times 10^{-2}$ (1) kPa^{-1} (1).

(iii) Forward reaction exothermic (1) so increasing temp. pushes equil. to the left and the value of K_p decreases (1).

3 a) $CH_3COOH + CH_3CH_2OH \rightleftharpoons CH_3COOCH_2CH_3 + H_2O$ (1).

b) (i)

	CH_3COOH +	CH_3CH_2OH ⇌	$CH_3COOCH_2CH_3$ +	H_2O
initial moles	1	1	0	0
at equil	0.34	0.34	0.66	0.66 (1)
Concentration/ mol dm^{-3}	$\frac{0.34}{0.1}$	$\frac{0.34}{0.1}$	$\frac{0.66}{0.1}$	$\frac{0.66}{0.1}$
(1)	3.4	3.4	6.6	6.6 (1)

(ii) K_c (No units) $= \frac{[CH_3COOCH_2CH_3][H_2O]}{[CH_3COOH][CH_3CH_2OH]}$ (1)

$= \frac{(6.6)(6.6)\ (1)}{(3.4)(3.4)} = 3.77$ (1)

c) (i) Catalyst (1).

(ii) Increases rate; (1) provides an alternative reaction pathway of with a lower E_a (1).

(iii) None (1) since the rates of the forward and reverse reactions are increased equally.

4 a) Moles: PCl_5 20.85/208.5 = 0.1 : PCl_3 20.625/137.5 = 0.15 : Cl_2 14.20/71 = 0.2: total moles 0.45 mole fraction: PCl_5 0.1/0.45 PCl_3 0.15/0.45 Cl_2 0.2/0.45

Answers: Module 4

Unit 2 Equilibria (continued)

b) Partial pressures:

PCl_5	0.10/0.45 × 100 = 22.22 kPa
PCl_3	0.15/0.45 × 100 = 33.33 kPa
Cl_2	0.20/0.45 × 100 = 44.44 kPa

$$K_p = \frac{(PPCl_3)(PCl_2)}{(PPCl_5)} = \frac{33.33 \times 44.44}{22.22} = 66.7\,\text{kPa}$$

5 a) As temp. increases value of K_c decreases
As temp. increases equilibrium shifts to left.
Higher temps favour endothermic reactions (1).
Forward reaction is exothermic (1).
b) (i) The equilibrium lies to the left (1).
(ii) Increase the pressure (1)/decrease the temperature (1)/ add more A or B (1). (Max. 2).

Unit 3 Acids and bases

Pages 34 – 54

1 a) H_2O acts a base and H_3O^+ acts as an acid.
b) $CH_3COOH + H_2O \rightleftharpoons CH_3COO^- + H_3O^+$:
CH_3COO^- is the conjugate base.

2 Ethanedioic acid.

3 $K_a = \dfrac{[C_6H_5COO^-][H^+]}{[C_6H_5COOH]}$

4 Lower: dissociation is endothermic and as temp. decreases dissociation decreases.

5 $CH_3NH_3^+$

6 a) $H_2SO_4 + CH_3COOH \rightleftharpoons HSO_4^- + CH_3COOH_2^+$
acid base base acid

b) $CH_3CONH_2 + NH_3 \rightleftharpoons CH_3CONH^- + NH_4^+$
acid base base acid

7 a) 1.60 b) 2.30 c) 0.90

8 a) 1×10^{-5} b) 3.162×10^{-4} c) 1.58 d) 5.62×10^{-5}
e) 1.12×10^{-7} f) 1.23

9 a) 0 b) 0.60 c) 0.52 (diprotic acid)

10 a) 0.025 M b) 0.30 M

11 a) $pH = -\log_{10}[H^+]$
b) pH = 2.88: $[H^+] = 1.318 \times 10^{-3}\,\text{mol dm}^{-3}$

$$K_a = \frac{[H^+]^2}{c} = \frac{(1.318 \times 10^{-3})^2}{0.1} = 1.74 \times 10^{-5}\,\text{mol dm}^{-3}$$

12 a) $pK_a = -\log_{10}K_a$
b) 4.70

13 a) $K_w = [H^+][OH^-]\,\text{mol}^2\,\text{dm}^{-6}$
b) pH = 7.6 therefore $[H^+] = 2.52 \times 10^{-8}\,\text{mol dm}^{-3}$
pure water so $[H^+] = [OH^-] = 2.52 \times 10^{-8}$
hence $K_w = 6.31 \times 10^{-16}\,\text{mol}^2\,\text{dm}^{-6}$

14 a) In pure water $[H^+] = [OH^-] = 3.162 \times 10^{-7}$
$K_w = 1 \times 10^{-13}\,\text{mol}^2\,\text{dm}^{-6}$
b) $[H^+] = K_w/[OH^-] = (1 \times 10^{-13})/(0.01)$
$= 1 \times 10^{-11}$ ∴ pH = 11

15 a) Strong acid and hence 0.1 M H^+ hence initial pH = 1.
b) Initial moles of $H^+ = MV/1000 = (0.1 \times 25)/1000 = 0.0025$
Moles of OH^- added $= MV/1000 = (0.1 \times 5)/1000 = 0.0005$
Moles of H^+ unreacted 0.0025 – 0.0005 = 0.002
New vol: 30 cm^3 : $[H^+] = (0.002 \times 1000)/30$
= 0.0667 ∴ pH = 1.18

16 a)

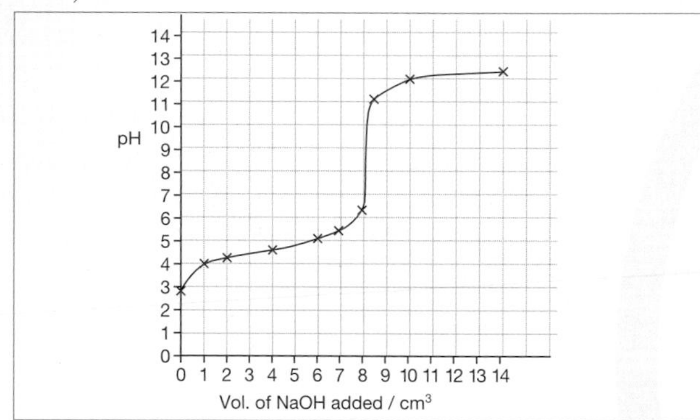

b) 7–10.5
c) Equivalence volume from graph is 8.2 cm^3
Moles of NaOH $= MV/1000 = (0.1 \times 8.2)/1000 = 8.2 \times 10^{-4}$
Moles of weak acid $= 8.2 \times 10^{-4}$
Molarity of weak acid = (moles × 1000)/V
$= (8.2 \times 10^{-4} \times 1000)/10$
= 0.082 M

17 a) Blue.
b) Expect pK_a to be 4.7. Indicators are weak acids that operate in range of ±1 pH units around their pK_a values.

18 a) and b)

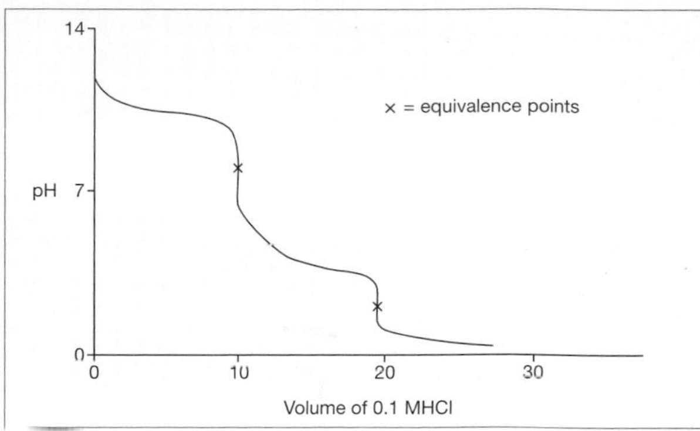

c) Phenolphthalein and methyl orange.

19 $K_a = \frac{[H^+][A^-]}{[HA]}$ and hence $[H^+] = \frac{K_a [HA]}{[A^-]}$

$= \frac{(2.4 \times 10^{-5} \times 0.25)}{0.5}$

Hence $[H^+] = 1.2 \times 10^{-5}$ pH = 4.92

20 $K_a = \frac{[CH_3COO^-][H^+]}{[CH_3COOH]}$

Hence $[CH_3COO^-] = \frac{K_a[CH_3COOH]}{[H^+]} = \frac{1.7 \times 10^{-5} \times 0.1}{1 \times 10^{-4}}$

$= 1.7 \times 10^{-2}$

(pH = 4 therefore $[H^+] = 1 \times 10^{-4}$ mol dm^{-3})

Moles of sodium ethanoate = $MV/1000$

$= (1.7 \times 10^{-2} \times 500)/1000 = 8.5 \times 10^{-3}$

Mass needed = moles × $M_r = 8.5 \times 10^{-3} \times 82 = 0.697$ g of CH_3COONa.

Unit 3 End-of-unit questions Page 55

1 a) (i) pH = $-\log_{10}[H^+]$ (1).

(ii) Strong acid hence pH = $-\log_{10}(0.1)$ = 1 (1)

b) Weak acid is only partially ionised in solution (1).

$CH_3CH_2COOH(aq) + H_2O(l) \rightleftharpoons CH_3CH_2COO^-(aq) + H_3O^+(aq)$ (1)

$K_a = \frac{[CH_3CH_2COO^-][H^+]}{[CH_3CH_2COOH]}$ (1)

$[CH_3CH_2COO^-] = [H^+]$ (1)

Therefore $K_a = \frac{[H^+]^2}{[CH_3CH_2COOH]}$

$\therefore [H^+] = \sqrt{K_a[CH_3CH_2COOH]} = \sqrt{K_a c}$ (1).

$[H^+] = \sqrt{1.35 \times 10^{-5} \times 0.1}$

$= 1.162 \times 10^{-3}$ mol dm^{-3} (1) ∴pH = 2.93 (1).

c) Fully dissociated (1) so $[H^+]$ is higher and pH is lower (1).

d) Dissociation is endothermic (1). As temp. increases dissociation increases (1): K_a increases (1).

2 a) Strong acid is 100% ionised in solution (1): monoprotic means that each acid molecule can donate only one hydrogen ion (proton) to a base (1).

b) $HCl + NaOH \rightarrow NaCl + H_2O$ (1).

c) Moles of HCl $MV/1000 = (25 \times 0.15)/1000 = 0.00375$ (1).

Moles of NaOH $MV/1000 = (30 \times 0.125)/1000 = 0.00375$ (1).

Equal moles (1) ∴ $[H^+] = [OH^-]$ (1).

$[H^+] = \sqrt{K_w}$ (1) $= \sqrt{1 \times 10^{-14}} = 1 \times 10^{-7}$ (1) ∴ pH = 7 (1).

3 a) $HA \rightarrow H^+ + A^-$ (1).

b) pH = –0.1 $[H^+] = 1.259$ mol dm^{-3} (1).

c) Moles of HA $MV/1000 = (1.259 \times 25)/1000$
= 0.03147(1)
= moles of NaOH needed (1)

Volume of NaOH needed = (moles × 1000)/M
= (0.03147 × 1000)/0.5
= 62.95 cm^3 (1).

4 a) (i) $K_w = [H^+][OH^-]$ (1).

(ii) 1×10^{-14} (1) $mol^2 dm^{-6}$ (1) at 298 K

b) (i) Pure water $[H^+] = [OH^-]$ (1).

Therefore $K_w = [H^+]^2$ (1)

$[H^+] = \sqrt{K_w} = \sqrt{1 \times 10^{-14}}$
$= 1 \times 10^{-7}$ mol dm^{-3}(1) ∴pH = 7 (1).

(ii) Final volume of the solution is 50 cm^3. The acid has been diluted by a factor of 10 (1). Final concentration of acid is 0.01 M (1). pH = 2 (1).

c) The dissociation of water is endothermic (1). By Le Chatelier's Principle dissociation decreases as temp. decreases (1) ∴ smaller value for K_w and $[H^+]$ (1): pH increases.

5 a) $pK_a = 5.45$ $K_a = 3.548 \times 10^{-6}$ mol dm^{-3} (1).

$[H^+] = \sqrt{K_a c}$ (1) $= \sqrt{(3.548 \times 10^{-6} \times 0.1)}$
$= 5.957 \times 10^{-4}$ mol dm^{-3} (1).

pH = 3.23 (1).

b) Moles of HA $MV/1000 = (20 \times 0.1)/1000 = 0.002$

Moles of NaOH $MV/1000 = (30 \times 0.1)/1000 = 0.003$ (1).

Excess NaOH = 0.001 moles (1).

Molarity of NaOH = $[OH^-]$ = (moles × 1000)/V
= (0.001 × 1000)/50
= 0.02 M (1).

pOH = 1.70

pH + pOH = 14 at 298 K ∴pH = 12.3 (1).

c)

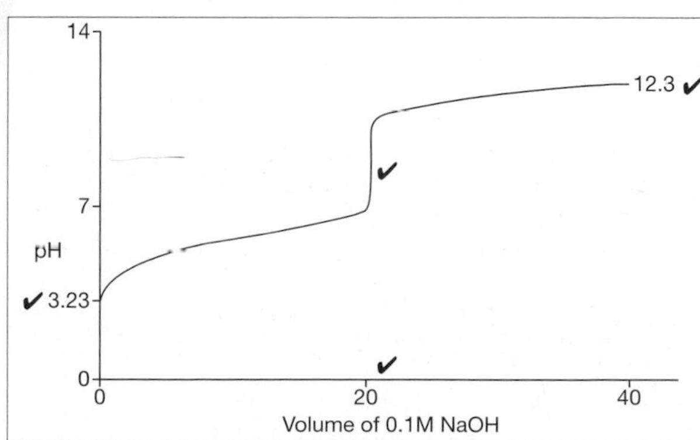

The pH change at equivalence is pH 7–10.

d) Becuse the pH change at equivalence is above 7 (1) and it is in this pH region that phenolphthalein changes colour (1).

Answers: Module 4

Unit 3 Acids and bases (continued)

6 a) (i) Brønsted–Lowry acid: proton donor (1): H_2O and NH_4^+ ion donate a proton (1).
Brønsted–Lowry base: proton acceptor (1): NH_3 and OH^- ion accept a proton (1).
(ii) Ammonia in water produces hydroxide ions (1) and hence the solution is alkaline with a pH above 7 ($[OH^-] > [H^+]$) (1).

b) $K_w = [H^+][OH^-]\ 1 \times 10^{-14}\,mol^2\,dm^{-6}$

$$[H^+] = \frac{K_w}{[OH^-]}\ (1)$$

$$= \frac{1 \times 10^{-14}}{4.5 \times 10^{-4}} = 2.222 \times 10^{-11}\,mol\,dm^{-3}\ (1)$$

pH = 10.65 (1).

c) e.g. ammonium chloride

7 a) (i) $HNO_3(aq) + HF(aq) \rightarrow NO_3^-(aq) + H_2F^+(aq)$ (1).
(ii) $HNO_3(aq) + H_2SO_4(aq) \rightarrow H_2NO_3^+(aq) + HSO_4^-(aq)$ (1).

b) Strengths are $H_2SO_4 > HNO_3 > HF$ (1).

c) 0.025 M HNO_3 pH = 0.602 (1).
0.025 M H_2SO_4 pH = 0.301 (diprotic acid!) (1).

8 a) Weak acid is only partially ionised in solution (1): monoprotic means that each acid molecule can only donate one proton (1).

b) $K_a = \frac{[H^+][F^-]}{[HF]}$ (1) $mol\,dm^{-3}$ (1).

c) $pK_a = 3.35\ K_a = 3.548 \times 10^{-4}\,mol\,dm^{-3}$ (1).
For a weak acid $[H^+] = \sqrt{K_a c}$ (1)
$= \sqrt{(3.548 \times 10^{-4} \times 0.2)}$
$= 8.424 \times 10^{-3}\,mol\,dm^{-3}$ (1).
pH = 2.07 (1)

d) This is the half-neutralisation point (1) and hence $K_a = [H^+]$ therefore pH = 3.45 (1).

e) Moles of NaOH = moles of NaF
$MV/1000 = (35 \times 0.2)/1000 = 0.007$ moles (1).
$[F^-] = [NaF] = (\text{moles} \times 1000)/V$
$= (0.007 \times 1000)/85 = 0.08235$ M (1).
Initial moles of HF = $MV/1000 = (50 \times 0.2)/1000 = 0.01$
Moles of unreacted HF = 0.01 – 0.007 = 0.003 mol (1).
$[HF] = (\text{moles} \times 1000)/V = (0.003 \times 1000)/85 = 0.03529$ M (1).

$$[H^+] = K_a \frac{[HF]}{[F^-]}\ (1) = 3.548 \times 10^{-4} \times \frac{0.03529}{0.08235}$$

$= 1.52 \times 10^{-4}\,mol\,dm^{-3}$ (1) pH = 3.82 (1).

9 a) A solution whose pH is resistant to change (1) on the addition of relatively small quantities an acid/alkali (1).

b) A mixture of ammonia solution and ammonium sulphate solution contains a large 'reservoir' of the weak base ammonia and its conjugate acid, the ammonium ion (1).
Any acid added is removed by the weak base, ammonia (1).
$NH_3 + H^+ \rightarrow NH_4^+$ (1).
Any alkali added is removed by the ammonium ion (1).
$NH_4^+ + OH^- \rightarrow NH_3 + H_2O$ (1).

Unit 4 Isomerism

Pages 57 – 62

1

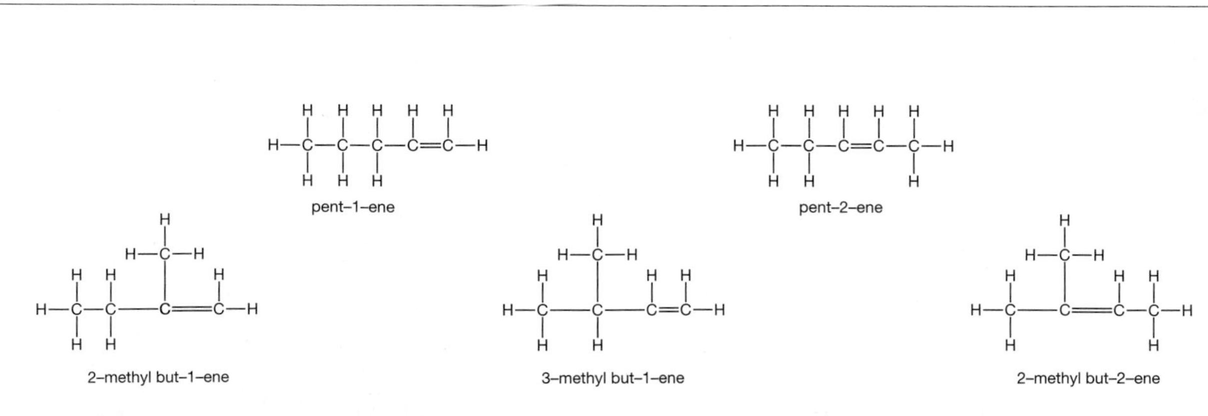

2

CH_2Cl CH_3 Cl CH_3 Cl CH_3 Cl

3 pent-2-ene.
4 b)
5 a) There is a chiral centre: a carbon atom is attached to four different groups of atoms.
b) In nature the compound is formed by enzymes which are stereospecific in their action.
6 The enantiomers will rotate the plane polarised light in opposite directions.

Unit 4 End-of-unit questions Page 63

1 a) (i) (2)

butane ✔ 2–methylpropane ✔

(ii) Branched chain isomer has lower boiling point (1) less points of contact between molecules (1) less van der Waals' forces (1).

b) (6)

$CH_3CH_2CH_2$ H C=C H H ✔✔
CH_3CH_2 CH_3 C=C H H ✔✔
CH_3CH_2 H C=C H CH_3 ✔✔

2 a) (2)

OH OH O O C C C C HO H H OH ✔✔
asymmetric carbon atoms

b) Molecule has two asymmetric carbon atoms (1) that act as chiral centres (1).

3 a) (4)

H–C–C–C–C–Br ✔ H–C–C–C–Br ✔
H–C–C–C–C–H (Br) ✔ H–C–C–C–H (Br) ✔

b) (4)

$CH_3CH_2CH_2$–C–Br ✔ ✔ :NH_3 ⟶ $CH_3CH_2CH_2$–C–N^+–H ✔ ✔ :NH_3

$CH_3CH_2CH_2CH_2NH_2$ + NH_4Br

4 a) (i) Optical (1).
(ii) Asymmetric carbon atom (1).
(iii) (2)

OH ✔ CH_3 C COOH H HO ✔ HOOC C CH_3 H

They are non-superimposable mirror images (1).

b) Lactic acid produced in the body is formed by enzyme activity (1) and only one enantiomer is formed (1). Lactic acid produced in the laboratory consists of equal amounts of the two enantiomers (a racemic mixture) (1).

5 a) (2)

CH_3 CH_3 C=C H ✔ H CH_3 H C=C H ✔ CH_3

b) Can only exhibit geometric isomerism when each (1) of the two carbon atoms in the C=C bond has two different groups attached (1).

Answers: Module 4

Unit 4 Isomerism (continued)

6 (6)

A

$CH_3CH_2CH_2CHO$ (aldehyde: C=O, C–H) ✔

or branched aldehyde

B

$CH_3CH_2COCH_3$ (CH_3CH_2 and CH_3 on C=O) ✔

C

$CH_3CH_2CH_2COOH$ (C=O, OH) ✔

or branched acid

D

$CH_3COOCH_2CH_3$ (C=O, OCH_2CH_3) ✔

or a different ester

E

$CH_3CH_2CH_2CH_2OH$ ✔

or other primary or secondary alcohol

F

$(CH_3)_3COH$ (CH_3—C—CH_3 with CH_3 and OH on the central C) ✔

7 a) Geometric (1): presence of C=C bond (1) which has restricted rotation (1).

b) Functional group (1): one isomer is an aldehyde (1) and the other is a ketone (1).

c) Functional group (1): one isomer is a carboxylic acid (1): the other one is an ester (1).

d) Positional (1): the functional group (C—C) (1) is in a different position (1).

8 a) (i) Compounds have the same molecular and structural formula (1) but have one or more atoms that have a different spatial orientation (1).

(ii) (4)

CH_3(H)C=C(H)CHO — *cis* but-2-enal ✔ (structure ✔)

CH_3(H)C=C(CHO)H — *trans* but-2-enal ✔ (structure ✔)

b) (2)

(i) CH_3—C(H)(Br)—C(H)(H)—CHO ✔ (circled C labelled: asymmetric carbon atom)

(ii) CH_3(H)C=C(H)COOH ✔

c) Optical (1) and asymmetric carbon atom labelled (1).

Unit 5 Carbonyl compounds

Pages 65 – 81

1

$CH_3CH_2CH_2CHO$ (C=O, H)

$CH_3CH_2CH_2COOH$ (C=O, OH)

CH_3—CH(CH_3)—CHO

CH_3—CH(CH_3)—COOH

$CH_3CH_2COCH_3$ (CH_3CH_2 and CH_3 on C=O)

Tertiary isomer does not undergo oxidation.

2 a) $CH_3CH_2CHO + 2[H] \rightarrow CH_3CH_2CH_2OH$ propan-1-ol

b) $CH_3COCH_2CH_3 + 2[H] \rightarrow CH_3CH(OH)CH_2CH_3$ butan-2-ol

c) $CH_3COCH_2CH(CH_3)_2 + 2[H] \rightarrow$ $CH_3CH(OH)CH_2CH(CH_3)_2$ 4-methylpentan-2-ol

3 a) The C=O bond is polar. The carbon atom carries a δ+ charge. Electron deficient carbon atoms are readily attacked by the lone pair of electrons on a nucleophile.

b)

$CH_3CH_2(CH_3)C=O$ + $:H^-$ → $CH_3CH_2(CH_3)C(H)O^-$ —H^+→ $CH_3CH_2(CH_3)C(H)OH$

4

$(CH_3)_2C=O$ + $:CN^-$ → $(CH_3)_2C(CN)O^-$ —H^+→ $(CH_3)_2C(CN)OH$

5 2-hydroxy, 2-methylpropanoic acid

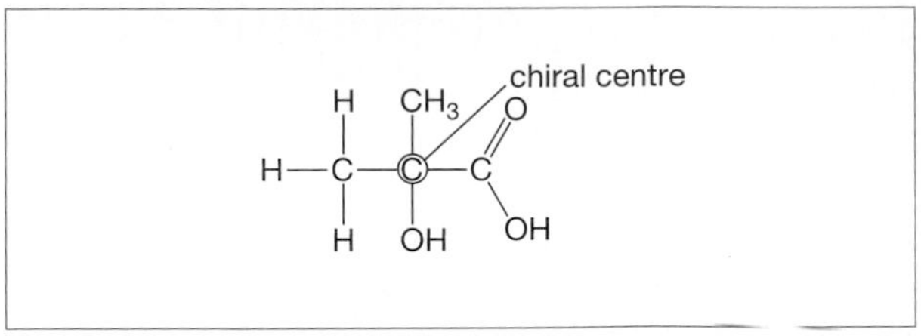

H CH$_3$ chiral centre
O
H—C—C—C
H OH OH

It has optical activity.

6 $CH_3CH_2OH + [O] \rightarrow CH_3CHO + H_2O$
$CH_3CHO + HCN \rightarrow CH_3CH(OH)CN$
$CH_3CH(OH)CN + 2H_2O + HCl \rightarrow$
$CH_3CH(OH)COOH + NH_4Cl$

7 a) Methanoic acid. b) Pentanoic acid.
c) 3-methylbutanoic acid. d) 4-methylpentanoic acid.

8

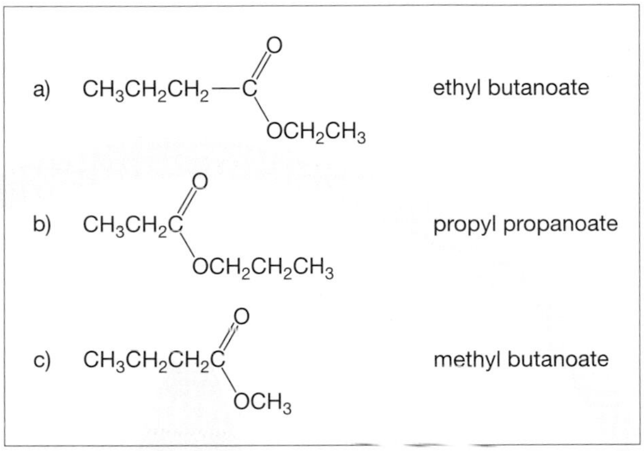

a) $CH_3CH_2CH_2$—C(=O)OCH_2CH_3 ethyl butanoate

b) CH_3CH_2C(=O)$OCH_2CH_2CH_3$ propyl propanoate

c) $CH_3CH_2CH_2C$(=O)OCH_3 methyl butanoate

9 a) $CH_3CH_2COOH + CH_3CH_2CH_2OH \rightarrow$
$CH_3CH_2COOCH_2CH_2CH_3 + H_2O$
b) $CH_3CH_2COOH + CH_3CH_2OH \rightarrow$
$CH_3CH_2COOCH_2CH_3 + H_2O$
c) $HCOOH + CH_3CH_2OH \rightarrow HCOOCH_2CH_3 + H_2O$.

10

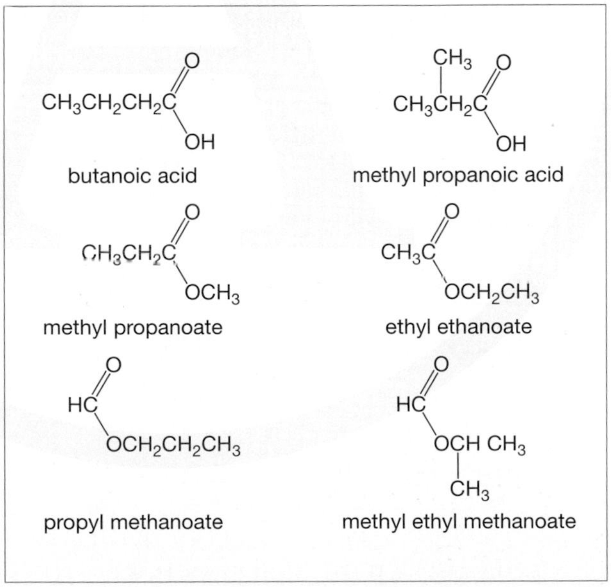

$CH_3CH_2CH_2C$(=O)OH butanoic acid

CH_3CH_2C(=O)OH with CH_3 methyl propanoic acid

CH_3CH_2C(=O)OCH_3 methyl propanoate

CH_3C(=O)OCH_2CH_3 ethyl ethanoate

HC(=O)$OCH_2CH_2CH_3$ propyl methanoate

HC(=O)OCH CH_3 with CH_3 methyl ethyl methanoate

11 a) $CH_3CH_2CH_2COOH$ butanoic acid and CH_3CH_2OH ethanol
b) CH_3CH_2COOH propanoic acid and $CH_3CH_2CH_2OH$ propan-1-ol
c) $CH_3CH_2CH_2COOH$ butanoic acid and CH_3OH methanol

12 a) $CH_3CH_2COCl + CH_3CH_2OH \rightarrow$
$CH_3CH_2COOCH_2CH_3 + HCl$ ethyl propanoate
b) $CH_3CH_2CH_2COCl + 2NH_3 \rightarrow$
$CH_3CH_2CH_2COONH_2 + NH_4Cl$ butanamide
c) $CH_3COCl + CH_3NH_2 \rightarrow CH_3CONHCH_3$
$+ HCl$ *N*-methylethanamide

13 a) $CH_3CH_2COCl + CH_3CH_2OH \rightarrow$
$CH_3CH_2COOCH_2CH_3 + HCl$

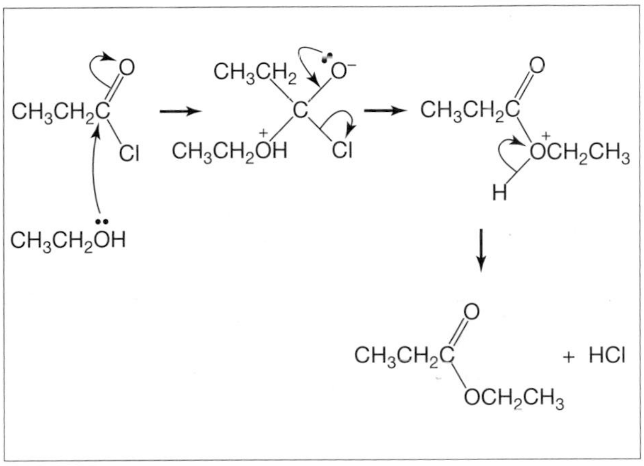

CH_3CH_2C(=O)Cl + $CH_3CH_2\ddot{O}H$ → CH_3CH_2C(O^-)(Cl)($CH_3CH_2\overset{+}{O}H$) → CH_3CH_2C(=O)$\overset{+}{O}(H)CH_2CH_3$ → CH_3CH_2C(=O)OCH_2CH_3 + HCl

b) $CH_3CH_2CH_2COCl + 2NH_3 \rightarrow$
$CH_3CH_2CH_2CONH_2 + NH_4Cl$

$CH_3CH_2CH_2C$(=O)Cl + :NH_3 → $CH_3CH_2CH_2$C(O^-)(Cl)($\overset{+}{N}H_3$) → $CH_3CH_2CH_2C$(=O)$\overset{+}{N}H_3$ + :NH_3 → $CH_3CH_2CH_2C$(=O)NH_2 + NH_4Cl

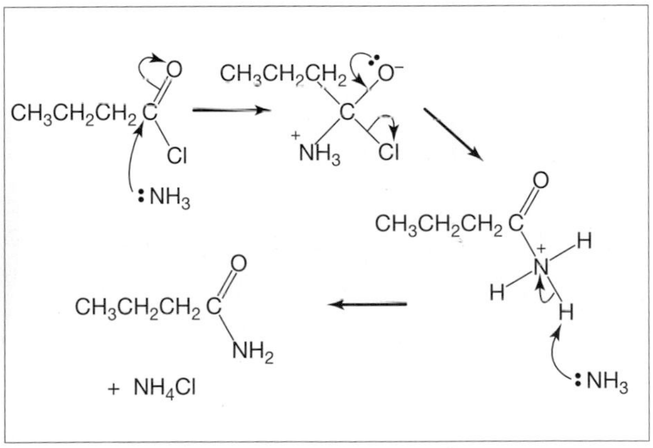

14 Reaction with carboxylic acid is equilibrium reaction so does not go to completion: reaction requires conc H_2SO_4 and heat. Need to separate product from reaction mixture.
Reaction with acyl chloride requires anhydrous conditions: reaction is very rapid. Reaction can be violent. Fumes of HCl.

Answers: Module 4

Unit 5 Carbonyl compounds (continued)

15

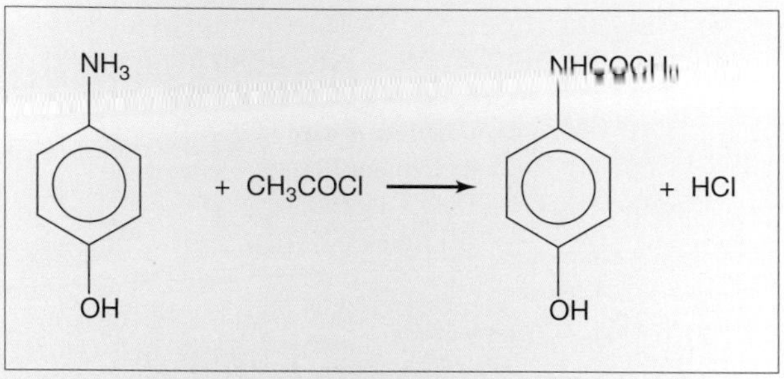

Unit 5 End-of-unit questions Page 82

1 a) Butanone (1) $CH_3CH_2COCH_3$ (1).
b) Butan-2-ol (1) $CH_3CH_2CH(OH)CH_3$ must be a secondary alcohol (1) since ketones are formed from secondary alcohols.
c) (i) Oxidation (1).
(ii) Potassium dichromate(VI) and dilute sulphuric acid (1) : heat (1).
(iii) $CH_3CH_2CH(OH)CH_3 + [O] \rightarrow CH_3CH_2COCH_3 + H_2O$ (1)
d) (2)

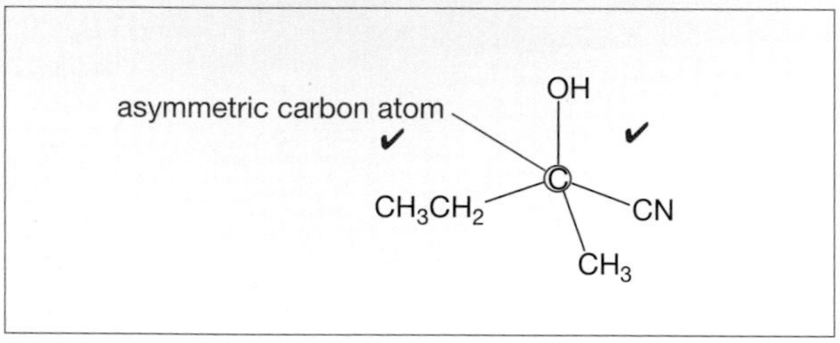

e) Nucleophilic addition (1).

2 a) (i) $CH_3COCl + CH_3NH_2 \rightarrow CH_3CONHCH_3 + HCl$ (1).
(ii) $CH_3COCl + CH_3OH \rightarrow CH_3COOCH_3 + HCl$ (1).
b) Nucleophilic addition–elimination (1).
(4)

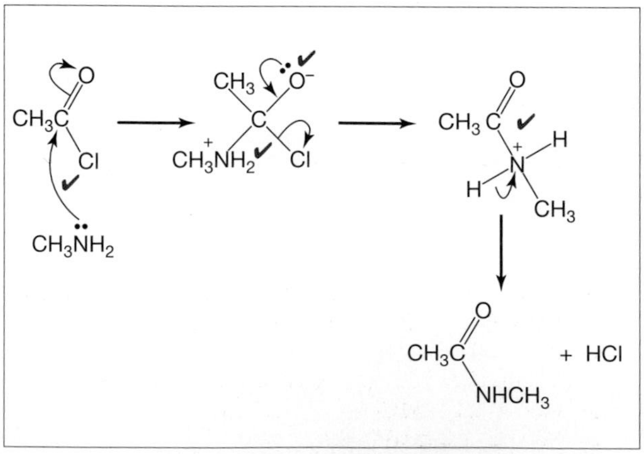

3 a) Propanal, CH_3CH_2CHO (1).
The isomers rotate the polarised light (1) in opposite directions (1).
(2)

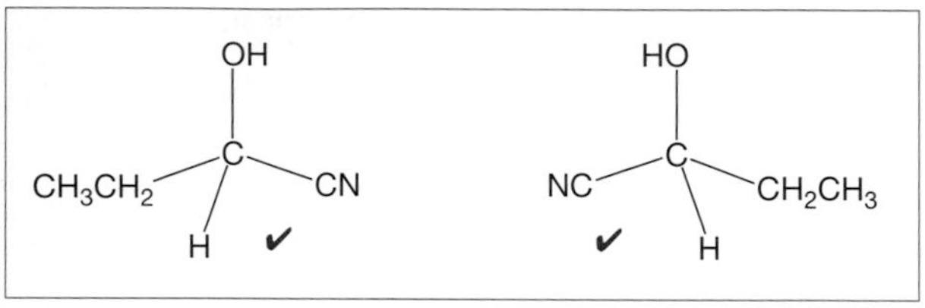

b) Nucleophilic addition. (1)
(3)

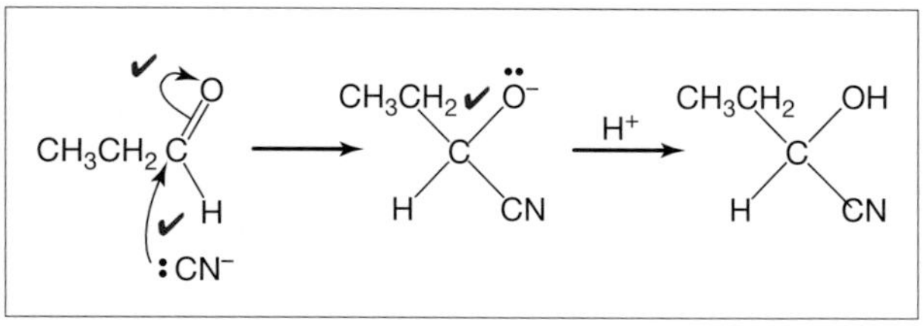

4 a) A = CH_3COOH (1) ethanoic acid (1).
B = $CH_3COCH_2CH_3$ (1) ethyl ethanoate (1).
C = $(CH_3CO)_2O$ (1) ethanoic anhydride (1).
b) (i) $CH_3COOH + CH_3CH_2OH \rightarrow CH_3COCH_2CH_3 + H_2O$ (1).
(ii) Catalyst (1).
c) (i) $(CH_3CO)_2O + NH_3 \rightarrow CH_3CONH_2 + CH_3COOH$ (1).
(ii) Nucleophilic addition–elimination (1).

5 a) (i) A = $(CH_3)_2CHCH_2OH$ (1).
B = $(CH_3)_2CHCHO$ (1).
C = $(CH_3)_2CHCH(OH)CN$ (1).
D = $(CH_3)_2CHCH(OH)COOH$ (1).
(ii) Changes from blue solution to brick-red ppt (1).
(iii) Butanal (1) would give positive test; butanone would give negative result (1).
b) Step 1 reduction (1).
Step 2 nucleophilic addition (1).
Step 3 (acid) hydrolysis (1).
c) Nucleophilic addition (1).
(3)

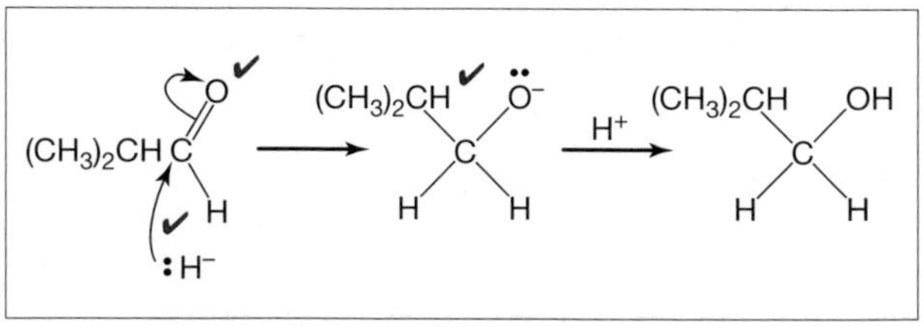

6 a) $CH_3COOH + CH_3OH \rightarrow CH_3COOCH_3 + H_2O$ (1).
$CH_3COCl + CH_3OH \rightarrow CH_3COOCH_3 + HCl$ (1).

b) Reaction with carboxylic acid: conc. sulphuric acid (1) and heat (1): conc sulphuric acid corrosive (1). Reaction with acyl chloride: anhydrous condition (1): reaction can be violent. (1) Acyl chlorides and hydrogen chloride are irritants (1). (Max 5.)

c) (4)

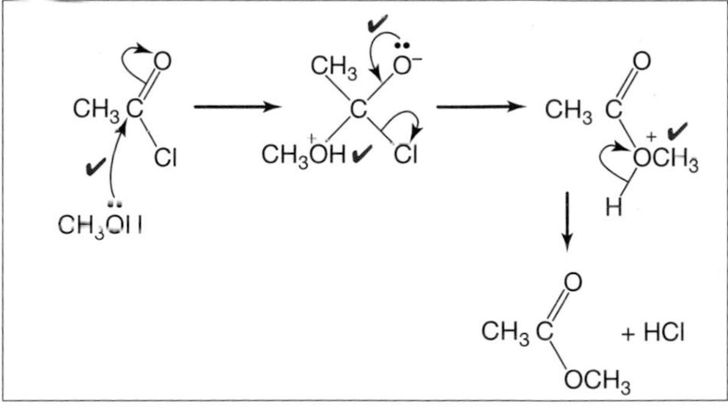

d) (2)

CH_3COOCH_3 + NaOH → $CH_3COO^-Na^+$ + CH_3OH ✔✔

7 a) $CH_3COCl + CH_3CH_2OH \rightarrow CH_3COOCH_2CH_3 + HCl$ (1).
ethanoyl chloride (1) ethanol (1) ethyl ethanoate(1)

b) $(CH_3CO)_2O + CH_3OH \rightarrow CH_3COOCH_3 + CH_3COOH$ (1).
ethanoic anhydride (1) methanol (1) methyl ethanoate (1) ethanoic acid (1).

c) $CH_3CH_2COCl + 2NH_3 \rightarrow CH_3CH_2CONH_2 + NH_4Cl$ (1).
propanoyl chloride (1) propanamide (1).

d) $(CH_3CO)_2O + CH_3CH_2CH_2NH_2 \rightarrow CH_3CONHCH_2CH_2CH_3 + CH_3COOH$ (1).
ethanoic anhydride propylamine (1).
N-propylethanamide (1) ethanoic acid (1).

e) $CH_3COCl + C_6H_5NH_2 \rightarrow CH_3CONHC_6H_5 + HCl$ (1).
ethanoyl chloride phenylamine (1).
N-phenylethanamide (1).

8 a) Step 1 water (1) Step 2 ethanol (1): anhydrous conditions (1).

b) X = methylpropanoic (or butanoic) acid (1).
$2(CH_3)_2CHCOOH + Na_2CO_3 \rightarrow 2(CH_3)_2CHCOO^-Na^+ + CO_2 + H_2O$ (2).
Y = methylethyl methanoate (2).
$HCOOCH(CH_3)_2 + NaOH \rightarrow HCOO^-Na^+ + CH_3CH(OH)CH_3$ (1).
$(CH_3)_2CHCOOH + 2[H] \rightarrow (CH_3)_2CHCHO + H_2O$ (1).

Unit 6 Aromatics

Pages 84 – 93

1 120°

2 Localised electrons are limited to the atomic orbitals whereas delocalised electrons are free to move from atom to atom.

3 A species that is electron deficient. It can accept a pair of electrons.

4

5 The catalyst is $AlCl_3$ as a Lewis acid. $AlCl_3$ readily hydrolysed by water.

6

7

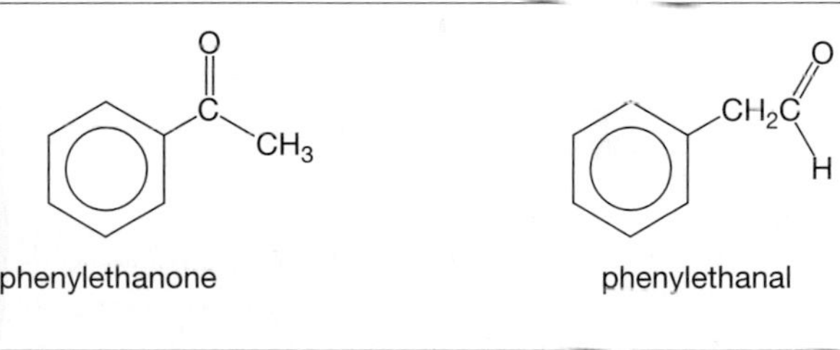

8 a)

b) Lewis acid accepting a pair of electrons from the CH_3COCl to form the electrophile.

9 Because chloroethane is made from ethene and hydrogen chloride. Using ethene saves money.

10 a) $CH_2{=}CH_2 + HCl \rightarrow CH_3CH_2Cl$

b) Electrophilic addition.

Answers: Module 4

Unit 6 Aromatics (continued)

11

$C_6H_6 + CH_2{=}CH_2 + HCl \longrightarrow C_6H_5CH_2CH_3$ regenerated

$\downarrow -2[H]$

$C_6H_5CH{=}CH_2 \longrightarrow [-CH(C_6H_5)-CH_2-]_n$

12 a) $(CH_3)_2\overset{+}{C}H$ and $CH_3CH_2CH_2^+$ First is a secondary carbocation which is more stable than the primary carbocation.

b) Major $C_6H_5CH(CH_3)_2$ Minor $C_6H_5CH_2CH_2CH_3$

13

$CH_3CH_2CH{=}CH_2 \; H{-}Cl \; AlCl_3 \longrightarrow CH_3CH_2\overset{+}{C}HCH_3 + AlCl_4^-$ + $CH_3CH_2CH_2\overset{+}{C}H_2$

$C_6H_6 + CH_3CH_2\overset{+}{C}HCH_3 \longrightarrow$ intermediate $\longrightarrow C_6H_5CH(CH_3)CH_2CH_3 + H^+$

$C_6H_6 + CH_3CH_2CH_2\overset{+}{C}H_2 \longrightarrow$ intermediate $\longrightarrow C_6H_5CH_2CH_2CH_2CH_3 + H^+$

Branched isomer is formed in a greater quantity since its formation involves a secondary carbocation which is more stable than the primary carbocation.

Unit 6 End-of-unit questions Page 94

1 a) Step 1 conc. nitric acid (1) and conc sulphuric acid (1).
Step 2 tin and conc. hydrochloric acid (1).

b) Step 1 electrophilic substitution (or nitration) (1).
Step 2 reduction (1).

c) $C_6H_6 + HNO_3 \rightarrow C_6H_5NO_2 + H_2O$ (1).
$C_6H_5NO_2 + 6[H] \rightarrow C_6H_5NH_2 + 2H_2O$ (1).

2 a) (4)

$CH_3CH_2{-}Cl \; AlCl_3 \longrightarrow CH_3\overset{+}{C}H_2 + AlCl_4^-$

$C_6H_6 + \overset{+}{C}H_2CH_3 \longrightarrow$ intermediate $\longrightarrow C_6H_5CH_2CH_3 + H^+$

b) (4)

$CH_3C(O)Cl \; AlCl_3 \longrightarrow CH_3{-}\overset{+}{C}{=}O + AlCl_4^-$

$C_6H_6 + CH_3\overset{+}{C}{=}O \longrightarrow$ intermediate $\longrightarrow C_6H_5COCH_3 + H^+$

c) Aluminium chloride is hydrolysed by water (1).

3 a) (1)

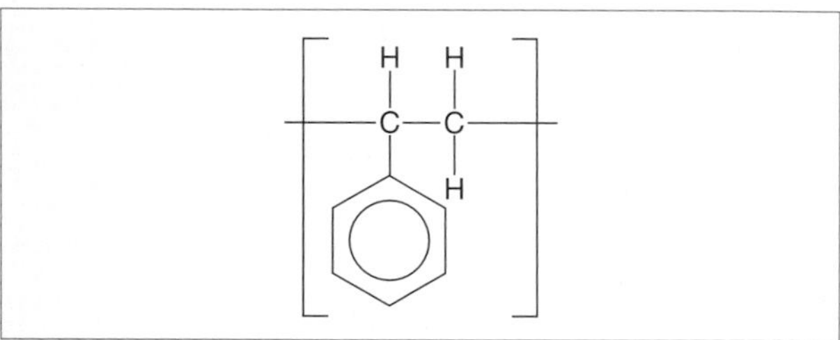

b) (i) Step 1: alkylation/Friedel–Crafts/electrophilic substitution (1).
Step 2: dehydrogenation (1).

(ii) (5)

$CH_2{=}CH_2 \; H{-}Cl \; AlCl_3 \longrightarrow CH_3\overset{+}{C}H_2 + AlCl_4^-$

$C_6H_6 + \overset{+}{C}H_2CH_3 \longrightarrow$ intermediate $\longrightarrow C_6H_5CH_2CH_3 + H^+$

(iii) Chloroethane (1).

4 a) (i) A species with a positively charged carbon atom (1).

(ii) (2)

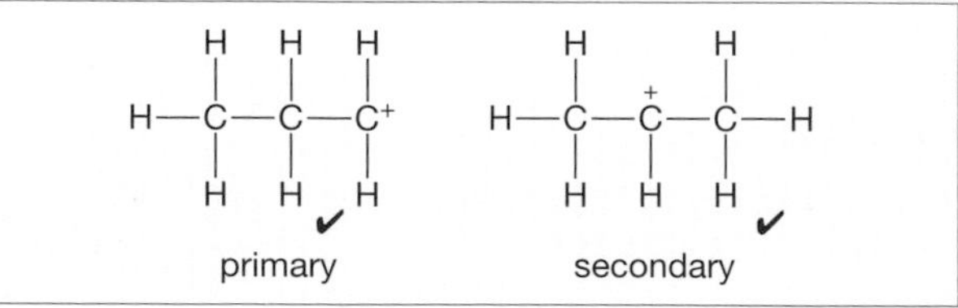

b) (i) $CH_3CH{=}CH_2 + HCl + AlCl_3 \rightarrow CH_3\overset{+}{C}HCH_3 + AlCl_4^-$ (1).
Generates the electrophile (1).

(ii) Major product is formed from secondary carbocation (1) which is in greater quantities (1) than the less stable primary carbocation (1).

(iii) $C_6H_5CH_2CH_2CH_3$ (1).

5 a) An electron deficient species: it can accept a pair of electrons (1).

b) In benzene the six carbon atoms form a planar hexagon with a ring of delocalised p electrons (1) above and below the plane of the molecule. Benzene susceptible to attack by electrophiles (1). Addition results in the loss of extra stability (1) conferred by the delocalised electrons. Substitution favoured as this retains the delocalisation (1).

c) (4)

6 a) (i) $C_6H_{10} + H_2 \rightarrow C_6H_{12}$ (1).

(ii) $C_6H_6 + 3H_2 \rightarrow C_6H_{12}$ (1).

b) Would expect the value to be 3 × 120 = 360 since three moles of H_2 added (1). Value is less than this since the p electrons are delocalised (1) around the benzene molecule and this makes the molecule more stable (1).

c) Add $Br_2(aq)$ (1): cyclohexene will decolourise $Br_2(aq)$ (1). No change with benzene (1).

7 a) Nitronium ion (1).

$HNO_3 + 2H_2SO_4 \rightarrow NO_2^+ + 2HSO_4^- + H_2O$ (1).

b) Electrophilic substitution (1).

c) (3)

8 a) Phenylethanone (1).

b) Ethanoyl chloride (1) and aluminium chloride (1).

c) (4)

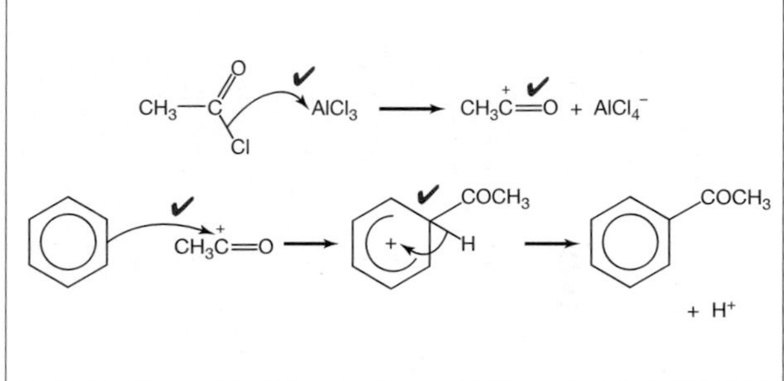

Unit 7 Amines

Pages 96 – 102

1 a) 2-aminopropane.

b) Phenylamine.

c) 2-aminobutane.

2 a) 1-aminopropane – primary.

b) *N*-methylpropylamine – secondary.

c) Propan-2-ol – secondary.

d) 2-chloro, 2-methylpropane – tertiary.

3

4 a) Reduction of propanenitrile with H_2/Ni or reaction of ammonia with 1-bromopropane.

b) First method. Only one product formed. With nucleophilic substitution other products are formed by successive substitution.

5 Act as Brønsted–Lowry bases. The lone pair on the nitrogen atom accept a proton from a water molecule. Results in the formation of OH^- ions and hence the pH is above 7.

$RNH_2 + H_2O \rightleftharpoons RNH_3^+ + OH^-$

6 a) Propylamine.

b) The alkyl group is electron–releasing compared to hydrogen. The lone pair on the nitrogen atom in propylamine are more available for bonding with an H^+.

Answers: Module 4

Unit 7 Amines (continued)

Unit 7 End-of-unit questions Page 103

1 a) (i) $CH_3COCl + CH_3CH_2NH_2 \rightarrow CH_3CONHCH_2CH_3 + HCl$ (1).
(ii) nucleophilic addition–elimination (1).

(5)

b) Ethanoic anhydride (1).

2 a) (i) Step 1 e.g. tin (1), concentrated HCl (1). Step 2 ethanoyl chloride (1).
(ii) Step 1 – reduction (1); Step 2 – acylation (1).

b) (5)

3 a) Primary $CH_3CH_2CH_2NH_2$ (1).
Secondary $CH_3CH_2NHCH_3$ (1).
Tertiary $(CH_3)_3N$ (1).

b) Bromoethane (1) and methylamine (1).
$CH_3CH_2Br + 2CH_3NH_2 \rightarrow CH_3CH_2NHCH_3 + CH_3NH_3^+Br^-$ (2).

c) (i) $R_4N^+X^-$ (1).
(ii) Cationic surfactants (1).

4 a) (i) OH^- ions are formed (1).
(ii) Accepts a proton from the water molecules (1) – Brønsted–Lowry base (1).
(iii) $K_w = [H^+][OH^-]$ (1) $= 1 \times 10^{-14}$
Hence $[H^+] = (1 \times 10^{-14})/(4.8 \times 10^{-4})$ (1).
$[H^+] = 2.083 \times 10^{-11}$ $pH = -\log_{10}[H^+]$ (1).
$= -\log_{10}(2.083 \times 10^{-11}) = 10.68$ (1).

b) (i) CH_3CH_2 group is electron–releasing relative to hydrogen (1). Lone pair on nitrogen atom are more available for bonding (1) ethylamine can accept a proton more readily (1).
(ii) In phenylamine the lone pair on the nitrogen atom interact (1) with the delocalised π electrons in the benzene ring (1) and hence are less available for bonding (1).

5 a) Ammonia (1).
$C_6H_5CH_2Cl + 2NH_3 \rightarrow C_6H_5CH_2NH_2 + NH_4Cl$ (1).
Hydrogen and a nickel catalyst (1).
$C_6H_5CN + 2H_2 \rightarrow C_6H_5CH_2NH_2$ (1).

b) (4)

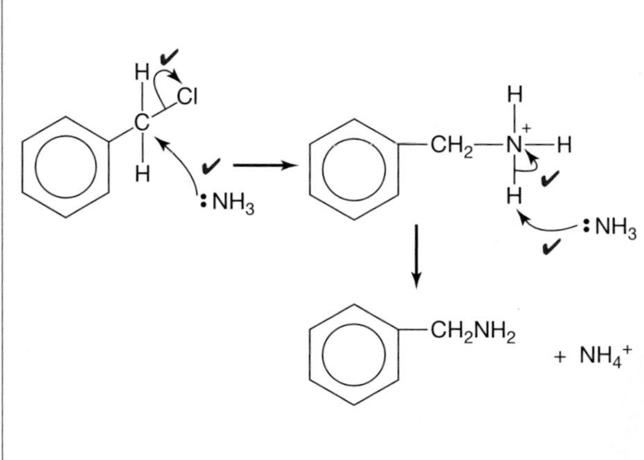

c) Stronger base is (phenylmethyl)amine (1).
In phenylamine the lone pair on the nitrogen atom interact (1) with the delocalised π electrons in the benzene ring (1) and hence are less available to form a co-ordinate bond with an H^+ ion (1).

d) Phenylamine is covalent molecule (1) which is insoluble in water. However being a base it reacts with hydrochloric acid to form an ionic salt (1) that dissolves in water.
$C_6H_5NH_2 + HCl \rightarrow C_6H_5NH_3^+Cl^-$ (1).

6 a) $CH_3CH_2Br + 2NH_3 \rightarrow CH_3CH_2NH_2 + NH_4Br$ (1).

(4)

b) $CH_3CH_2NH_2 + CH_3CH_2Br \rightarrow (CH_3CH_2)_2NH + HBr$ (1).
$(CH_3CH_2)_2NH + CH_3CH_2Br \rightarrow (CH_3CH_2)_3N + HBr$ (1).
$(CH_3CH_2)_3N + CH_3CH_2Br \rightarrow (CH_3CH_2)_4N^+Br^-$ (1).

c) Reduction of ethanenitrile using hydrogen and nickel catalyst (1).
$CH_3CN + 2H_2 \rightarrow CH_3CH_2NH_2$ (1).

7 a) nucleophilic substitution (1).
$CH_3CHClCH_3 + 2NH_3 \rightarrow CH_3CH(NH_2)CH_3 + NH_4Cl$ (1).

b) Reduction (1).
$CH_3CH_2CN + 2H_2 \rightarrow CH_3CH_2CH_2NH_2$ (1).

c) Reduction (1).
$C_6H_5NO_2 + 6[H] \rightarrow C_6H_5NH_2 + 2H_2O$ (1).

d) Nucleophilic substitution (1).
$CH_3CH_2NH_2 + CH_3CH_3Cl \rightarrow (CH_3CH_2)_2NH + HCl$ (1).

e) Nucleophilic addition–elimination (1).
$CH_3CH_2NH_2 + CH_3COCl \rightarrow CH_3CONHCH_2CH_3 + HCl$ (1).

8 a) $CH_3NH_2 + H_2O \rightleftharpoons CH_3NH_3^+ + OH^-$ (1).

b) The lone pair on the nitrogen atom (1) interact with the delocalised p electrons in the benzene ring (1). This makes the lone pair less available (1) to form a co-ordinate with an H^+. Hence phenylamine is a weaker base (1) than the aliphatic amines and hence its conjugate acid is a stronger acid and hence has a lower pK_a value.

c) $CH_3CH_2CH_2NH_2 + HCl \rightarrow CH_3CH_2CH_2NH_3^+Cl^-$ (1).
$CH_3CH_2CH_2NH_3^+Cl^- + NaOH \rightarrow CH_3CH_2CH_2NH_2 + NaCl + H_2O$ (1).

Unit 8 Amino acids and polymers

Pages 105 – 112 [Polymers]

1 Plastic bottles – cling film.

2 Poly(chloroethene).

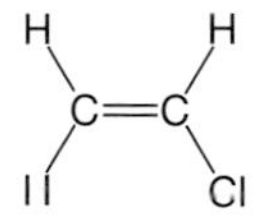

3 Poly(tetrafluoroethane) PTFE.

4 Faster reaction.

5

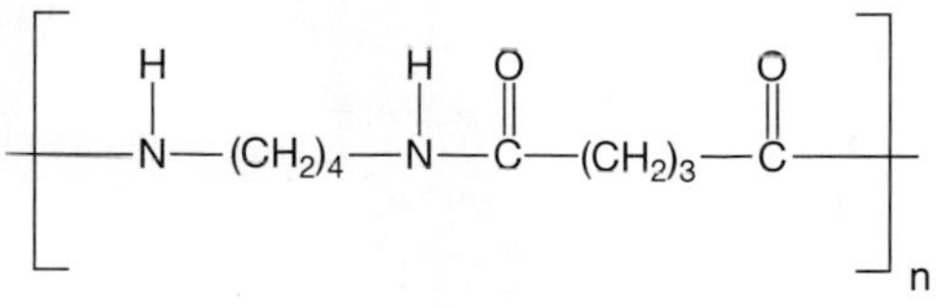

6

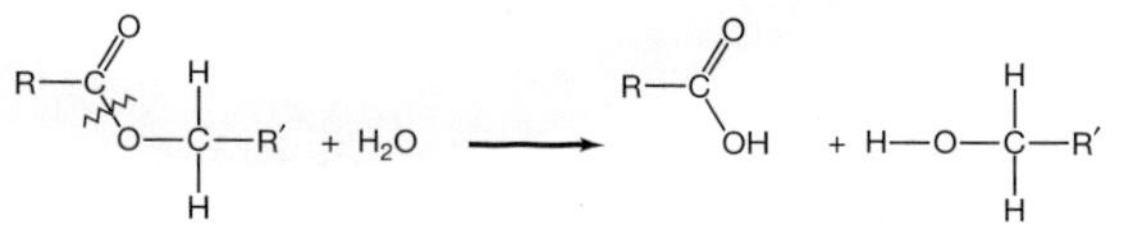

7 a)

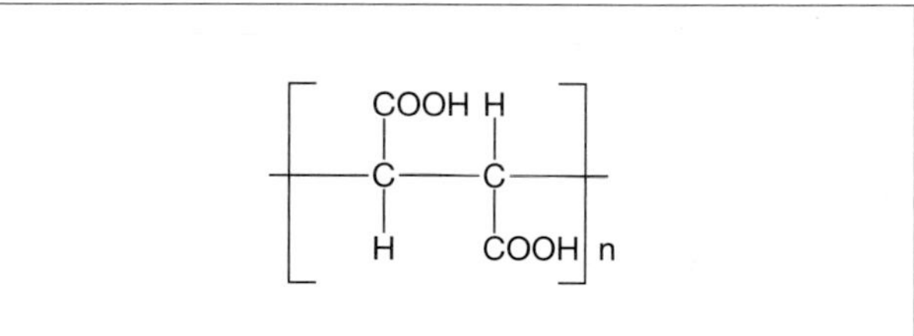

b) Both the same since all the bonds can rotate.

Amino acids

8 Secondary amine.

9 3-hydroxy, 2- aminopropanoic acid.

10

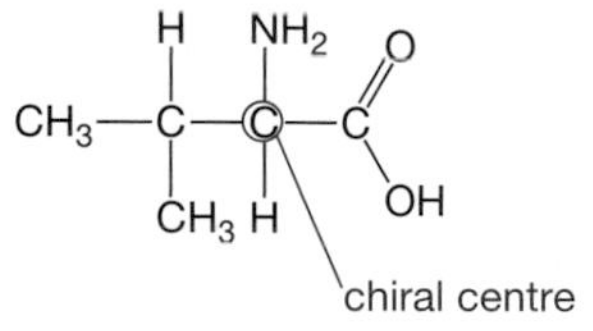

11

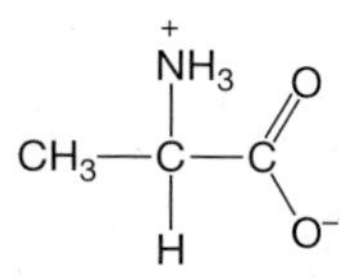

Answers: Module 4

Unit 8 Amino acids and polymers (continued)

12 a)

b) The tripeptide has an amino group and a carboxylic acid group which can be used to form further peptide linkages

Unit 8 End-of-unit questions Page 113

1 a) (2)

b) (4)

n HOOC–C_6H_4–COOH + n $HOCH_2CH_2OH$ ⟶

c) (4)

n ClOC $(CH_2)_4$ COCl + n H_2N $(CH_2)_6$ NH_2

d) Terylene/nylon are biodegradable: the ester/amide linkages are broken by hydrolysis (1).

2 a) (1)

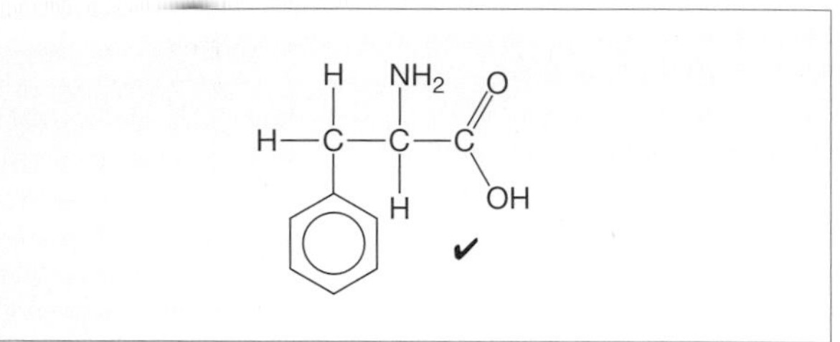

b) Optical isomerism (1) isomers rotate plane polarised light in opposite directions (1).

c) (i) Phenylalanine exists as the zwitterion (1); there is ionic bonding present (1). This is stronger than the hydrogen bonding in 2-hydroxy-3-phenylpropanoic acid (1).

(ii) (3)

3 a) $H_2NCH_2COOH + OH^- \rightarrow H_2NCH_2COO^- + H_2O$ (1).
$H_2NCH_2COOH + H^+ \rightarrow H_3N^+CH_2COOH$ (1).

b) (i) $CH_3COCl + H_2NCH_2COOH \rightarrow CH_3COHNCH_2COOH + HCl$ (1).

(ii) Nucleophilic addition–elimination (1).

(iii) (4)

c) $H_2NCH_2COOH + CH_3CH_2OH \rightarrow H_2NCH_2COOCH_2CH_3 + H_2O$ (1).

4 a) (i) and (ii) (3)

n R–C(NH₂)(H)–COOH ✔ → [–NH–CHR–CO–NH–CHR–CO–]ₙ ✔✔

b) All contain the amide (peptide) link –NH–CO– (1)

c) Nylon has peptide links (1) which will undergo hydrolysis with the alkali (1).

5 a) (1)

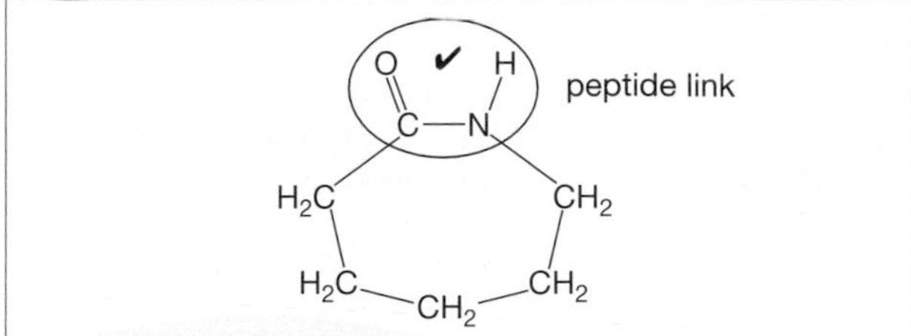

b) (2)

$H_2NCH_2CH_2CH_2CH_2CH_2COO^-$ Na^+ ✔✔

c) (2)

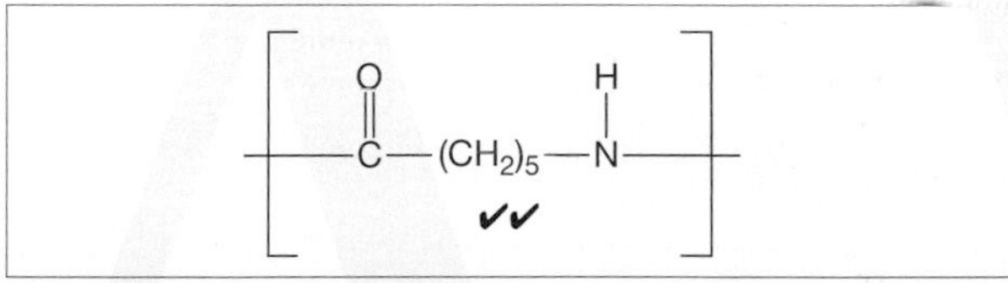

d) There is hydrogen bonding (1) between the hydrogen atoms on the N—H bonds and the oxygen atoms in the C=O bonds on adjacent chains (1).

6 a) $CH_3CHBrCOOH + 2NH_3 \rightarrow CH_3CH(NH_2)COOH + NH_4Br$ (2).

b) Nucleophilic substitution (1). The amino acid acts as nucleophile and could react with 2-bromopropanoic acid. (1) Excess NH_3 reduces chance of successive substitution (1).

c) Natural alanine is optically active: formed by stereospecific enzyme reactions (1). Only one enantiomer is formed (1). Synthetic alanine is formed by chemical reactions: equal quantities (1) of the enantiomers (1) are formed, resulting in no apparent optical activity.

d) Proteins (1) (or polypeptides).

—C(=O)—N(H)—

7 a) (1)

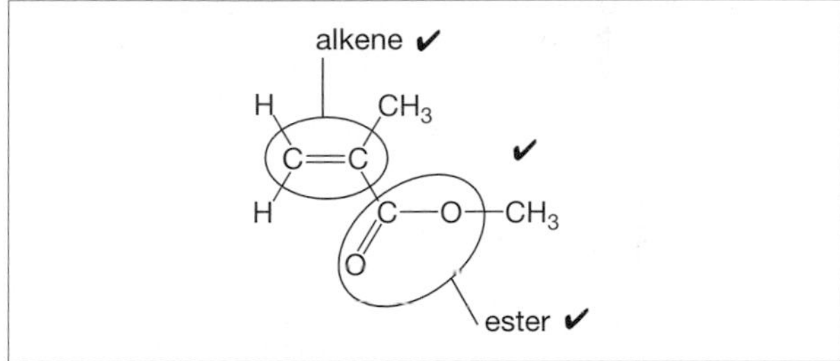

b) Alkene (1) and ester (1).

c) $CH_2{=}C(CH_3)COOCH_3 + H_2O \rightarrow CH_2{=}C(CH_3)COOH + CH_3OH$ (2).

8 Poly(ethene) (1). The reaction is addition polymerisation (1). Structure $-(CH_2CH_2)_n-$ (1).

Unit 9 Structure determination

Pages 115 – 135

1 a) 46 b) 6

2 a)

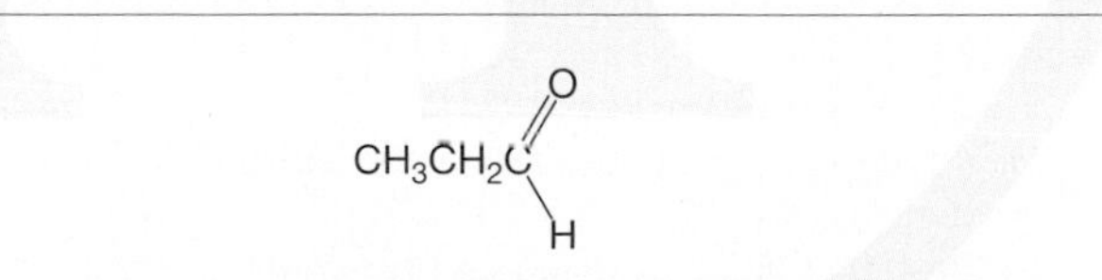

Add a few drops of each to Tollen's reagent and warm; the aldehyde forms a silver mirror.

b) $CH_3CH_2CHO^{+\bullet} \rightarrow CH_3CH_2^{+} + CHO^{\bullet}$

$CH_3CH_2CHO^{+\bullet} \rightarrow CH_3CH_2^{\bullet} + CHO^{+}$

Both ions have an m/z value of 29.

3 a) $C^{35}ClH{=}CH^{35}Cl$

b) $C^{35}ClH{=}CH^{37}Cl$

c) $C^{37}ClH{=}CH^{37}Cl$

4

5 Br has two isotopes ^{79}Br and ^{81}Br which occur in a ratio of 1:1

6 **C** is $C_7H_{10}O_2$

7 Nitrogen and oxygen do not have a dipole (non-polar bonds). In water and hydrogen fluoride the bonds are between atoms with different electronegativities: bonds are polar.

8 Carbon dioxide absorbs infra-red radiation.

Answers: Module 4

Unit 9 Structure determination (continued)

9 Sharp absorption at 1680 cm^{-1} indicates a carbonyl group. The compound has two oxygen atoms and this suggests that it is an ester.
If X is CH_3COOCH_3 methyl ethanoate – then fragmentation of molecular ions gives:
$CH_3COOCH_3^{+\bullet} \rightarrow CH_3CO^+ + {}^{\bullet}OCH_3$ $m/z = 43$
$CH_3COOCH_3^{+\bullet} \rightarrow CH_3CO^{\bullet} + {}^{+}OCH_3$ $m/z = 31$

CH_3—C(=O)—O—CH_3
$m/z = 43$
$m/z = 31$
methyl ethanoate

10 Fingerprint region (1500-400 cm^{-1}). Each compound has unique pattern in this region.
11 a) 3:1 b) 3:2:2:1.
12 $CH_3CH_2CH_2CH_2Br$ gives four peaks with a peak ratio of 3:2:2:2.
$CH_3CH_2CHBrCH_3$ gives four peaks with a peak ratio of 3:2:1:3.
13

butan-1-ol
$CH_3CH_2CH_2CH_2OH$
5 peaks 3 : 2 : 2 : 2 : 1

butan-2-ol
CH_3CH_2—C(OH)(H)—CH_3
5 peaks 3 : 2 : 1 : 1 : 3

methyl propan-1-ol
CH_3—C(CH_3)(H)—CH_2OH
4 peaks 6 : 1 : 2 : 1

methyl propan-2-ol
CH_3—C(CH_3)(OH)—CH_3
2 peaks 9 : 1

ethoxyethane
CH_3CH_2—O—CH_2CH_3
2 peaks 6 : 4

14 TMS – tetramethylsilane
15 a) four b) 2:1:6:3
(c)

CH_3CH_2—C(CH_3)(CH_3)—OH
2-methylbutan-2-ol

Unit 9 End-of-unit questions Page 136

1 a) (i) (4)

Ion	$CH_3CH_2OH_2^+$(1)	$CH_3CH_2OH^+$(1)	CH_2OH^+(1)	CH_3^+(1)
m/z values	47	46	31	15

(ii) $CH_3CH_2OH^{+\bullet}$ (1) $\rightarrow CH_3^{\bullet} + [CH_2OH]^+$ (1).
$CH_3CH_2OH^{+\bullet} \rightarrow CH_3^+ + {}^{\bullet}CH_2OH$ (1).

b) (i) 3400 cm^{-1} (1).
(ii) 1500–400 cm^{-1} (1) Each compound has a unique absorption pattern in the fingerprint region (1). Fingerprint region is compared to that of known samples (1).

c) (i) 1680–1750 cm^{-1} (1).
(ii) Add acidified potassium dichromate(VI) solution and warm (1). Ethanol: colour change orange to green (1): with the propanone solution will remain orange (1).

2 a) Cl has two isotopes (1) ^{35}Cl and ^{37}Cl in a 3:1 ratio (1). Peak at $m/z = 64$ is chloroethane with ^{35}Cl (1) is three times as high as peak at $m/z = 66$ containing ^{37}Cl (1).
b) $[CH_3CH_2]^+$ (1).
$CH_3CH_2Cl^{+\bullet} \rightarrow [CH_3CH_2]^+ + Cl^{\bullet}$ (2).

3 a)

	C	H	O
mass	60	13.3	26.6
A_r	12	1	16
moles	5	13.3	1.66
simplest ratio	3	8	1 (1)

Empirical formula C_3H_8O (2).
b) (i) Molecular formula is C_3H_8O (1).
(ii) $m/z = 60$ for molecular ion (1) isomers have same molecular mass (1).
c) Both absorb strongly at 3300 cm^{-1} in infra-red: indicates —OH group (1).
Both are alcohols: propan-1-ol and propan-2-ol.
d) (i) C will be $CH_3CH{=}CH_2$ (1).
(ii) Elimination (1).
e) Oxidation of alcohols by acidified potassium dichromate(VI).
Propan-1-ol is oxidised to propanal (CH_3CH_2CHO) which has three peaks in its proton n.m.r. spectrum (or propanoic acid) (1).
Propan-2-ol is oxidised to propanone (CH_3COCH_3) which has only one peak in its proton n.m.r. spectrum (1).
D = propanal (1) C = propanone (1).
A = propan-1-ol (1) B = propan-2-ol (1).
f) Peak will be caused by $[CH_3CH(OH)]^+$ (1).
$CH_3CH(OH)CH_3^{+\bullet} \rightarrow [CH_3CH(OH)]^+ + CH_3^{\bullet}$ (2).

4

	C	H	O
mass	66.6	11.1	22.2
A_r	12	1	16
moles	5.55	11.1	1.387
simplest ratio	4	8	1 (1)

Empirical formula C_4H_8O (1).
$m/z = 72$ is molecular ion peak so $M_r = 72$ (1).
Molecular formula is C_4H_8O (1).

X is an aldehyde or a ketone (1).
Confirmed by i.r. data – strong absorption at 1680 cm^{-1} (1).
X can be reduced to an alcohol which confirms that it is an aldehyde or a ketone (1).
Resistant to mild oxidation indicates a ketone (1).
Hence X could be butanone $CH_3CH_2COCH_3$ (1).
In mass spectrum peak at $m/z = 57$ caused by $[CH_3CH_2CO]^+$: (1) peak at $m/z = 43$ caused by $[CH_3CO]^+$ (1).
proton n.m.r CH_3–CH_2–CO–CH_3 (1) (Max. 10.)
t q s

Unit 10 Organic synthesis and analysis

Unit 10 End-of-unit questions Page 148

1 a) Step 1 acylation; (1) CH_3COCl (1) and $AlCl_3$ (1).
Step 2 reduction: (1) $NaBH_4$ (1).
Step 3 elimination: (1) concentrated H_2SO_4 (1).

b) (4)

c) (4)

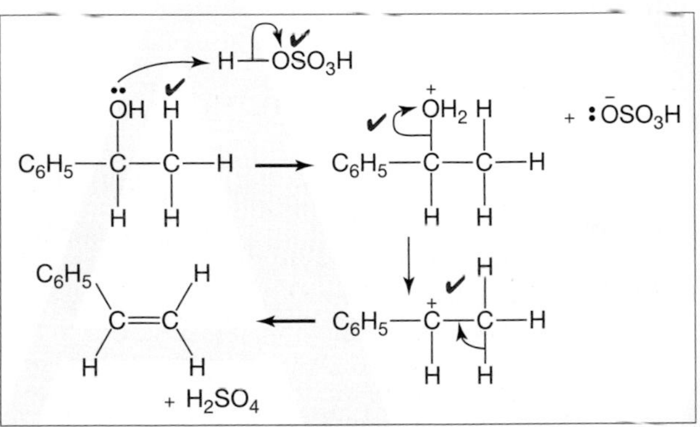

d) (1)

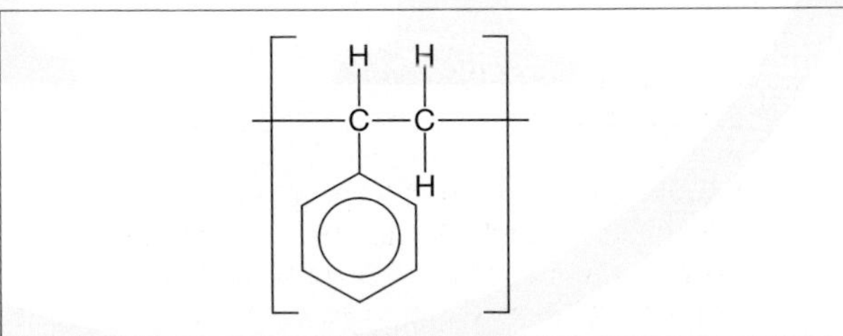

2 a) Step 1 free radical substitution (1): Cl_2 (1).
Step 2 nucleophilic substitution (1): KCN in ethanol (1).
Step 3 reduction (1): H_2/Ni (1).
b) Ultraviolet light (1).

c) (2)

d) Phenylamine is a weaker base (1): the lone pair on the nitrogen atom interact with the π electrons (1) in the benzene ring and are less available to accept H^+ ion (1).

3 Name or formula
A – 1,4-diaminobutane (1) $H_2NCH_2CH_2CH_2CH_2NH_2$
B – hexane-1,6-dinitrile (1) $NCCH_2CH_2CH_2CH_2CN$
C – hexane-1,6-dioic acid (1) $HOOCCH_2CH_2CH_2CH_2COOH$
D – nylon 46 (1) $-(OOC(CH_2)_6CONH(CH_2)_4NH)-$

4 a) A – $(CH_3)_2CHCH_2Br$ (1).
B – $(CH_3)_2CHCH_2OH$ (1).
C – $(CH_3)_2CHCHO$ (1): aldehyde.
D – $(CH_3)_2C{=}CH_2$ (1).
E – $(CH_3)_3CBr$ (1).
F – $(CH_3)_3COH$ (1): tertiary alcohol.

b)

Conversion 1	nucleophilic substitution or hydrolysis (1).
Conversion 2	oxidation (1).
Conversion 3	oxidation/redox (1).
Conversion 4	elimination (1).
Conversion 5	electrophilic addition (1).

Answers: Module 4

Unit 10 Organic synthesis and analysis (continued)

c) (i) Butanal (1).
(ii) But-2-ene (1).
(iii) 2-bromobutane (1).

5 a) (i) 74 (1).
(ii) $m/z = 29$ $CH_3CH_2^+$ (1).
$m/z = 45$ $COOH^+$ (1).
$m/z = 57$ $CH_3CH_2CO^+$ (1).

b) i.r. absorption at 2670 cm^{-1} indicates a carboxylic acid. (1) M_r of 74 indicates CH_3CH_2COOH. (1) Hence **Y** is propanoic acid. Fragmentation data supports the identification.

c) **Z** must be a secondary alcohol since it forms a ketone (1).

	C	H	O
mass	60	13.3	26.7
divide by A_r	12	1	16
moles	5	13.3	1.6875
ratio	3	8	1 (1)

Empirical formula C_3H_8O (1).
M_r is 60 so molecular formula is C_3H_8O (1).
Z must be propan-2-ol $CH_3CH(OH)CH_3$ (1).

d)

(2)

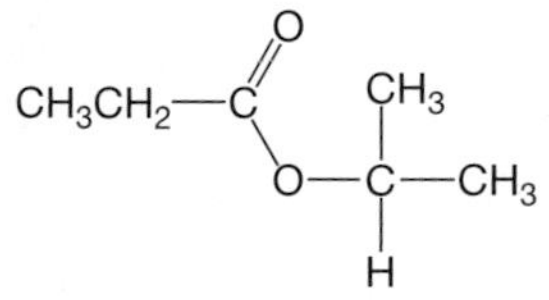

CH_3CH_2—C(=O)—O—C(H)(CH_3)—CH_3

Answers: Module 5

Unit 11 Thermodynamics

Pages 156 – 173

1

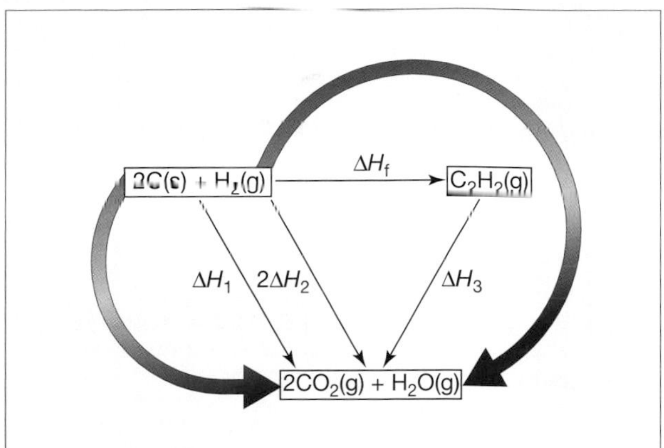

$\Delta H_f + \Delta H_3 = 2\Delta H_1 + \Delta H_2$
$\Delta H_f = 2\Delta H_1 + \Delta H_2 - \Delta H_3$
$= 2(-394) + (-286) - (-1300) = +226\,\text{kJ mol}^{-1}$

2 a) Mean bond enthalpy is the average bond energy value for the same type of bond (e.g. C—H) in a range of different compounds.

$CH_2{=}CH_2 + H_2 \rightarrow CH_3CH_3$

Bonds broken	Bonds formed
C=C 612	C—C 348
H—H 436	2 × C—H 824
total 1048	total 1172

Bonds broken – bonds formed 1048–1172
$= -124\,\text{kJ mol}^{-1}$

3

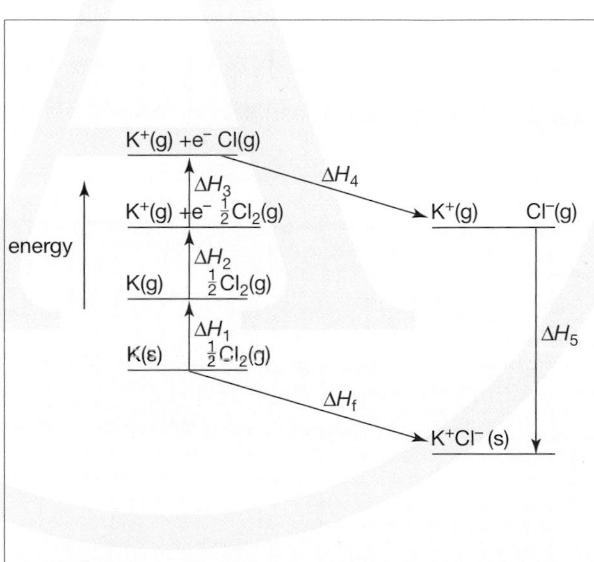

$\Delta H_f = \Delta H_1 + \Delta H_2 + \Delta H_3 + \Delta H_4 + \Delta H_5$
$\Delta H_f = +90 + (+419) + (+121) + (-364) + (-711)$
$= -445\,\text{kJ mol}^{-1}$

4

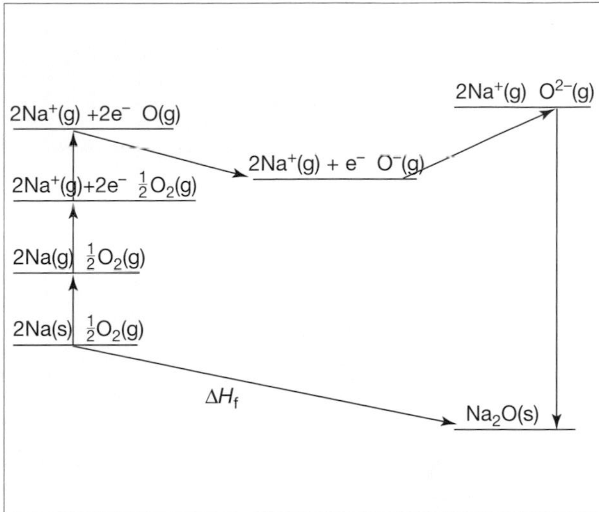

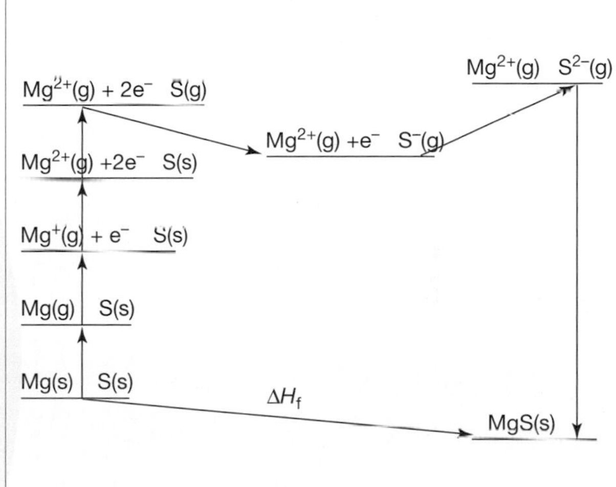

5 a) Force of attraction between ions depends upon the size and charge on the ions. Both involve Na^+: Cl^- is smaller than I^-: force of attraction is less with the larger ion.

b) Theoretical values of lattice enthalpies are calculated assuming that the compound is 100% ionic. NaCl is nearly 100% ionic whereas AgCl has some covalent character.

Answers: Module 5

Unit 11 Thermodynamics (continued)

6 a)

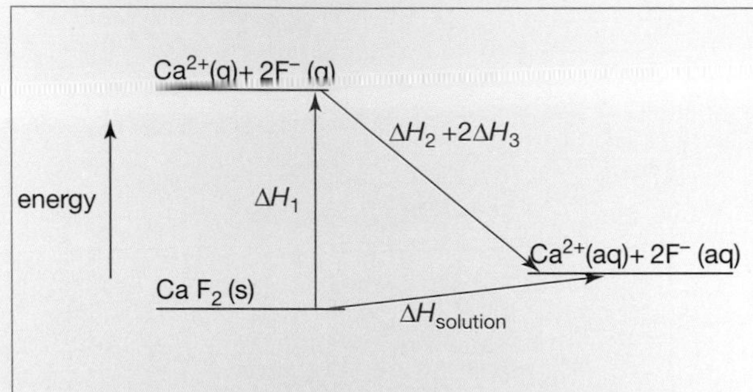

b) The enthalpy of solution is endothermic. Endothermic reactions are favoured by an increase in temp. (Le Chatelier's Principle): the solubility increases as temp. increases.

7 Ion–dipole forces are formed when ions are hydrated. The size of the ion–dipole forces increases as the size of the ions decreases and as the charge on the ion increases. The three ions have the same charge. The size of the ion increases from lithium to potassium and hence the enthalpy of hydration becomes less negative from lithium to potassium.

8 $\Delta H_{solution} = +905 + (-446) + (-364) = +95\,kJ\,mol^{-1}$

9 a) Increases. b) Increases.
c) Decreases. d) Decreases.

10 $\Delta G = \Delta H - T\Delta S$

$\Delta G = +65 - 400 \times \frac{(+167.5)}{1000}$ $\Delta G = +65 - 67 = -2\,kJ\,mol^{-1}$

11 Reaction is feasible when ΔG is zero or negative: this occurs when:

$T > \frac{\Delta H}{\Delta S}$ when $T > \frac{825 \times 1000}{275} > 3000\,K$.

Unit 11 End-of-unit questions Page 174

1 a) $\Delta G = \Delta H - T\Delta S$ (1)

b) (i) A measure of the disorder in a system. (1)
(ii) A reaction that occurs without an outside agency e.g. heat energy. (1)
(iii) A reaction in which heat energy is absorbed from the surroundings (1).

c) (i) $NaHCO_3(s) + HCl(aq) \rightarrow NaCl(aq) + CO_2(g) + H_2O(l)$ (1).
(ii) ΔH is positive (1) ΔS is positive (1).
(iii) $T\Delta S$ is larger than ΔH (1) and so ΔG is negative (1).

2 $C_5H_{12}(l) + 8O_2(g) \rightarrow 5CO_2(g) + 6H_2O(g)$

a)

Bonds broken		Bonds formed
4 × C—H	1392	10 × C=O 7430
12 × C—H	4944	12 × O—H 5556
8 × O=O	3968	
Total 10304 (1)		Total 12956 (1)

Bonds broken – bonds formed = 10304 – 12956 = –2682 (1) $kJ\,mol^{-1}$ (1).

b) $C_5H_{12}(l) + 8O_2(g) \rightarrow 5CO_2(g) + 6H_2O(g)$
$\Delta H_{reaction} = \Sigma\Delta H_f\,(products) - \Sigma\Delta H_f\,(reactants)$ (1).
$\Delta H = [5(-394) + 6(-242)] - [(-146)]$ (1).
$= -3276\,kJ\,mol^{-1}$ (1).

c) Mean bond enthalpies are average values (1), whereas enthalpies of combustion are accurate figures (1).

d) $C_5H_{12}(l) + 8O_2(g) \rightarrow 5CO_2(g) + 6H_2O(g)$
$\Delta S = \Sigma S_{(products)} - \Sigma S_{(reactants)}$ (1).
$\Delta S = [5(214) + 6(189)] - [348 + 8(205)]$ (1)
$= +216\,J\,K^{-1}\,mol^{-1}$ (1).

e) $\Delta G = \Delta H - T\Delta S$ (1)
$\Delta G = -3276 - 310 \times \frac{(+216)}{1000}$ (1) $= -3342.96\,kJ\,mol^{-1}$ (1).

3 a) (iii) ΔS positive (1).
b) Change from liquid to gas. 1) In the gas the molecules are moving randomly – highly disordered system compared to the more ordered liquid state (1).

4 a) (2)

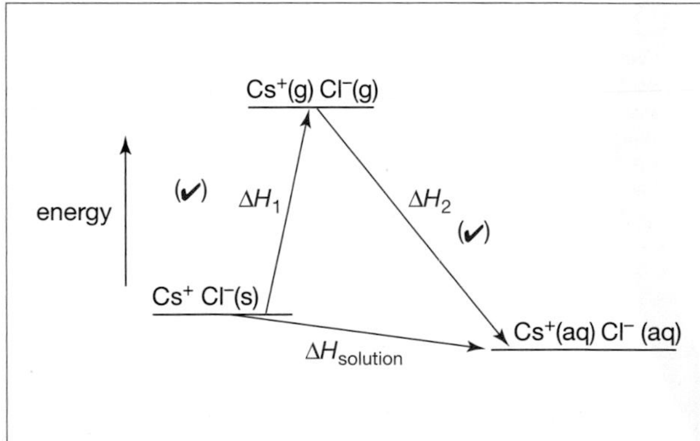

b) Ions are hydrated, ion–dipole forces (1) are formed resulting in release of energy (1).
c) $\Delta H = +70 + 380 + (-270)$ (1) $= +180\,kJ\,mol^{-1}$ (1).

5 a) $2Al(s) + 3/2O_2(g) \rightarrow Al_2O_3(s)$ (1)
b) (5)

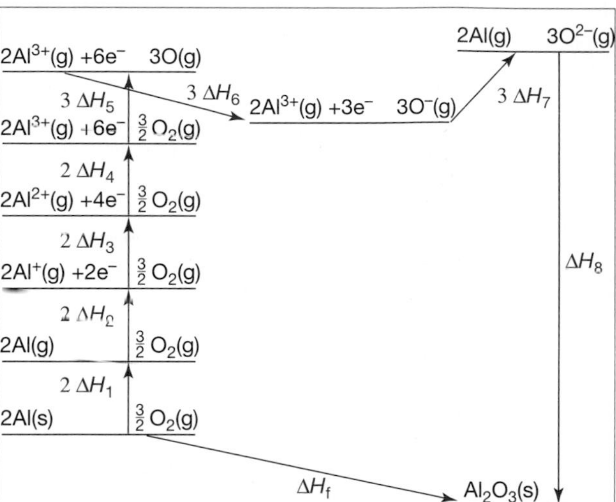

c) Lattice enthalpy, $\Delta H_8 = \Delta H_f - 2\Delta H_1 - 2\Delta H_2 - 2\Delta H_3 - 2\Delta H_4 - 3\Delta H_5 - 3\Delta H_6 - 3\Delta H_7$ (2).

6 a) $\Delta G = \Delta H - T\Delta S$ (1).
$\Delta G = +130 - [298 \times \frac{(+335)}{1000}]$ (1).
$= +\ 30.17\,\text{kJ mol}^{-1}$ (1).
b) Action of heat releases carbon dioxide gas (1). which is trapped in the pastry/dough, causing the pastry/dough to 'rise' (1).
Decomposition only occurs when ΔG is negative: occurs when T is greater than ΔH.
$T > \frac{\Delta H}{\Delta S}$ (1) $T > \frac{(130 \times 1000)}{335} > 388\,\text{K}$ (1) (5 max)

7 a) For a change of state ΔG is zero (1). Hence $\Delta H - T\Delta S = 0$ (1).
$\Delta S = \frac{\Delta H}{T}$ (1) $= \frac{(4.6 \times 1000)}{156} = +\ 29.49\,\text{J K}^{-1}\,\text{mol}^{-1}$ (1).
b) $\Delta S = \frac{\Delta H}{T} = \frac{(13.5 \times 1000)}{352} = +\ 123.58\,\text{J K}^{-1}\,\text{mol}^{-1}$ (1).
c) Solids are highly ordered and liquids contain some degree of disorder (1): in a gas the particles are moving randomly and the system is highly disordered (1). Hence ΔS for vaporisation much larger than ΔS for melting.

Unit 12 Periodicity

Pages 176 – 185

1 $1s^2 2s^2 2p^6$
2 $2Li(s) + 2H_2O(l) \rightarrow 2LiOH(aq) + H_2(g)$
3 Sulphur(VI) oxide, SO_3. Prepared by the reaction of sulphur(IV) oxide, SO_2, and oxygen gas in the presence of a catalyst of vanadium(V) oxide (Contact process).
4 Magnesium (Y) burns in oxygen to form magnesium oxide (X) which is a white solid.
$2Mg + O_2 \rightarrow 2MgO$
5 Sulphur (Z) is a yellow solid: burns in oxygen to form colourless sulphur dioxide gas.
6 a) Trigonal planar.
b) Tetrahedral.
c) Triangular bipyramid.
7 Bauxite.
8 Both ions are $1s^2 2s^2 2p^6$ but the nuclear charge of magnesium is greater than that of sodium. The greater nuclear charge draws the electrons closer, reducing the size of the ion.
9 The molecule is trigonal planar with three polar bonds. There is has no overall dipole because of the symmetry of the polar bonds. The intermolecular forces are van der Waals' not permanent dipole–dipole forces.
10 $MgO + 2HNO_3 \rightarrow Mg(NO_3)_2 + H_2O$
11 NaOH is very soluble in water. The ionic salt dissolves to release hydroxide ions into solution. $Mg(OH)_2$ is only sparingly soluble in water and only a few hydroxide ions are released into solution.
12 Ionic oxides are basic: covalent oxides are acidic.
13 Hydration is the addition of water in a physical process.
Hydrolysis is a reaction in which water is a reactant and the water molecule dissociates.
14 Al^{3+} has a large charge/size ratio and is highly polarising. It polarises the chloride ions resulting in the sharing of electrons.

Unit 12 End-of-unit questions Page 186

1 a) Passing dry Cl_2 gas (1) over heated Al (1).
$2Al + 3Cl_2 \rightarrow 2AlCl_3$ (1).
b) $AlCl_3$ dissolves in water
$AlCl_3 + 6H_2O \rightarrow [Al(H_2O)_6]^{3+} + 3Cl^-(aq)$ (1).
Hydrolysis of the complex releases H^+ ions into the water and pH is about 3. (1).
$[Al(H_2O)_6]^{3+} + H_2O \rightarrow [Al(H_2O)_5(OH)]^{2+} + H_3O^+$ (1).
When NaCl dissolves in water the ions are hydrated.
$NaCl + \text{water} \rightarrow Na^+(aq) + Cl^-(aq)$ (1).
No hydrolysis occurs and the solution is neutral (1).
c) (2)

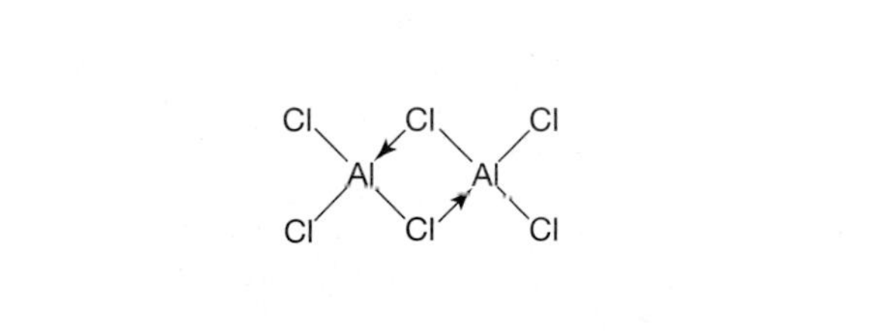

Co-ordinate bonds (1) are formed by the lone pair of electrons on a chlorine atom (1) and the vacant orbital on the aluminium atom (1) in an adjacent $AlCl_3$ molecule.

Answers: Module 5

Unit 12 Periodicity (continued)

2 a) (i) $2Na + 2H_2O \rightarrow 2NaOH + H_2$ (1).
(ii) $Na_2O + H_2O \rightarrow 2NaOH$ (1).
Presence of hydroxide ions (1) from the 100% dissociated sodium hydroxide (1).
b) Magnesium reacts with steam (1).
$Mg + H_2O \rightarrow MgO + H_2$ (1).
c) (i) Can react with both acids and bases (1).
(ii) Al_2O_3 dissolves to form a colourless solution (1).
$Al_2O_3 + 2OH^- + 3H_2O \rightarrow 2[Al(OH)_4]^-$ (1).

3

Compound	Sketch of shape	Name of shape
PCl_3	(1)	pyramidal or distorted tetrahedral (l)
$SiCl_4$	(1)	tetrahedral (1)
$AlCl_3$	(1)	trigonal planar (1)
SO_3	(1)	trigonal planar (1)

4 a) $SiCl_4$ exists as a simple covalent molecules with weak intermolecular forces between the molecules (1).
SiO_2 is a giant covalent structure (1). A large number of covalent bonds have to be overcome to break down the giant lattice structure (1).
b) (i) $1s^22s^22p^63s^23p^3$ (1).
(ii) By sharing three 3p electrons (1), phosphorus forms PCl_3. By sharing all five electrons in the third principal energy level (1) and exceeding its octet, phosphorus forms PCl_5.
c) $PCl_5 + 4H_2O \rightarrow H_3PO_4 + 5HCl$ (1).

5 a) $AlCl_3$ dissolves exothermically (1) and misty fumes (1) are given off.
b) $AlCl_3 + 6H_2O \rightarrow [Al(H_2O)_6]^{3+} + 3Cl^-(aq)$ (1).
c) $[Al(H_2O)_6]^{3+} + H_2O \rightarrow [Al(H_2O)_5(OH)]^{2+} + H_3O^+$ (1).
Hydrolysis (1).

6 a) (i) Ionic (1).
(ii) Covalent (1).
b) (i) $Na_2O + H_2O \rightarrow 2NaOH$ (1).
$SO_2 + H_2O \rightarrow H_2SO_3$ (1).
(ii) Sodium hydroxide (1): pH 13/14 (1).
Sulphuric(IV) acid (1): pH $\approx$ 3 (1).

7 a) Max. 8.
NaCl: dissolves to form colourless solution (1), $Na^+(aq)$ (1).
$AlCl_3$: dissolves exothermically and gives off misty fumes (1), $[Al(H_2O)_6]^{3+}$ (1).
$SiCl_4$: dissolves very exothermically (violent) (1). Fumes and a white ppt (1) $Si(OH)_4$ (1) (and HCl).
PCl_5: dissolves exothermically and gives off misty fumes (1), H_3PO_4 (1) (and HCl).
b) (i) Trend is from neutral (NaCl) to acidic (PCl_5) (1).
(ii) Ionic chlorides dissolve in water (1).
Covalent chlorides are hydrolysed by water to form acidic solutions (1).

8 a) The outer electrons are in the third principal energy level (1).
b) Filling of the third principal energy level: 3s (1). and 3p (1).
c) Full outer energy level and as a result little tendency to gain, lose or share electrons (1).
Process requires too much energy/ionisation energy too large (1).

Unit 13 Redox equilibria

Pages 188 – 209

1 Dichlorovanadium(IV) oxide.

2 a) +4 manganese(IV) oxide.
b) +4 titanium(IV) chloride.
c) +4 oxovanadium(IV).
d) +6 manganate(VI).

3 a) CuCl c) $Fe(OH)_3$ c) CrO_4^{2-} d) VO_3^-

4 $MnO_2(s) + 4H^+(aq) + 2e^- \rightarrow Mn^{2+}(aq) + 2H_2O(l)$:
It is an oxidising agent.

5 $MnO_2(s) + 2H_2O(l) \rightarrow MnO_4^{2-}(aq) + 4H^+(aq) + 2e^-$:
It is a reducing agent.

6 $Cr_2O_7^{2-}(aq) + 3H_2S(g) + 8H^+(aq) \rightarrow$
$2Cr^{3+}(aq) + 3S(s) + 7H_2O(l)$

7 a) $SO_3^{2-}(aq) + H_2O(l) \rightarrow SO_4^{2-}(aq) + 2H^+(aq) + 2e^-$
b) $2MnO_4^-(aq) + 5SO_3^{2-}(aq) + 6H^+(aq) \rightarrow$
$2Mn^{2+}(aq) + 5SO_4^{2-}(aq) + 3H_2O(l)$

8 The colour is from the $Cu^{2+}(aq)$ ions and they are removed as Cu(s): the colour fades.

9 0.5 M

10 a) Salt bridge, e.g. filter paper soaked in KNO_3 solution which allows the ions to move.
b) Copper wire, which allows the electrons to flow – needs to be a good conductor.

11 Zinc dissolves to form a colourless solution with effervescence of hydrogen.

12 No reaction.

13 One molar solutions, temperature of 298K and a pressure of 100 kPa.

14 a) $E^{\ominus}_{cell} = +0.34 - (-2.38) = +2.72\,V$
b) $E^{\ominus}_{cell} = +0.34 - (+0.27) = +0.07\,V$
c) $+1.03 = (+0.27) - E^{\ominus}_{lhs}$
$E^{\ominus}_{lhs} = +0.27 - (+1.03) = -0.76\,V$
The metal is zinc.

15 $Al^{3+}(aq) + 3e^- \rightleftharpoons Al(s)$

16 +1.66 V

17 a) Yes: $Sn^{2+}(aq) + 2Ag^+(aq) \rightarrow Sn^{4+}(aq) + 2Ag(s)$
b) Yes: $2Fe^{2+}(aq) + Cl_2(g) \rightarrow 2Fe^{3+}(aq) + 2Cl^-(aq)$
c) No.

18 a) $Sn^{2+}(aq) + Ni(s) \rightarrow Sn(s) + Ni^{2+}(aq)$
b) $Sn^{2+}(aq) + Fe(s) \rightarrow Sn(s) + Fe^{2+}(aq)$

19 Iron(III) is reduced to iron(II) and iodide ions are oxidised to iodine. Iodine will be observed as a brown solution (darker than the iron(III) solution).

20 a) Purple colour of solution will fade to colourless, with effervescence of chlorine gas.
b) No change.

21 MnO_4^- has a more positive $E^{\ominus}$ value than the chlorine electrode potential. Reaction of manganate(VII) with 1M HCl will produce chlorine. MnO_2 and dichromate have less positive $E^{\ominus}$ values than the chlorine electrode potential and will not form chlorine with 1 M HCl.

Unit 13 End-of-unit questions Page 210

1 a) Reducing agent (1).
b) $H_2SO_4(aq) + 8H^+(aq) + 8e^- \rightarrow 4H_2O(l) + H_2S(g)$ (2)

2 a) MnO_4^- +7 (1). MnO_4^{2-} +6 (1). MnO_2 +4 (1).
b) $E^{\ominus}_{tot} = E^{\ominus}_{rhs} - E^{\ominus}_{lhs}$
$E^{\ominus}_{tot} = (+2.260) - (+0.564) = +1.696\,V$ (1).
$3MnO_4^{2-}(aq) + 4H^+(aq) \rightarrow$
$2MnO_4^{2-}(aq) + MnO_2(s) + 2H_2O(l)$ (2).
c) Disproportionation. (1)

3 a) (i) The absolute value of an electrode potential cannot be measured (1). One electrode was selected as a reference (1).
(ii) 1 M solutions of ions (1), a temperature of 298 K (1) and a pressure of 100 kPa (1).
b) (i) The hydrogen electrode (1).
(ii) 0.00 V (1).
(iii) Pure H_2 gas (1) at 100 kPa pressure (1), bubbled over a platinum electrode (1) in a 1 M solution of H^+ ions (1).
c) (i) A calomel electrode (1):
$Hg_2Cl_2(aq) + 2e^- \rightarrow 2Hg(l) + 2Cl^-(aq)$ (1).
(ii) Hydrogen electrode is difficult to set up and use (1).

4 a) (i) $Zn(s) + 2Ag^+(aq) \rightarrow Zn^{2+}(aq) + 2Ag(s)$ (1).
(ii) Zinc redox couple has a more negative $E^{\ominus}$ value (1) than the silver redox couple and therefore zinc metal will reduce silver(I) ions (1).
Overall $E^{\ominus} = +0.08 - (-0.76) = +1.56\,V$ (1).
b) As the reactions occur in the cell the concentration of the silver(I) ions will be reduced (1) and the concentration of the the zinc(II) ions will increase (1). This will cause voltage to decrease steadily to zero (1).

5 a) $Fe^{3+}(aq)$ (1) and $Cr^{3+}(aq)$ (1).
b) $Cr^{3+}(aq)$ and $Zn^{2+}(aq)$ (1).
c) No reaction (1).

6 a) Species that donates electrons (1).
b) Cadmium, Cd (1).
c) Ag^{2+} (1).
d) $E^{\ominus}_{cell} = E^{\ominus}_{rhs} - E^{\ominus}_{lhs}$ (1).
$E^{\ominus}cell = (+0.80) - (-0.40) = +1.20\,V$ (1).
e) (i) The bromine redox couple has a more positive $E^{\ominus}$ than the iodine redox couple and so bromine will oxidise iodide ions (1).
$Br_2(l) + 2I^-(aq) \rightarrow 2Br^-(aq) + I_2(s)$ (1).
Overall $E^{\ominus}$ value = +1.07 – (+0.54) = +0.53 V (1).
(ii) $2Ag^+(aq) \rightarrow Ag^{2+}(aq) + Ag(s)$ (1).
The overall $E^{\ominus}$ for the reaction is + 0.80 – (+1.98) = – 1.18 V (1).
Reaction is thermodynamically not possible (1).

7 a) (i) $C_2O_4^{2-}(aq) \rightarrow 2CO_2(g) + 2e^-$ (1).
(ii) $MnO_4^-(aq) + 8H^+(aq) + 5e^- \rightarrow$
$Mn^{2+}(aq) + 4H_2O(l)$ (1).
(iii) $2MnO_4^-(aq) + 5C_2O_4^{2-}(aq) + 16H^+(aq) \rightarrow$
$2Mn^{2+}(aq) + 10CO_2(g) + 8H_2O(l)$ (1).
b) M_r $Na_2C_2O_4$ = 134 (1).
Concentration of $Na_2C_2O_4 = (1.713/134) \times 4$
$= 0.05113$ (1).
Moles of $Na_2C_2O_4 = MV/1000 = (0.05113 \times 25)/1000$
$= 0.001278$ mol (1).
Moles of $MnO_4^- = 0.001278 \times 2/5$
$= 0.00051134$ (1).
Concentration of MnO_4^- (moles × 1000)/V =
(0.0005113 × 1000)/23.90 = 0.0214 M (1).

Answers: Module 5

Unit 14 Transition metals

Pages 212 – 239

1 a) $1s^2 2s^2 2p^6 3s^2 3p^6 3d^1$
b) $1s^2 2s^2 2p^6 3s^2 3p^6 3d^5$
c) $1s^2 2s^2 2p^6 3s^2 3p^6 3d^3$

2 The electronic structures of the two ions are:
iron(II): $1s^2 2s^2 2p^6 3s^2 3p^6 3d^6$ and
iron(III): $1s^2 2s^2 2p^6 3s23p^6 3d^5$
Iron(III) has the more stable electronic structure because of the half-filled 3d sub-level and hence iron(II) will lose an electron (oxidised) to form the more stable structure.

3 a) Donates a lone pair.
b) Accepts a lone pair.
c) A transition metal ion surrounded by ligands which form co-ordinate bonds with the metal ion.

4 a) +2, six.
b) +1, two.
c) +2, six.

5 a) Transition metal has a partially filled 3d sub-level in the metal or its ions. A co-ordinate bond is formed between a species with a lone pair and a species with a vacant orbital. It is a shared pair of electrons in which both of the electrons have come from the same species. Co-ordination number is the number of co-ordinate bonds formed between the ligands and the metal ion.
b) $[CoCl_4]^{2-}$

6 NH_3 only has one lone pair whereas in 1,2-diaminoethane there are two nitrogen atoms, each of which has a lone pair that it uses to form co-ordinate bonds.

7 Yes. There is a lone pair on the nitrogen atom.

8 There are three ligands attached but each ligand forms two co-ordinate bonds with the chromium ion. Hence six co-ordinate bonds are formed – co-ordination number is six.

9 The bond has to be weak so that the oxygen can be released from the complex in the blood to the cells in the body.

10 a) Octahedral, six and +2.
b) Octahedral, six and +2.
c) Octahedral, six and +3.
d) Linear, two and +1.

11 a) Hexaquacobalt(II).
b) Tetrachlorocuprate(II).
c) Hexamminecobalt(III).
d) Dichloroargentate(I).

12 a) $[Sc(H_2O)_6]^{3+}$
b) $[MnCl_4]^{2-}$
c) $[Co(NH_3)_6]^{2+}$
d) $[Ag(H_2O)_2]^+$

13 $[Co(H_2O)_6]^{2+}$

14 Colourless, since the ion contains silver(I) with a full 4d sub-level ($[Kr]4d^{10}$).

15 Blue.

16 Complementary colours.

17 Green-blue.

18 a) The Cu^{2+} ion has a partially filled 3d sub-level. The 3d sub-level splits to two slightly different energies. The 3d electrons are 'excited' from the lower energy level to the higher energy level by some frequencies in the visible region of the electromagnetic spectrum. The colour depends upon the frequencies absorbed.
b) Violet.

19 No reaction: ketones are resistant to oxidation.

20 At the positive electrode: $Ag(s) - e^- \rightarrow Ag^+(aq)$
At the negative electrode: $Ag^+(aq) + e^- \rightarrow Ag(s)$

21 $2AgBr \rightarrow 2Ag + Br_2$

22 a) (i) $1s^2 2s^2 2p^6 3s^2 3p^6 3d^1$
(ii) $1s^2 2s^2 2p^6 3s^2 3p^6$
(iii) $1s^2 2s^2 2p^6 3s^2 3p^6 3d^1$
(iv) $1s^2 2s^2 2p^6 3s^2 3p^6 3d^8$
b) Ti(IV) since it does not have a partially full 3d sub-level.

23 VO_2^+ +5: VO_3^- +5: MnO_4^- +7: CrO_4^{2-} +6: $Cr_2O_7^{2-}$ +6

24 $6Fe^{2+}(aq) + Cr_2O_7^{2-}(aq) + 14H^+(aq) \rightarrow$
$6Fe^{3+}(aq) + 2Cr^{3+}(aq) + 7H_2O(l)$

25 The oxidation state of vanadium is +5 and hence all three 3d electrons are involved in bonding.

26 Violet → green → blue (+4 is the most stable oxidation state of vanadium).

27 V^{2+} since it has the lowest oxidation state (+2) and is more likely to lose electrons.

28 Dichromate(VI) and chromate(VI).

29 $Zn + 2HCl \rightarrow ZnCl_2 + H_2$

30 In acidic solution the chromate(VI) changes to dichromate (VI).
$2CrO_4^{2-}(aq) + 2H^+(aq) \rightarrow Cr_2O_7^{2-}(aq) + H_2O(l)$
orange

31 a) A – $[Cr(H_2O)_6]^{3+}$ B – CrO_4^{2-} C – $Cr_2O_7^{2-}$
b) H_2O_2 (or Na_2O_2)

32 First permanent pink colour.

33 $6Fe^{2+}(aq) + Cr_2O_7^{2-}(aq) + 14H^+(aq) \rightarrow$
$6Fe^{3+}(aq) + 2Cr^{3+}(aq) + 7H_2O(l)$
Moles of $Cr_2O_7^{2-}$ $MV/1000 = (0.02 \times 26.5)/1000$
= 0.00053 mol
Moles of Fe^{2+} = 0.00053 × 6 = 0.00318 mol
Concentration of Fe^{2+} (moles × 1000)/V
= (0.00318 × 1000)/25 = 0.127 M

34 $6Fe^{2+}(aq) + Cr_2O_7^{2-}(aq) + 14H^+(aq) \rightarrow$
$6Fe^{3+}(aq) + 2Cr^{3+}(aq) + 7H_2O(l)$
Moles of $Cr_2O_7^{2-}$ $MV/1000 = (0.017 \times 26.50)/1000$
= 0.0004505 mol
Moles of Fe^{2+} in 25 cm^3 = 0.0004505 × 6 = 0.002703
Moles of Fe^{2+} in 250 cm^3 = 0.002703 x 10 = 0.02703
Hence 0.02703 mol of the compound has a mass of 7.490 g
M_r = moles/mass = 7.490/0.02703 = 277.1
M_r $FeSO_4$ = 152
Therefore xH_2O = 271.6 – 152 = 125.1
Therefore x = 125.1/18 = 6.95 ∴ x = 7

35 $5Fe^{2+}(aq) + MnO_4^-(aq) + 8H^+(aq) \rightarrow 5Fe^{3+}(aq) + Mn^{2+}(aq) + 4H_2O$

First titration

Moles of MnO_4^- $MV/1000 = (0.02 \times 21.90)/1000 = 0.000438$ mol

Moles of $Fe^{2+} = 0.000438 \times 5 = 0.00219$ mol

Concentration of Fe^{2+} (moles × 1000)/V = $(0.00219 \times 1000)/25 = 0.0876$ M

Second titration

Moles of MnO_4^- $MV/1000 = (0.02 \times 36.60)/1000 = 0.000732$ mol

Moles of $Fe^{2+} = 0.000732 \times 5 = 0.00366$ mol

Concentration of Fe^{2+} (moles × 1000)/V = $(0.00366 \times 1000)/25 = 0.1464$ M

The second titration gives the total concentration of iron ions present.

Therefore concentration of Fe^{3+} is $0.1464 - 0.0876 = 0.0588$ M

Concentration of Fe^{2+} in g dm^{-3} is $0.0876 \times 56 = 4.906$ g dm^{-3} = 4.91 g dm^{-3}

Concentration of Fe^{3+} in g dm^{-3} is $0.0588 \times 56 = 3.293$ g dm^{-3} = 3.29 g dm^{-3}

36 $H_2SO_4 + 2NaOH \rightarrow Na_2SO_4 + 2H_2O$

$H_2C_2O_4 + 2NaOH \rightarrow Na_2C_2O_4 + 2H_2O$

First titration gives total concentration of the acids.

Moles of NaOH $MV/1000 = (0.100 \times 37.5)/1000 = 0.00375$ mol

Moles of acid $0.00375/2 = 0.001875$ mol

Concentration of acids (moles ×1000)/V = $(0.001875 \times 1000)/25 = 0.075$ M

Second titration gives concentration of the ethanedioic acid.

$5C_2O_4^{2-}(aq) + 2MnO_4^-(aq) + 16H^+(aq) \rightarrow 10CO_2(aq) + 2Mn^{2+}(aq) + 8H_2O$

Moles of MnO_4^- $MV/1000 = (0.02 \times 12.5)/1000 = 0.00025$ mol

Moles of $H_2C_2O_4 = 0.00025 \times 5/2 = 0.000625$ mol

Concentration of $H_2C_2O_4$ (moles × 1000)/V = $(0.000625 \times 1000)/25 = 0.025$ M

Hence concentration of H_2SO_4 is $0.075 - 0.025 = 0.05$ M

37 $2H_2O_2 \rightarrow 2H_2O + O_2$: H_2O_2 slowly decomposes to form water and oxygen.
MnO_2 acts as a catalyst.

38 a) E_a for the reaction is very high and few collisions result in a reaction.
b) V_2O_5 provides an alternate reaction pathway of lower activation energy.
c) The catalyst has no effect on the equilibrium position, since it speeds up the forward and backward reactions equally.

39 The cyclic molecule is very 'strained' and the carbon–oxygen bonds readily break.

40 The reaction is exothermic and by lowering the temp. the reaction rate is slower and less heat energy is released. This reduces the possibility of the epoxyethane reacting.

41 The symbol is W.

42 Iron is a more efficient catalyst and is cheaper.

43 They are very efficient catalysts.

44 a) Iron in the Haber Process and nickel in hydrogenation reactions.
b) The reactant molecules adsorb onto active sites on the surface of the catalyst. The adsorption results in some bonds being weakened or broken/ an increase in concentration/ favourable orientation for a reaction. The products once formed desorb from the surface leaving the active sites available for further reaction.

45 They have variable oxidation states.

46 a) $MnO_4^-(aq) + 4Mn^{2+}(aq) + 8H^+(aq) \rightarrow 5Mn^{3+}(aq) + 4H_2O(l)$
b) $C_2O_4^{2-}(aq) + 2Mn^{3+}(aq) \rightarrow 2CO_2 + 2Mn^{2+}(aq)$

47 a) $S_2O_8^{2-}(aq)$ and $I^-(aq)$ are both negative ions (1) and the repulsion between the ions reduces the chance of successful collisions occurring. (1)
b) Iron(II) reduces the peroxodisulphate ion
$S_2O_8^{2-}(aq) + 2Fe^{2+}(aq) \rightarrow 2SO_4^{2-}(aq) + 2Fe^{3+}(aq)$ (1)
Overall $E^\ominus = +2.01 - (+0.77) = +1.24$ V (1)
Iron(III) oxidises the iodide ions.
$2Fe^{3+}(aq) + 2I^-(aq) \rightarrow 2Fe^{2+}(aq) + I_2(s)$ (1)
Overall $E^\ominus = +0.77 - (+0.54) = +0.23$ V (1)
Both reactions have a positive $E^\ominus$ value.

48 A homogeneous catalyst is in the same state (phase) as the reactants.
A heterogeneous catalyst is in a different state than the reactants.

Unit 14 End-of-unit questions Page 240

1 a) (i) Ligand has a lone pair that it uses to form a co-ordinate bond (1) or lone-pair donor.
(ii) Water (1) and the chloride ion (1).
b) (i) Co-ordinate bond (1).
(ii) Lone pair (1) on the ligand transferred to vacant orbital on transition metal ion (1).

2 a) (i) Reducing agent – donates electrons (1).
Lewis base – donates a pair of electrons (1).
(ii) 1. Reduction. 2. Neither. 3. Neither. 4. Reduction. 5. Oxidation.
b) Process 2 — NH_3 (1).
Process 3 — an acid e.g. H_2SO_4 (1).
Process 4 — Zn and an acid (1).
Process 5 — H_2O_2 (1).

3 $[CoCl_4]^{2-}$ tetrahedral (1). Four (1). Blue (1). +2 (1).
$[Ag(NH_3)_2]^+$ linear (1). Two (1). Colourless (1). +1 (1).
$[Cu(H_2O)_2(NH_3)_4]^{2+}$ octahedral (1). six (1).
Deep blue (1). +2 (1).

4 a) Provides an alternate reaction pathway (1) that has a lower E_a (1).
b) (i) $2SO_2(g) + O_2(g) \rightleftharpoons 2SO_3(g)$ (1).
(ii) $S_2O_8^{2-}(aq) + 2I^-(aq) \rightarrow 2SO_4^{2-}(aq) + I_2(s)$ (1).
(iii) $2MnO_4^-(aq) + 5C_2O_4^{2-}(aq) + 16H^+(aq) \rightarrow 2Mn^{2+}(aq) + 10CO_2(g) + 8H_2O(l)$ (1).
c) They have variable oxidation state (1).

5 a) (i) $1s^22s^22p^63s^23p^63d^{10}4s^1$ (1).
(ii) $1s^22s^22p^63s^23p^63d^{10}$(1).
(iii) $1s^22s^22p^63s^23p^63d^9$ (1).
b) Transitional (1) if the species has a partially filled 3d sub-level. (1).
c) Colourless. (1). Oxidation state is +1 and is not transitional (1).

Answers: Module 5

Unit 14 Transition metals (continued)

6 a) Forms complexes (1). Has coloured ions (1). Has variable oxidation state (1).

b) (i) $MnO_4^-(aq) + 8H^+(aq) + 5e^- \rightarrow Mn^{2+}(aq) + 4H_2O(l)$ (1).

(ii) $Fe^{2+}(aq) \rightarrow Fe^{3+}(aq) + e^-$ (1).

(iii) $5Fe^{2+}(aq) + MnO_4^-(aq) + 8H^+(aq) \rightarrow 5Fe^{3+}(aq) + Mn^{2+}(aq) + 4H_2O(l)$ (1).

c) (i) Moles of MnO_4^- $MV/1000$ $= (0.02 \times 23.3)/1000 = 0.000466$ mol (1).

(ii) Moles of iron(II) $0.000466 \times 5 = 0.00233$ mol (1).

(iii) Mass of iron(II) $0.00233 \times 56 = 0.1305$ g (1).

(iv) Percentage iron(II) in tablet

$$\frac{0.1305}{0.700} \times 100 = 18.64\% \text{ (1).}$$

7 a) (i) Can use two lone pairs (1) to form two co-ordinate bonds (1) in a complex.

(ii) (2)

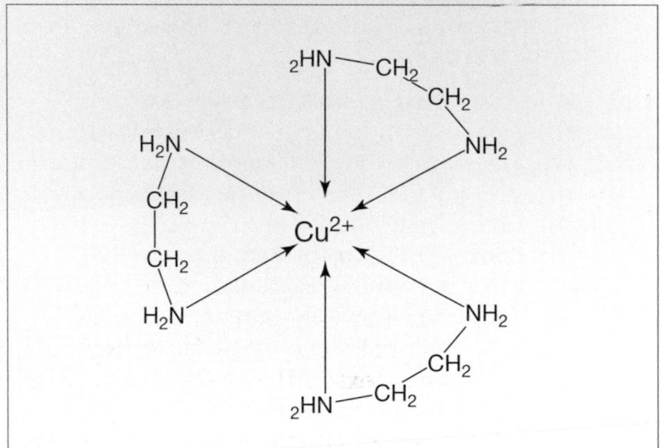

b) (i) Haem (1) or haemoglobin.

(ii) Iron (1).

(iii) Multidentate (1).

(iv) Oxygen transport in the blood (1).

8 a) Both have a lone pair (1).

b) (i) $[CuCl_4]^{2-}$ (1).

(ii) $[Cr(NH_3)_6]^{3+}$ (1).

(iii) $[Ag(NH_3)_2]^+$ (1).

c) (i) (1)

Cl, NH$_3$, Pt, Cl, NH$_3$

(ii) Cancer (1).

(iii) the ammonia ligands are on the same side of the complex (1).

Unit 15 Reactions of inorganic compounds in aqueous solution

Pages 242 – 257

1 a) Iron(II) sulphate heptahydrate.

b) Cobalt(II) chloride hexahydrate.

2 a) $CoCl_2(s) + 6H_2O(l)$ ($[Co(H_2O)_6]^{2+}(aq) + 2Cl^-(aq)$

b) Blue solid dissolves to form a pink solution.

3 $[Cr(H_2O)_6]^{3+} + 6NH_3 \rightleftharpoons [Cr(NH_3)_6]^{3+} + 6H_2O$

4 a) $[Cu(H_2O)_6]^{2+} + 4Cl^- \rightleftharpoons [CuCl_4]^{2-} + 6H_2O$

b) $[Cu(H_2O)_6]^{2+} + 4NH_3 \rightleftharpoons [Cu(NH_3)_4(H_2O)_2]^{2+} + 4H_2O$

5 a) Yellow/green.

b) $[Cu(H_2O)_6]^{2+} + 4Cl^- \rightleftharpoons [CuCl_4]^{2-} + 6H_2O$

6 a) Cl^- or CN^-

b) NH_3 or H_2O

7 a) e.g. $[Cu(H_2O)_6]^{2+}$

b) e.g. $[CuCl_4]^{2-}$

8 a) $CuSO_4(s) + 6H_2O \rightarrow [Cu(H_2O)_6]^{2+} + SO_4^{2-}(aq)$

white blue

$[Co(H_2O)_6]^{2+} + 6NH_3 \rightleftharpoons [Co(NH_3)_6]^{2+} + 6H_2O$

pink pale yellow

$[Co(NH_3)_6]^{2+} \rightarrow [Co(NH_3)_6]^{3+} + e^-$

brown

9 X = $[Cu(H_2O)_6]^{2+}$. On addition of conc. HCl the water ligands are replaced by chloride ligands forming a tetrahedral complex with a co-ordination number of four.

10 a) It can form six co-ordinate bonds using six different lone pairs of electrons.

b) e.g. water softener.

11 Chromium – green, iron – yellow/orange, vanadium – green, aluminium – colourless.

12 $[Cr(H_2O)_6]^{3+} + H_2O \rightleftharpoons [Cr(H_2O)_5(OH)]^{2+} + H_3O^+$

13 Fe^{2+} is much less polarising than Fe^{3+} (smaller charge/size ratio): water ligands are less polarised and hence the aqua ion has less tendency to donate a proton.

14 a) $Fe^{3+}(aq) + 3OH^-(aq) \rightarrow Fe(OH)_3$

b) $Al^{3+}(aq) + 3OH^-(aq) \rightarrow Al(OH)_3$

15 In both cases the ppt will dissolve to form a solution.

$[Fe(H_2O)_3(OH)_3] + 3H^+ \rightarrow [Fe(H_2O)_6]^{3+}$ yellow/orange

$[Al(H_2O)_3(OH)_3] + 3H^+ \rightarrow [Al(H_2O)_6]^{3+}$ colourless

16 $Cr(OH)_3 + 3OH^- \rightarrow [Cr(OH)_6]^{3-}$

$Al(OH)_3 + 3OH^- \rightarrow [Al(OH)_6]^{3-}$

17 $[Cu(H_2O)_6]^{2+} + 2H_2O \rightarrow [Cu(H_2O)_4(OH)_2] + 2H_3O^+$

18 A = $Co(OH)_2$ B = $Co(OH)_3$

$Co^{2+}(aq) + 2OH^-(aq) \rightarrow Co(OH)_2(s)$

19 White ppt is formed which is insoluble in excess aqueous ammonia.

20 X = $[Cr(H_2O)_6]^{3+}$ Y = $[Cr(H_2O)_3(OH)_3]$ Z = $[Cr(NH_3)_6]^{3+}$

21 With iron(II) a green ppt of $FeCO_3$ is formed. With iron(III) a red/brown ppt of $Fe(OH)_3$ is formed together with effervescence of CO_2.

22 The tripositive aqua ion will be acidic. The metal hydroxide ppt will form together with effervescence of CO_2.

$[Sc(H_2O)_6]^{3+} + 3H_2O \rightarrow [Sc(H_2O)_3(OH)_3] + 3H_3O^+$

$CO_3^{2-} + 2H_3O^+ \rightarrow CO_2 + 3H_2O$

23 a) e.g Add excess NaOH solution and filter off the insoluble $Fe(OH)_3$ ppt. The filtrate will contain $[Al(OH)_4]^-$

b) e.g. Add excess $NH_3(aq)$ and filter off the insoluble $Al(OH)_3$ ppt. The filtrate will contain $[Cr(NH_3)_6]^{3+}$

24 a) $[Al(H_2O)_6]^{3+}$

b) $[Al(H_2O)_6]^{3+} + H_2O \rightleftharpoons [Al(H_2O)_5(OH)]^{2+} + H_3O^+$

c) The gas is hydrogen and the precipitate is $Al(OH)_3$

$[Al(H_2O)_6]^{3+} + 3H_2O \rightarrow [Al(H_2O)_3(OH)_3] + 3H_3O^+$

$Zn + 2H_3O^+ \rightarrow Zn^{2+} + H_2 + 2H_2O$

Unit 15 End-of-unit questions Page 258

1 a) A – $[Co(H_2O)_6]^{2+}$ (1). B – $[CoCl_4]^{2-}$ (1).
C – $Co(OH)_2$ (1). D – $[Co(NH_3)_6]^{2+}$ (1).

b) $[Co(H_2O)_6]^{2+} + 4Cl^- \rightleftharpoons [CoCl_4]^{2-} + 6H_2O$ (1).

$Co^{2+}(aq) + 2OH^-(aq) \rightarrow Co(OH)_2$ (1)

or $[Co(H_2O)_6]^{2+} + 2NH_3 \rightarrow [Co(OH)_2(H_2O)_4] + NH_4^+$

$[Co(H_2O)_6]^{2+} + 6NH_3 \rightleftharpoons [Co(NH_3)_6]^{2+} + 6H_2O$(1).

c) Oxidation (1) to $[Co(NH_3)_6]^{3+}$ (1).

d) Chloride ligands replaced by water ligands (1) to form $[Co(H_2O)_6]^{2+}$ (1).

2 a) Reaction 1 Cu^{2+} or Co^{2+}(1) Reaction 2 Ag^+ (1).
Reaction 3 Co^{2+} or Cr^{3+} (1).
Reaction 4 Cu^{2+} (1) Reaction 5 Fe^{3+} ,Cr^{3+} or Al^{3+}(1).
Reaction 6 Co^{2+}, Cu^{2+} or Fe^{2+} (1).

b) Tetrahedral (1). Linear (1) Octahedral (1).

c) Electroplating (1).

d) Tripositive ions undergo hydrolysis reaction releasing H^+ ions into solution (1). The acidic solution reacts with CO_3^{2-} ions (1) to form CO_2 and the metal hydroxide ppt (1).
Dipositive ions in solution are not sufficiently acidic to release carbon dioxide and instead they react with the carbonate ions and the metal carbonate is precipitated (1).

3 a) (i) Grey-green ppt(1) which dissolves in excess $NH_3(aq)$ (1) to form a violet solution (1).

(ii) Grey-green ppt (1) which dissolves in excess NaOH to form a green solution (1).
On oxidation the green solution changes colour to yellow (1).

(iii) Grey-green ppt (1) which is insoluble in excess Na_2CO_3 (1). Effervescence of CO_2 (1).

b) They are all hydrolysis reactions (1) where acidic (1) aqueous chromium(III) ion reacts with a base (1), forming $Cr(OH)_3$ (1) – the grey/green ppt.

c) Can react as a base and as an acid (1).
As a base $[Cr(OH)_3(H_2O)_3] + 3H^+ \rightarrow [Cr(H_2O)_6]^{3+}$ (1).
As an acid $Cr(OH)_3 + OH^- \rightarrow [Cr(OH)_4]^-$ (1).

4 a) (i) White solid dissolves exothermically (1) to form a blue solution (1).

(ii) $[Cu(H_2O)_6]^{2+}$(1). Octahedral (1).

b) (i) $Cu(OH)_2$ (1). Pale blue (1).

(ii) $[Cu(H_2O)(NH_3)_4]^{2+}$ (1). Deep blue (1).

(iii) $[CuCl_4]^{2-}$ (1). Green/yellow(1).

5 a) A – Aluminium (1); B – $[Al(OH)_4]^-$ (1);
C – $Al(OH)_3$ (1); D – $[Al(H_2O)_6]^{3+}$ (1).

b) E – $CoSO_4$ (1); F – $[Co(H_2O)_6]^{2+}$ (1);
G – $BaSO_4$ (1); H – $[CoCl_4]^{2-}$ (1).

6 a) The charge/size ratio is greater (1) for Fe^{3+} and the ion is more polarising (1). Fe^{3+} polarises water ligand to such an extent that it can donate a proton to a water molecule (1).
$[Fe(H_2O)_6]^{3+} + H_2O \rightarrow [Fe(OH)(H_2O)_5]^{2+} + H_3O^+$ (1).
The Fe^{2+} is less polarising and the tendency to donate a proton is much less (1).

b) (i) Green ppt is $Fe(OH)_2$ (1) and in air it is oxidised to form $Fe(OH)_3$ (1).
$[Fe(H_2O)_6]^{2+} + 2OH^- \rightarrow [Fe(OH)_2(H_2O)_4] + 2H_2O$ (1).

(ii) $[Fe(H_2O)_6]^{3+}$ undergoes hydrolysis (1) releasing H^+ ions (1) which react with the CO_3^{2-} to form CO_2. The hydrolysis reaction leads to the formation of the metal hydroxide ppt (1).
$[Fe(H_2O)_6]^{3+} + 3H_2O \rightarrow [Fe(OH)_3(H_2O)_3] + 3H_3O^+$(1).
$CO_3^{2-} + 2H_3O^+ \rightarrow CO_2 + 3H_2O$ (1).

Answers: Module 6

Unit 16 Synoptic questions

Pages 270 – 271

1 a) (i) B = butenedioic acid (1).
C = 2-hydroxybutanedioic acid (1).
B: geometric isomerism (1) due to the presence of a carbon–carbon double bond (1), which is resistant to rotation (1). The two carboxylic acid groups can be on the same side or on opposite sides (1). C: optical isomerism (1), since the molecule has an asymmetric carbon atom (1) resulting in enantiomers (1), which are 3D mirror images of each other (1).

(ii) The synthetically formed compound will contain equal quantities of each enantiomer (1) and hence will appear to be optically inactive (1). The naturally produced compound C is formed by enzyme activity. Enzymes are stereospecific in their action (1) and only one of the enantiomers is formed; hence the product is optically active (1).

b) Step 1: Reaction with cold conc. H_2SO_4 (1), followed by the addition of water (1) and heating (1).
$HOOCCH{=}CHCOOH + H_2O \rightarrow HOOCCH(OH)CH_2COOH$ (1).

Step 3: Oxidation using acidified potassium dichromate(VI) (1) and heat (1).
$HOOCCH_2CH(OH)COOH + [O] \rightarrow HOOCCH_2COCOOH$ (1).

2 a) (i) (1)

H ×• O •× H

Shape is V-shaped (distorted tetrahedral) (1), with a bond angle of 105° (1).

(ii) (2)

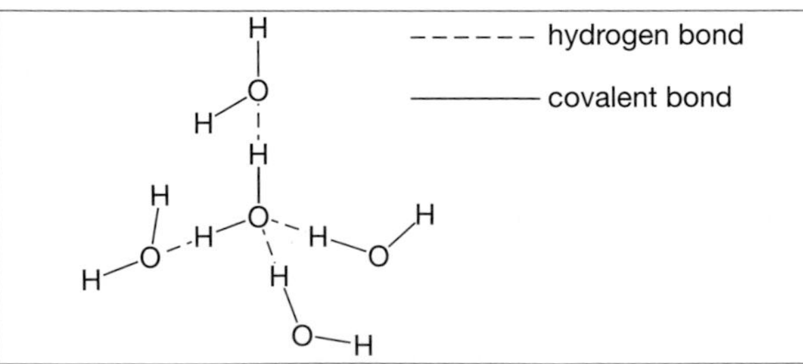

(iii) In ice the lone pair of electrons (1) on the water molecules are involved in forming hydrogen bonds (1) with the hydrogen atoms on adjacent water molecules. Each oxygen atom forms four bonds (1) – two covalent bonds and two hydrogen bonds (1). This results in the repulsion between the pairs of electrons being similar (1) and results in a tetrahedral shape with bond angles of 109.5° (1). (Max. 10.)

b) $AlCl_3 + 6H_2O \rightarrow [Al(H_2O)_6]^{3+} + 3Cl^-(aq)$ (1).
$[Al(H_2O)_6]^{3+} + H_2O \rightarrow [Al(H_2O)_5(OH)]^{2+} + H_3O^+$(1).
Hydrolysis in which the aluminium complex donates protons to solvent water molecules (1).

c) Brønsted–Lowry acid – proton donor (1).
$NH_3 + H_2O \rightleftharpoons NH_4^+ + OH^-$ (1).
Brønsted–Lowry base – proton acceptor:
$HCl + H_2O \rightarrow H_3O^+ + Cl^-$ (1).

3 a) (i) (3)

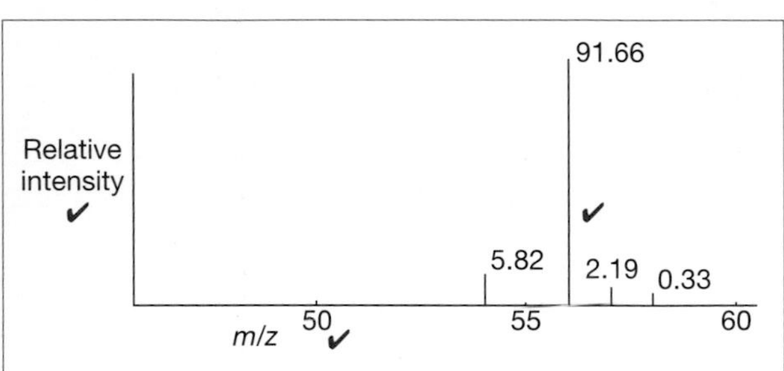

(ii) Relative atomic mass:

$$\frac{(5.82 \times 54) + (91.66 \times 56) + (2.19 \times 57) + (0.33 \times 58)\ (1)}{(5.83 + 91.66 + 2.19 + 0.33)\ (1)}$$

$$= \frac{5591.21}{100} = 55.91\ (1).$$

b) (i) Fe^{2+} 26 protons: 30 neutrons: 24 electrons (1).
Fe^{3+} 26 protons: 30 neutrons: 23 electrons (1).

(ii) $Fe^{2+}\ 1s^2 2s^2 2p^6 3s^2 3p^6 3d^6$ (1).
$Fe^{3+}\ 1s^2 2s^2 2p^6 3s^2 3p^6 3d^5$ (1).
Both ions have a partially filled 3d sub-level (1).

c) Heterogeneous: catalyst is in a different state to the reactants (1).
Homogeneous: catalyst is in the same state as the reactants (1).
Iron is used as a heterogeneous catalyst in the Haber Process (1). The reaction occurs on the surface of the solid catalyst (1).
Aqueous iron(II) or iron (III) are homogeneous catalysts in the reaction between $S_2O_8^{2-}$(aq) and I^-(aq) (1). These are both negative ions and the mutual repulsion reduces the chances of the ions colliding (1). They undergo separate redox reactions with positive iron(II) and iron(III) ions (1).

d) (i) Iron is present in haemoglobin in the blood (1). The iron forms a loose complex with oxygen (1) and transports oxygen around the body.

(ii) Carbon monoxide is formed by the incomplete combustion of fossil fuels (1). Carbon monoxide forms a stable complex with haemoglobin and hence reduces the transport of oxygen in the body (1).

4 a) Fractional distillation: separation of a mixture (1) by differences in boiling points (1).
Finite resource – a resource that cannot be replaced once it has been used (1).
Feedstock – raw materials for reactions (1).

b) ΔH reaction = $\Sigma\Delta H_f$ (products) – $\Sigma\Delta H_f$ (reactants) (1).
(i) *Reaction 1*
$\Delta H = [-111] - [-242]$ (1) = +131 kJ mol^{-1} (1) units (1).
(ii) *Reaction 2*
$\Delta H = [-169 + 8(-242)] - [8(-111)]$ (1)
= –1217 kJ mol^{-1} (1).

c) Reaction 1 involves an increase in the number of gaseous moles (1) and is favoured by a low pressure (1). Lower pressures result in lower rate of reaction (1). The reaction is endothermic (1) and is favoured by high temperatures, which also increase the rate of reaction (1). Use standard pressure and high temperatures (1).
Reaction 2 involves a decreases in the number of gaseous moles and is favoured by a high pressure (1), but higher pressures involve greater cost (1). The reaction is exothermic and is favoured by low temperatures (1), but at lower temperatures the reaction rate is slower (1). Use compromise conditions that produce a reasonable yield at a reasonable rate and cost (1).
The heat energy released in Reaction 2 can be used in Reaction 1 (1). (Max. 11).
A suitable catalyst can be used in Reaction 2 (1).

d) High pressure are dangerous (1). The reaction produces carbon monoxide (1), which is a toxic gas (1). Hydrogen is highly inflammable (1). (Max. 3).

5 a) Titration with a standard solution of HCl (1): indicator is methyl orange (1).

b) Add excess potassium iodide (1) and titrate the released iodine (1) with a standard solution of sodium thiosulphate, $Na_2S_2O_3$ (1), using starch as the indicator (1).

c) Dissolve the iron tablet in a mixture of water and dilute sulphuric acid (1): titrate with a standard solution of potassium manganate(VII) solution (1): potassium manganate is self-indicating (1).

6 Shape depends upon the number of pairs of electrons around the central atom (1). These can be pairs of electrons in covalent bonds or lone pair of electrons (1). Pairs of electrons are as far apart as possible to reduce the mutual repulsion (1). Lone pairs are more concentrated (1) and will cause greater mutual repulsion (1) and a distortion of the shape by pushing bonds closer together (1).
BF_3 : Three pairs of electrons: trigonal planar (1).
$[Cu(H_2O)_6]^{2+}$: six pairs of electrons: octahedral (1).
PF_5 : five pairs of electrons: triangular bipyramid (1).
$[CoCl_4]^{2-}$: four pairs of electrons: tetrahedral (1).
PCl_3 : four pairs of electrons including a lone pair (1).
Distorted tetrahedral or pyramidal (1).

b) ICl_2^- : two bond pairs and three lone pairs (1).
Distorted triangular bipyramid (1).
PF_6^- : six bond pairs (1). Octahedral (1).
NH_4^+ : four bond pairs (1). Tetrahedral (1).
$[Zn(NH_3)_4]^{2+}$: four bond pairs (1). Tetrahedral (1).

Unit 16 End-of-unit questions Page 272

Multiple choice questions
7) D 8) C 9) B 10) D.

Matching pairs questions
11) D 12) C 13) B 14) C.

Multiple completion questions
15) A 16) D 17) A 18) C 19) B.

Glossary

acid A species that can donate a hydrogen ion (proton donor).

acid dissociation constant Equilibrium constant for a weak acid in solution.

activation energy, E_a The minimum energy required for a collision between particles to result in a reaction.

addition reaction A reaction in which a double covalent bond is broken to form a single bond and each atom in the double bond forms a bond with another atom or group of atoms.

alkali A soluble base.

alkyl group Part of an aliphatic chain: CH_3, CH_3CH_2 etc.

amphoteric Describes a compound that can react as an acid and as a base.

anhydrous The absence of water.

arene A species containing at least one benzene ring.

aryl group An aromatic group such as C_6H_5–.

atomic number The number of protons in the nucleus of an atom.

base A species that can accept a hydrogen ion (a proton acceptor).

batch process A process in which the products are removed at the end of the reaction. The reaction is then started again with a new supply of reactants.

bidentate A term for a ligand that has two donor atoms and forms two co-ordinate bonds.

bond angle The angle formed between two bonds attached to the same atom.

bond dissociation energy The energy needed to break a particular covalent bond.

Born–Haber cycle An energy cycle showing the theoretical energy changes that occur in the formation of an ionic solid.

buffer A solution that is resistant to change on the addition of a relatively small amount of an acid or a base.

calorimeter An apparatus in which heat energy changes are measured.

carbocation A species with a positive charge on a carbon atom.

carbonium ion An alternative name for a **carbocation**.

catalyst A substance that alters the rate of a chemical reaction, without itself being changed by the reaction.

chain isomers Isomers in which the carbon atoms in the chain are arranged in a different pattern.

chelate A species formed when a transition metal bonds with ligands that have more than one donor atom.

chemical shift The relative position of a peak in a proton n.m.r. spectrum compared to the reference peak.

chiral centre An asymmetric carbon atom that results in optical activity.

conjugate acid/base The relationship between an acid and the base formed when it loses a proton.

complex ion A species containing co-ordinate bonding.

continuous process A reaction in which more reactants are added as the products are removed.

co-ordinate bond A covalent bond in which both members of the pair of electrons are provided by one of the atoms.

co-ordination number The number of co-ordinate bonds formed in a complex.

covalent bond A bond formed by the sharing of a pair of electrons.

dative bond A different name for a co-ordinate bond.

dehydration A reaction in which a compound forms a new compound by the loss of a molecule of water.

delocalised this term applies to electrons that are free to move from atom to atom – for example in the benzene ring or in metals.

dimer A species formed when two molecule are bonded together.

dynamic A term applied to chemical equilibria indicating that reactions continue to occur.

electrochemical series A list of redox potentials arranged in numerical order.

electrode potential The potential difference between an oxidised and a reduced species.

electronegativity A measure of the ability of an atom to attract the pair of electrons in a covalent bond.

electronic structure The arrangement of the electrons in the energy levels of an atom or ion.

electrophile An electron-deficient species that can accept a lone pair of electrons.

element A substance made up of one sort of atom.

elimination reaction A reaction in which a double bond is formed and a small molecule is lost from a compound.

e.m.f. Electromotive force – the electrical power of a cell.

empirical formula The simplest whole-number ratio of the atoms present in a molecule.

enantiomers Optical isomers.

endothermic reaction A reaction that absorbs heat energy (from the surroundings).

enthalpy change, Δ*H* The heat energy change in a reaction occurring at constant pressure.

entropy, *S* A measure of the disorder of a substance.

equilibrium A reaction in which the rates of the forward and reverse reactions are equal.

equivalence point This is the point in a titration when equimolar quantities (given by the equation for the reaction) of the reactants are present.

esterification A reaction in which an ester is formed by the reaction of a carboxylic acid with an alcohol.

exothermic reaction A reaction that releases heat energy (to the surroundings).

feasible reaction A reaction that is thermodynamically possible.

fingerprint region The section (1500–400 cm^{-1}) of an infra-red spectrum of a compound that has a pattern unique to that compound.

fragmentation Occurs when a particle breaks down into smaller particles in a mass spectrometer.

free energy ΔG The balance between the enthalpy change and the entropy change in a reaction.

free radical A reactive species with an unpaired electron.

functional group isomers Isomers that contain a different functional group.

geometrical isomers Isomers in which a double bond results in the different orientation of some atoms or groups of atoms.

Hess's law The enthalpy change in a reaction is independent of the route of the reaction.

heterogeneous A term applied when the reactants and products in a reaction are not in the same phase (state).

homogeneous A term applied to a reaction in which all of the reactants and products are in the same phase (state).

homologous series A group of compounds that have the same functional group, similar chemical properties and a gradation in physical properties.

hydration The addition of water.

hydrocarbon A compound containing carbon and hydrogen only.

hydrogenation A reaction in which hydrogen is added to a compound.

hydrogen bond The strongest type of intermolecular bonding. It occurs between the molecules of a compound which has a hydrogen atom covalently bonded to a fluorine, oxygen or nitrogen atom.

hydrolysis A reaction with water.

intermolecular forces The weak forces of attraction between molecules.

ion A species that has a charge.

ion–dipole force The force of attraction between an ion and a polar molecule.

ionic bond The force of attraction between oppositely charged ions.

ionic product of water The product of concentrations of hydrogen ions and hydroxide ions formed by the dissociation of water.

ionisation enthalpy The energy required to remove an electron from a gaseous atom.

isomers Compounds with the same molecular formula but different properties.

isotopes Atoms of the same element that have different numbers of neutrons.

lattice enthalpy The enthalpy change when one mole of an ionic compound is formed from its constituent gaseous ions.

Le Chatelier's principle When one or more of the factors affecting the position of a chemical equilibrium change, then the equilibrium moves so as to oppose the change.

Lewis acid A species that accepts a lone pair of electrons.

Lewis base A species that donates a lone pair of electrons.

ligand A species that provides the lone pair of electrons used in co-ordinate bond formation.

lone pair A pair of electrons in the outer occupied energy level that are not involved in bonding.

macromolecule A giant molecule formed by covalent bonding.

mass number The sum of the protons and neutrons in an atom.

mean bond enthalpy The average bond energy for a particular covalent bond in different compounds.

mechanism The individual steps by which bonds are formed and broken in a reaction.

metallic bonding The force of attraction between the delocalised outer electrons and the resulting positive centres of the metal atoms

molarity The concentration of a solution in mol dm^{-3}.

mole The working qualitative unit used in calculations. One mole of a substance is the mass in grams of Avogadro's number of atoms, molecules or ions of the substance.

mole fraction The ratio of the number of moles of a compound to the total number of moles present.

molecular ion A molecule that has lost or gained electrons.

molecule A compound formed by covalent bonding.

monomers The small molecules that are joined together to form a long chain polymer.

monoprotic An acid in which each molecule of the acid can only donate one proton.

neutralisation A reaction in which an acid and a base react together to form a salt and water.

noble gas Any of the elements in Group 8 of the Periodic Table

nucleon number the number of subatomic particles (protons and neutrons) in the nucleus of an atom.

nucleophile A species with a lone pair of electrons that can attack an electron-deficient carbon atom.

optical isomers Isomers that have the same molecular and structural formula but a different effect on the rotation of plane polarised light.

order of reaction Shows how the rate of a reaction changes as the concentration of the reactants change.

oxidation A reaction in which a species loses electrons.

oxidation state (number) The number of electrons of an atom used in forming bonds.

oxidising agent A species that gains electrons from a different species.

partial pressure In a mixture of gases the partial pressure of a gas is the pressure that one of the component gases would exert if it alone occupied the volume.

peptide link A link formed by the condensation reaction of an amine and a carboxylic acid (—NH—CO—).

periodic trend A trend in the physical or chemical properties of the elements in a Period of the Periodic Table that is repeated in other periods.

pH A measure of the hydrogen ion concentration.

polar bond A covalent bond in which the pair of electrons are not shared equally.

polyamide A large molecule containing many amide linkages.

polyester A large molecule containing many ester linkages.

polymer A large molecule made by joining together many thousands of smaller molecules.

polypeptide A long-chain polymer formed by joining many amino acid units by peptide linkages.

position isomers Isomers in which the functional group is attached to different carbon atoms.

quantitative A term concerned with the amount of a substance.

racemate and racemic mixture A mixture of enantiomers that has no overall optical activity.

radical cation A positively charged species which also has an unpaired electron.

rate constant The constant of proportionality in a rate equation.

rate equation An experimentally derived equation that shows how the concentration of reactants affects the rate of a reaction.

redox couple A species and its reduced/oxidised form.

redox reaction A reaction in which oxidation and reduction occur.

reducing agent A species that gives electrons to a different species.

reduction A reaction in which a species gains electrons.

relative atomic mass of an element The average mass of an atom of an element (taking into account the natural occurrence of its isotopes) compared to the mass of one atom of carbon-12.

saturated compound A compound in which all the covalent bonds are single bonds.

spin–spin coupling Occurs when the magnetic field experienced by a proton is altered by the magnetic field from adjacent non-equivalent protons.

spontaneous reaction A reaction that occurs without heat energy being supplied.

standard reference electrode The electrode which is used as the standard against which the electrode potential of a redox couple is measured.

stereoisomers Isomers that have the same molecular and structural formulae but differ in the orientation of one or more atoms

structural isomers Isomers that have the same molecular formula, but different structural formulae.

substitution A reaction in which an atom or group of atoms is replaced by a different atom or group of atoms.

transition metal An element in which the atom or an ion contains an incomplete 3d sub-level.

unsaturated compound A compound containing one or more multiple covalent bonds.

wavenumber reciprocal of wavelength – used in infra-red spectra.

zwitterion An amino acid carrying both a positive and a negative charge.

Appendix A

Periodic Table

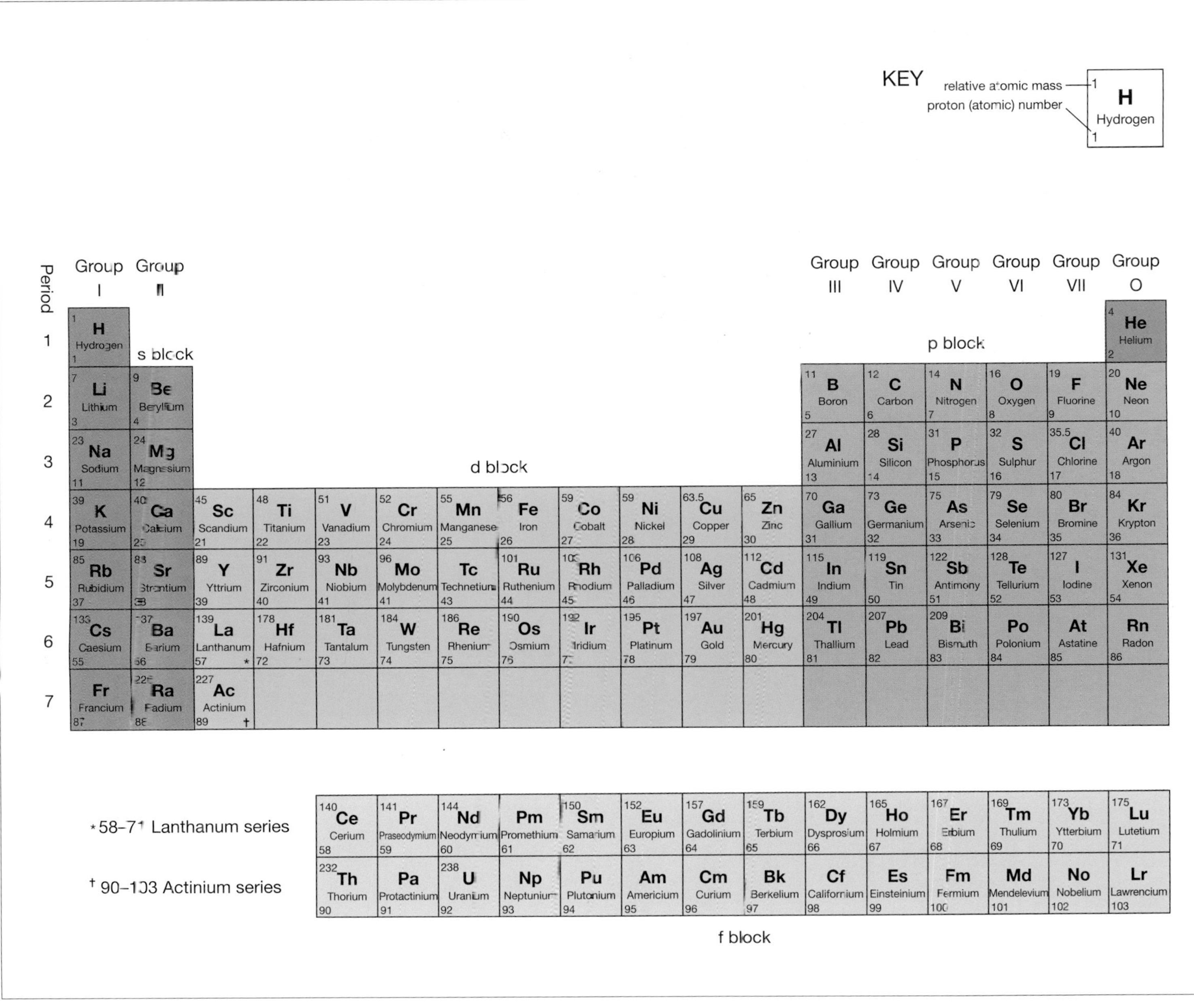

KEY: relative atomic mass (1), proton (atomic) number (1) — H Hydrogen

Period	Group I	Group II											Group III	Group IV	Group V	Group VI	Group VII	Group O
1	1 H Hydrogen 1																	4 He Helium 2
2	7 Li Lithium 3	9 Be Beryllium 4											11 B Boron 5	12 C Carbon 6	14 N Nitrogen 7	16 O Oxygen 8	19 F Fluorine 9	20 Ne Neon 10
3	23 Na Sodium 11	24 Mg Magnesium 12											27 Al Aluminium 13	28 Si Silicon 14	31 P Phosphorus 15	32 S Sulphur 16	35.5 Cl Chlorine 17	40 Ar Argon 18
4	39 K Potassium 19	40 Ca Calcium 20	45 Sc Scandium 21	48 Ti Titanium 22	51 V Vanadium 23	52 Cr Chromium 24	55 Mn Manganese 25	56 Fe Iron 26	59 Co Cobalt 27	59 Ni Nickel 28	63.5 Cu Copper 29	65 Zn Zinc 30	70 Ga Gallium 31	73 Ge Germanium 32	75 As Arsenic 33	79 Se Selenium 34	80 Br Bromine 35	84 Kr Krypton 36
5	85 Rb Rubidium 37	88 Sr Strontium 38	89 Y Yttrium 39	91 Zr Zirconium 40	93 Nb Niobium 41	96 Mo Molybdenum 41	Tc Technetium 43	101 Ru Ruthenium 44	103 Rh Rhodium 45	106 Pd Palladium 46	108 Ag Silver 47	112 Cd Cadmium 48	115 In Indium 49	119 Sn Tin 50	122 Sb Antimony 51	128 Te Tellurium 52	127 I Iodine 53	131 Xe Xenon 54
6	133 Cs Caesium 55	137 Ba Barium 56	139 La Lanthanum 57 *	178 Hf Hafnium 72	181 Ta Tantalum 73	184 W Tungsten 74	186 Re Rhenium 75	190 Os Osmium 76	192 Ir Iridium 77	195 Pt Platinum 78	197 Au Gold 79	201 Hg Mercury 80	204 Tl Thallium 81	207 Pb Lead 82	209 Bi Bismuth 83	Po Polonium 84	At Astatine 85	Rn Radon 86
7	Fr Francium 87	226 Ra Radium 88	227 Ac Actinium 89 †															

s block; d block; p block

Series														
* 58–71 Lanthanum series	140 Ce Cerium 58	141 Pr Praseodymium 59	144 Nd Neodymium 60	Pm Promethium 61	150 Sm Samarium 62	152 Eu Europium 63	157 Gd Gadolinium 64	159 Tb Terbium 65	162 Dy Dysprosium 66	165 Ho Holmium 67	167 Er Erbium 68	169 Tm Thulium 69	173 Yb Ytterbium 70	175 Lu Lutetium 71
† 90–103 Actinium series	232 Th Thorium 90	Pa Protactinium 91	238 U Uranium 92	Np Neptunium 93	Pu Plutonium 94	Am Americium 95	Cm Curium 96	Bk Berkelium 97	Cf Californium 98	Es Einsteinium 99	Fm Fermium 100	Md Mendelevium 101	No Nobelium 102	Lr Lawrencium 103

f block

Appendix B

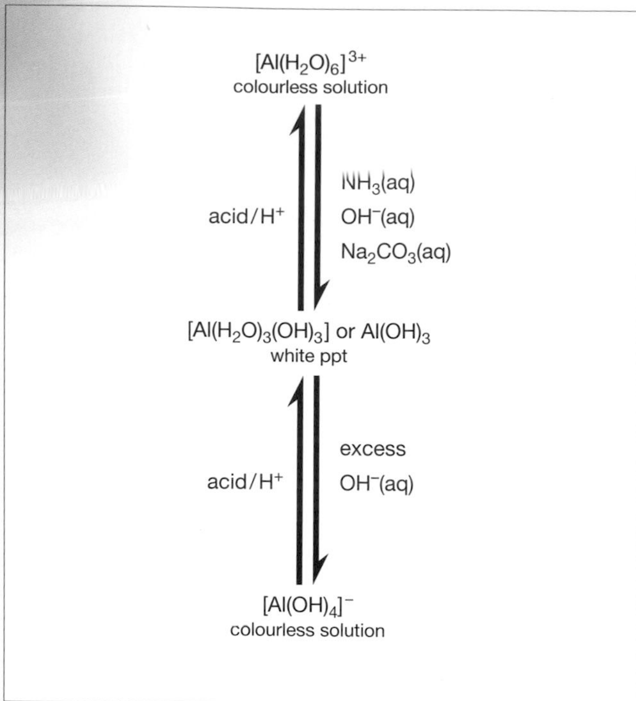

Figure A01 *Reactions of $Al^{3+}(aq)$*

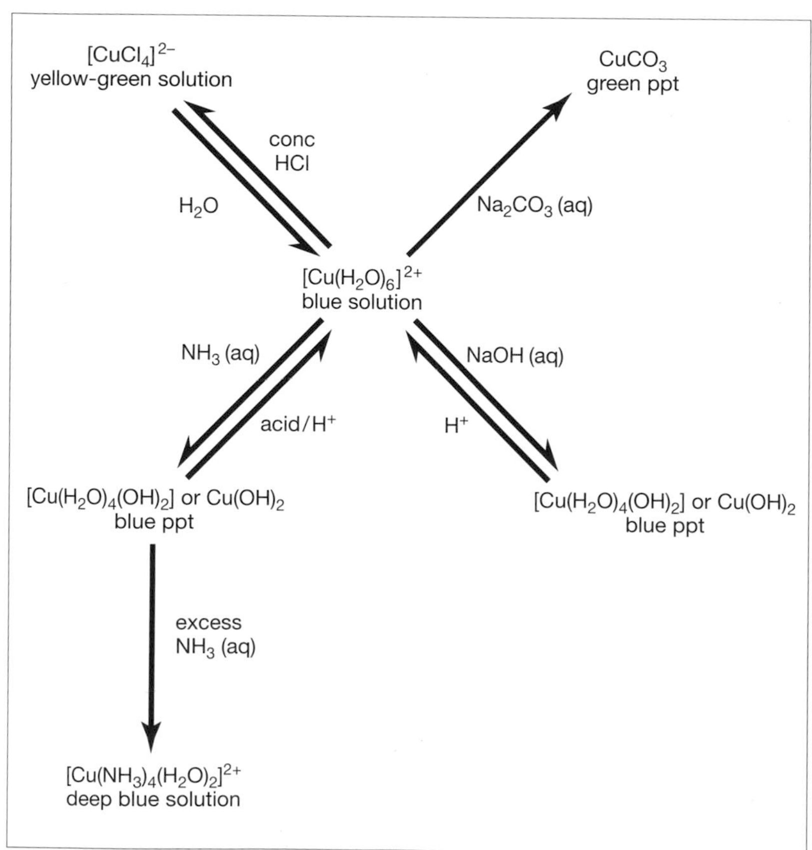

Figure A02 *Reactions of $Cu^{2+}(aq)$*

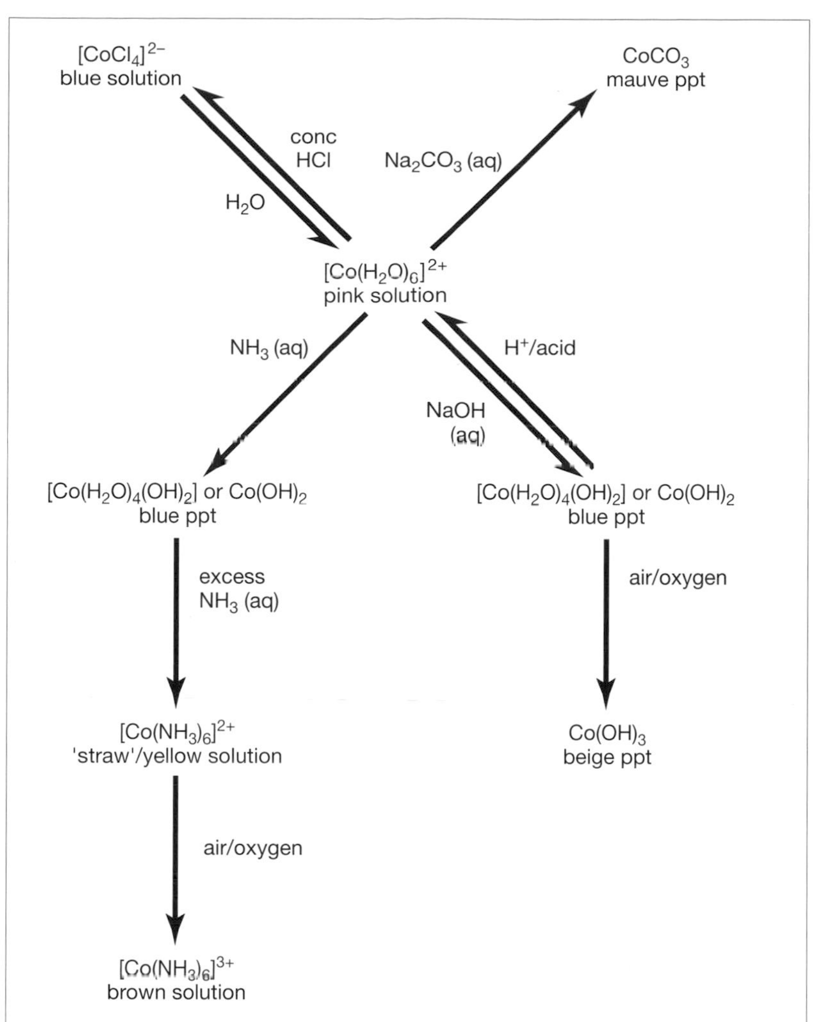

Figure A03 *Reactions of $Co^{2+}(aq)$*

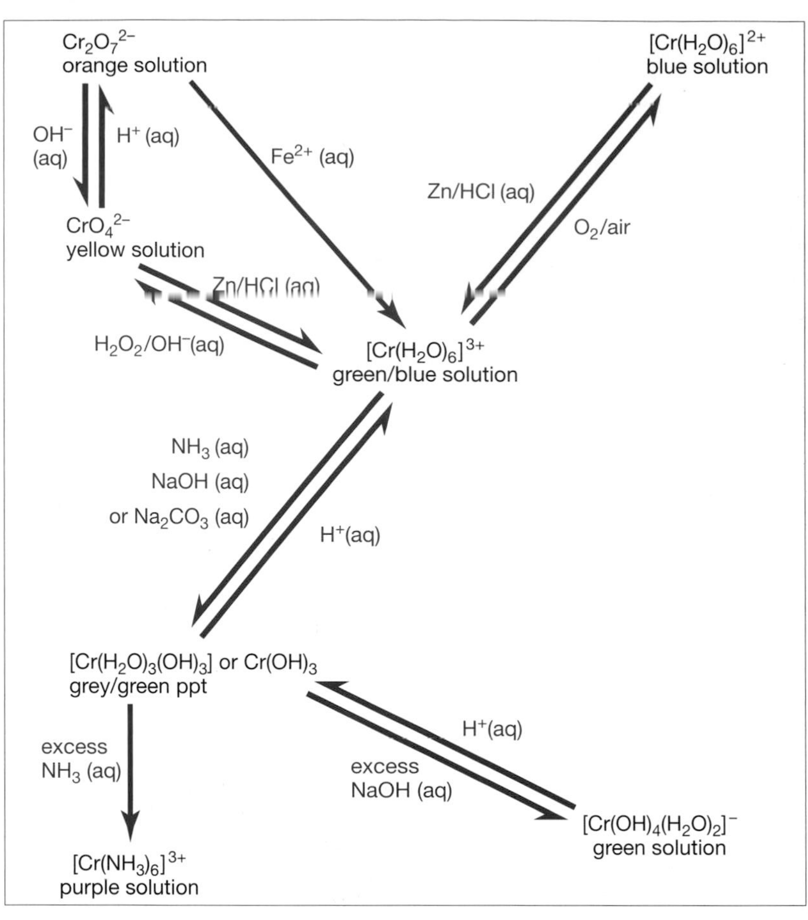

Figure A05 *Reactions of Cr^{3+}(aq)*

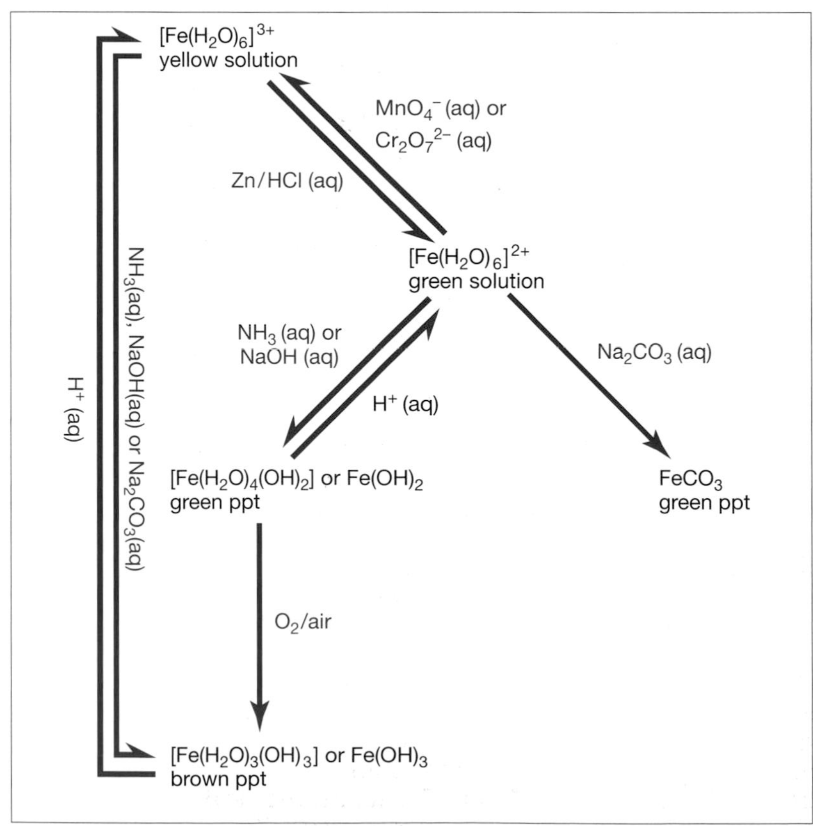

Figure A06 *Reactions of Fe^{2+}(aq) and Fe^{3+}(aq)*

Index